Oklahoma Run

Oklahoma Run

ALBERTA WILSON CONSTANT

NEW YORK
THOMAS Y. CROWELL COMPANY

Library of Congress Catalog Card No. 55-5395

To Edwin Constant

Many people know that Oklahoma was first opened to settlement in 1889 with a Run for land, but not so many know that this was only the first of the land openings in Oklahoma Territory, later combined with Indian Territory into the state of Oklahoma. This story, *Oklahoma Run*, concerns the second land opening in which the surplus lands of the Iowa, the Sac and Fox, the Pottawatomie, and the Absentee Shawnee reservations were thrown open to homesteaders. It took place on September 22, 1891, and consisted of 868,414 acres lying east of the Indian Meridian and adjoining the area settled in '89. This new addition to the Territory was made up of what is now Lincoln and Pottawatomie counties and portions of Logan, Oklahoma, and Cleveland counties on the west, and of Payne county on the north.

This is a story and not a history. The author has tried to make the background authentic, but the characters who take part in the story are known only to the author's mind. The names of a few nationally known persons and a few persons identified with the early history of Oklahoma are mentioned to create a feeling of reality, but the active characters are entirely fictional. If any character has the name of a real person, living now or in the period in which the story is set, it is an unintended coincidence.

Chapter 1

The Princess Elaine lifted her golden scepter.

"Elaine! Elaine the Fair!" her thronging subjects shouted again and again. A knight in golden armor and a golden helmet with a waving white plume stepped proudly forth. He said . . .

"Laineeeeeee! Laineeeeeeee! Time you were getting dressed. Laineeeeee!"

In a flash the knight was gone. Lainey Sheridan scrambled down the pear tree. Sharp little sprouting branches caught at her brown calico dress, humping it around her middle and letting coolness curl through the two petticoats that Aunt Ellen demanded for everyday wear. Lainey swung back and forth on the low limb, enjoying the breeze, feeling her body weight stretch her legs down and down till her feet felt heavy as lead. She calculated the chance of hitting the chickens' water pan and let go. The ground came up and smacked her and her teeth bounced. The chickens ran off, squawking.

The Dominicker rooster refused to run and Lainey picked up a last year's pear, dry and withered as a mummy, and chunked it at him. He flew up in the air, beating his spurred yellow legs. Then he eyed the pear, turned it over with his beak and pecked at it. Silly thing! He'd seen that same pear a thousand million times. His speckled tail feathers curved over his back; they would make elegant trimmings for doll hats. Lainey stepped toward the rooster, calling in false, gentle tones, "Coo-chick, coo-chick, coo-chick . . ."

"Laineeeeeee!"

"I'm coming!" she screamed.

Aunt Ellen sounded mad. She always wanted everything done right away. Uncle Hod just looked over his book and said, "Do

1

it to-reckly." Married people weren't much alike. Mr. and Mrs. Bucklin were like Jack Sprat and his wife. And Mama and Bush weren't alike, not one bit.

Bush! Her heart skipped. He was coming home today!

Lainey made a wild swipe at the rooster's tail feathers, then ran toward the calling voice. Bush was coming! Today!

Ellen Saunders Crump waited for her niece at the back door, hair-brush in hand. Lainey groaned inside. She hated to have Aunt Ellen to fix her hair.

"Did you hear me calling you?"

"Yes ma'am," Lainey panted, yanking at her stockings through the layers of her dress and petticoats. Now that she was eleven her stockings were forever too short. Aunt Ellen never had to pull up her stockings, her dress never wrinkled, and her hair looked as if it had been born in an iron-gray pompadour pinned with bone hairpins. The very same hairpins, Aunt Ellen often remarked, that she had owned when she was married. Sloppy people lost hairpins and sloppiness was one thing Aunt Ellen could not abide.

"Well, if you heard me, why didn't you answer me?"

"I did answer you," Lainey said righteously, "just as soon as I heard you."

It was the same question and answer they went through at least three times a day.

"Come along," Aunt Ellen sighed and drew Lainey into the house. "Allegra asked me to fix your hair. She's getting ready to go to the depot."

"I'm going, too," Lainey announced, sliding her hand out of the cool, dry palm. It was late summer in Missouri and everybody else was hot and sweaty, but for Aunt Ellen to break out in a sweat, or mention the heat, would have been an admission of weakness and a criticism of Snyder County weather. "I'm going with Mama to meet Bush." She repeated it, wanting to strengthen her position.

"I *know* you are!" The brush hit a tangle that went right through to the short hairs on Lainey's neck. "The way you call your father by his first name! It's enough to make your Grandmother Saunders turn over in her grave."

2

It was an old quarrel. For as long as she could remember Lainey had called Bushrod Sheridan "Bush." Mama said she started it in her cradle, saying "Bush" one day, plain as anything. From that time on she refused to say Papa or Father or any of the things they tried to teach her. They did everything from washing her mouth out with soap to making her recite the Fifth Commandment twenty-five times. Bush, himself, settled it when she was four.

"After all, it's my name," he said, swinging her up in the air and holding her there so that she looked down on his black hair, his sun-browned face, and his eyes that were either green or brown, you were never sure which. "It's my name and she's my girl so let it go. Glory be!"

With that he swung her down between his legs that looked like sturdy tree trunks encased in twill, then up again until she almost touched the prisms on the hall chandelier, and she screamed with terror and delight. "Bush! Bush!" Then Allegra made him put her down and she took Lainey upstairs for her nap but even there in the cool, high-ceilinged bedroom she had gone on whispering to the pillow, "Bush . . . Bush . . . Bush . . ."

And now, after months and months, Bush was coming back. It had been February when he left to go down to Indian Territory, or to the part they called Oklahoma Territory, though Aunt Ellen said it was all wilderness and why make such a fuss about what to call it. When Uncle Hod reminded her that the country had been opened in '89 and this was '91 and two years make a difference, she had just snorted and begun to crochet faster so that her needle flashed in the lamplight.

After Bush went away the evenings were the worst. The pain of missing him was like having a rock in your shoe that you could never, never stop to take out. She would wander aimlessly about the house, going from one big ghostly room to another, a little like a ghost, herself, in the deepening twilight. Often she went to the kitchen where Mattie, her face as dark as the shadows behind her, sat with her "boy," Jimdandy. They rarely talked much but they let her share their silence. Mattie sucked on her corncob pipe and Jimdandy whittled, now and then reaching out with his bare toes to flip a piece of kindling into the stove. Sometimes he

3

would take down his guitar and sing funny songs, chording an accompaniment to his deep rich voice. Then she would laugh and forget for a while the nameless fears for Bush that haunted her. Or maybe the fears would be too strong and she couldn't laugh and the songs were noisy jangles and Mattie would put out her skinny black hand and silence the guitar.

"Leave her be. The's a time to laugh an' a time to weep. The's a time to dance an' a time to mo'n."

Then she would go out on the back porch and lean against the solid brick wall of the house. Pushing her back against the wall until every bit of it touched she would whisper, "Bushrod Sheridan, my father. Bushrod Sheridan my father . . ." and after a while the lump in her throat would soften so that she could go back inside.

Every evening in the downstairs sitting room Mama and Aunt Ellen played backgammon and Uncle Hod read. He flipped the pages expertly with the same hand that held his book, for Uncle Hod had left an arm at the Battle of Westport when the Yankees and the Confederates fought back and forth across the Blue River. Lainey could not remember seeing him without a book in his hand; he even carried one with him when he went to Marney for the mail, in case the train was late.

The room where they sat was so quiet that when Lainey entered she softened her steps. The dice clicked, the counters slid over the board, the pages rustled and, as summer came on, the moths thudded against the high narrow windows. It was a hard room to enjoy yourself in, but late in the evening, just before Lainey was sent up to bed, Uncle Hod would read aloud. In spite of his frail body and the little hacking cough that bothered him, he had a voice that could call like a silver trumpet. "Once more, once more into the breach, dear friends, or close the wall up with our English dead!" Or he could whisper with the soft murmur of pigeons at the end of the day, "Good night . . . good night . . . parting is such sweet sorrow . . ." Lainey, listening, shivered and pressed her hands into the tufted sofa.

Aunt Ellen pulled the hair tight on the last black braid and wound the combings around the end. "There! Such a pity you

4

didn't get Allegra's hair. When she was your age she could sit on her hair and I was the only person who could comb it."

To be tenderheaded was part of being a lady. Lainey was ashamed to admit that she actually liked the scrape of the brush on her scalp. It was one more thing that set her apart from Mama. The beauty and glory of Allegra's hair was part of the Saunders legend. Golden as cane syrup from the first boiling, it was wavy but tractable too and it stayed wherever it was pinned. It made Lainey hate her own stubborn black hair and with it her green-brown eyes, the skin that buttermilk would not bleach, and the other things Aunt Ellen lumped together and called "all Sheridan."

"Now go up to your mother's room and get your clean dress, and those new white stockings, and be sure to wash good around your neck and don't forget that the sash of your dress sags and put those beauty pins Cousin Marian gave you in to hold it, and . . ."

The list trailed after Lainey like a swarm of gnats. You couldn't be neat enough or clean enough or ladylike enough to please Aunt Ellen if you were "all Sheridan."

Allegra was brushing her beautiful hair. She held her head down so that the hair almost touched the carpet, and with every stroke of the brush it followed her arm, fluttering like a great golden fan. As she brushed she sang, for she hated counting strokes, and two verses and three choruses of "My Old Kentucky Home" came out to just one hundred. Lainey stood in the doorway, waiting for the dramatic instant when Mama flung her head back as she sang, "My Old Kentucky Home . . . Goo-ood ni-hight!" Up the hair came, flying, and settled like a golden mantle around the shoulders of the embroidered combing jacket. Allegra's face was flushed pink, her eyes . . . blue as the Wedgwood rose-petal jar in the parlor . . . were shining.

"Almost time to go for Bush," she said and went on humming.

"Mama, why did he go off down there?"

"Oh, honey, men like to . . . to go places. He'd heard a lot about it. That Mr. Payne that used to come here, he was always talking about it."

"The one Aunt Ellen didn't like? The one they called King of the Boomers?"

5

"Yes. But he's dead now and we mustn't . . . but he did get Bush unsettled." She filled her mouth with hairpins and began to coil her hair into a neat figure eight, spacing a row of curls across her forehead. The shine had gone out of her eyes and a shadow of a frown came between her dark gold eyebrows. But even when she was troubled Mama was still pretty. She was more than that; she was "A Beauty." It was something like being a queen or a princess. The Saunders kin spoke of it that way. "I tell you, Allegra was A Beauty. She could have had any man in Snyder County." And once Lainey had heard Cousin Martha May add, leaning over her bulging bosom to Cousin Phronia, "And then she picked Bush. The hired man! Imagine!" At that Lainey had flown at Cousin Martha May and had had to be forcibly put to bed.

Now Allegra peeled off Lainey's clothes and had her step into the washbowl placed on the floor on a big huck towel. Lainey's feet slid on the slick china surface as she washed herself with Mama's violet-scented soap. Then she turned to the pile of starched underclothes on the bed. Every garment was hand-worked the way a lady always wore them and they made little crackling sounds as Lainey put them on. Last came the blue lawn dress with the panel of sheaves down the front done in wheat stitch. It had taken Aunt Ellen a month to make that panel and Lainey was uncomfortably conscious that she was already outgrowing the dress; it seemed downright ungrateful. Finished, she sat down in a chair by the window and felt a dew of sweat break out all over as the cocoon of starched clothes settled against her.

She liked to watch Mama get dressed. Allegra loved her pretty things. She had a way of patting each one, calling it by name as she picked it up. "My new surrah." It went over her head and settled with a swishing sound around her slim hips. "My kid gloves." Folded and left for the last minute. "My driving gloves." Loose cotton ones, strictly for protection. "My mesh purse." A silver affair of tiny flat links. "My parasol?" She hesitated, then put aside the ruffled pink confection with an extra pat as if for consolation. Then, "My hat!" It was white straw with white doves poised on the front and side and covered by a misty white veil. It had come from Kansas City.

6

"Do you really like it?" she asked Lainey, an amethyst-headed hatpin in her lifted hand. "You don't think it looks the least bit . . . flighty?"

Lainey was saved from answering by the sound of wheels on the pike.

"It's Bucklins," she announced, "Addie told me they were going to town today and she's going to get some red shoes with white silk tossels. I wish I had some."

"Tassels," Allegra corrected, "and if you're going to copy somebody, for goodness sakes don't pick the Bucklins. It makes me sick to see them in the old Gladwyn house. They always look as if they're just moving in or just moving out."

"I like Addie," Lainey said stubbornly.

"Now, honey," Allegra adjusted her veil, "you know how Aunt Ellen feels."

"I like Mr. Bucklin, too. He gave me a sack of jawbreakers last time I was in Marney. And Bush likes him. He said . . ."

She knew she had gone too far. This was not the time to remind Mama of the quarrel that had broken out when Bush wanted to sell Mr. Bucklin the bay colts. That quarrel, Lainey knew vaguely, had something to do with Bush's going away but it was one of those things that grown-ups keep hidden so that you trip on them when you least expect to and always get blamed.

"Elaine! The idea! Taking things from that man!"

"It was only jawbreakers," she sulked, "and a coconut flag."

"That makes no difference and you know it."

"Well, I can't help it because Mr. Bucklin's father was in the gang that set fire to Cousin Trenny's house and ran off her stock, can I? Besides, it was a thousand million years ago and Bush says . . ."

"Young lady, you're being impudent! Just for that . . . Oh, my heavens, look at the time. Why did you have to get me all upset?" She looked distractedly into the mirror. "I don't think Bush will like this hat! I'm sure he won't!"

"But Mama, it's your new hat *from Kansas City.*"

"I know, but he won't like it. Something tells me. Now you go on downstairs. Scat!"

7

Lainey went down the hall and trailed her hand over the walnut bannister of the long, curving stairway. Right down there, straight down, so that she could spit on the spot if she had a mind to, was the place where the quarrel over the bay colts had exploded. There Aunt Ellen had caught up with Bush when he stalked away from the table.

"It's foolish to talk about it, Bushrod," she had said with the chill of water flowing under ice. "I won't sell a horse off this place to Mot Bucklin."

"But, Ellen, we need the money. Need it for taxes. Mules. Nails for the barn."

"Then we'll have to find it someplace else."

"Mot's got the money in his hand. He wants to break that pair for carriage horses."

"Carriage horses!" Aunt Ellen snorted. "He came here in a wagon, barefoot at that!"

Allegra had come up to Bush then and put her hand on his arm. "Bush, those are Hector's colts . . ."

"For gosh sake!" Bush shook her off. "Do we have to consider the stallion's feelings, too? Now, look here, Ellen . . ."

But Aunt Ellen was not listening. She had launched into an angry recital of the evils done by the gangs that harassed western Missouri in the Fifties. Forerunners of the war, they rode through the country terrorizing, burning, stealing. Snyder County staunchly pro-slavery, had suffered bitterly from them. It was common talk that old Brant Bucklin was the leader of such a gang. That his son, Mot, had been allowed to settle in Snyder County was to Ellen's mind a disgrace. If she had her way . . .

"Ellen," Uncle Hod said, "that's all been over for years."

She turned on him in icy fury. "It'll never be over as long as I'm alive. Never!"

"Mot had nothing to do with it and old Brant's dead. Mot was just a boy then."

"Blood will tell," Aunt Ellen said ominously, "Let him get his carriage horses from some of the stock his father stole. He'll never own any off this place."

"I should have known better," Bush said and from the corner

8

by the hatrack Lainey could see his big hands behind his back, clenching and unclenching. "You've shown me where I stand often enough."

"Don't talk like that," Allegra begged. "What's mine's yours and Ellen . . ."

"I'm a Sheridan working Saunders' land," Bush went on as if she had not spoken. "And I'll never be anything else, no, not if I live to be a thousand."

"Now, Bush, there's no call for you to feel that way," Uncle Hod said uneasily.

"Please," Allegra touched his arm again, "Please . . . please . . . Listen, Bush . . ."

Aunt Ellen said nothing.

"I should have known when I ran away with Allegra . . ."

"You didn't run away with me any more than I ran away with you!"

How pretty Mama was with her dark blue eyes looking up at Bush. If only he would look at her. But he stared, blindly, straight ahead. "I should have known," he repeated.

Then Jimdandy came pounding to the back door bawling like a bull calf.

"Mist' Bush! The hawgs is out! They' headin' fo' the pike. Mist' Bush . . ."

"I guess that's my answer," Bush laughed harshly. "The Saunders own Riverview but it takes a Sheridan to chase hogs. Head 'em off Jim; I'll let out the dogs."

They stood, listening, to the feet of the two men running on the frozen ground and the yelping of the dogs as Bush opened the pen.

"If Longstreet had come up like *that* at Gettysburg," Uncle Hod said.

"Horace Crump!"

"Historical allusion, my dear. Nothing personal." He coughed softly. "Now I trust you ladies will join me while I finish my apple pudding."

Jimdandy had the buggy, washed and shining, at the horse block by the front door. He was standing by Trixie, the bay mare, and

9

it almost seemed that they were talking to each other. Jimdandy was a boss hand with horses. He'd been offered jobs lots of times at the horse and mule barns at St. Joe but he wouldn't leave Riverview. Lainey watched the mare nuzzle at his shoulder and flick her ears so as to catch what he muttered to her, too low for overhearing. Then she got into the buggy and leaned her head against the sidebar and gave herself up to waiting for Mama.

She stared at the house and the house stared back at her, the cornices over the upstairs windows like lifted eyebrows. It was a big house for a Missouri farm. It had been built in 1839 to hold Jeb Saunders, his wife, Laice, their ten children, the Kentucky kinfolks who came to visit, and any friends or strangers needing shelter for a night or a month. Aunt Ellen said it had been patterned after a French chateau Jeb Saunders admired on the grand tour he took as a young man. Certainly it was not part of the landscape now any more than it had been when it was first built but its size and beauty dominated everything around it just as the Saunders family dominated the county.

Lainey lifted her eyes to the tower, framed with black, lace-like iron. This was her refuge. On the farm or in the house she had to be what Mama or Bush or Aunt Ellen or Uncle Hod or Jimdandy or Mattie wanted her to be. But on the tower she belonged to herself.

From the front of the tower you could catch glimpses of the river. It had a name, but in Snyder County you simply called it the river as if it were the only one in the world. Around the other sides of the tower lay the Saunders' land. The cleared fields were divided by zig-zag rail fences or by the thorny green hedge that old timers called Osage orange. On the slopes ranged apple orchards, bouquets in the spring, cornucopias of goodness in the summer and fall. In the pasture mares grazed and long-legged colts raced up and down. Nearer the house were the big barns and the clutter of small buildings that no farm seemed able to do without. "Riverview," Jeb Saunders called his farm, writing it on the account book, now browned by time, that he started as a kind of diary. He must have known that a hundred other places would have that name in this river-blessed country, but he chose it all the same with the mixture of simplicity and arrogance that marked him, knowing that as long as he and his descendants lived that it would be known as "the Saunders place."

When Allegra finally came out the front door Lainey sat up and blinked. She was wearing an old pink voile with tiny green ribbon bows that shimmered like green butterflies. On her head was a wide-brimmed straw hat with a velvet ribbon the color of apple leaves in the springtime. Her hair was low on her neck in a soft, heavy knot, the way she wore it in the mornings.

"I guess you think I'm crazy," Allegra blushed, "but Bush likes this dress."

Jimdandy gave a final polish to a harness buckle with the sleeve of his torn shirt, and handed her the reins.

"Sho be glad to see Mist' Bush!"

"So will I," Allegra said and, smiling, spoke to the mare. She drove with the light sure hand of all the Saunders. The wheels grated on the gravel drive and then were muffled in the dust of the pike.

"Is Bush coming home to stay?" Lainey asked as they hit the rattling bridge over the south branch.

"What makes you ask that?" Allegra spoke so sharply that Trixie's ears flicked back.

"Nothing. I just wondered," Lainey mumbled. "I just wondered, that's all."

"I don't know why he wouldn't," Allegra said. "He's been gone long enough."

All the way into town Lainey wondered if her question had been answered or not.

Ump-bump, ump-bump. The buggy bounced over the first railroad crossing. Only a mile to the depot now. The rails shone as if they had been polished especially to bring Bushrod Sheridan home.

Chapter 2

A dozen men stood bunched in the shade of the depot. The area around them was dotted with the ambeer of Snyder County tobacco. Allegra lifted her pink-voile skirt: the green bows trembled.

"Howdy Miz Sheridan." Hats came off in a flurry.

Only Pappy Vickers who had been a captain in the regiment with Allegra's father called her by her first name. He winked at Lainey as she followed along.

"Can I walk the rails?" Lainey asked as they stepped out on the platform that stretched down to the water tank.

"Why *do* you have to be such a romp? Well, go on but don't get dirty. I'll stay by the water tower. Those men . . ."

Lainey stepped on a rail, balancing, her hands out. She wished Addie Bucklin were here to walk on the other one. Everything was more fun when Addie was along. She walked clear to the crossing without stepping off and stood there, teetering, about to turn around when Bucklin's new democrat wagon rumbled toward her. She blinked feeling that she had brought this about all by herself just by wishing. Bush coming home and now Addie . . . Lainey waved frantically. Mot Bucklin pulled up his horses and leaned over to her.

"Howdy, Lainey, ain't you kind of far from home? Fixin' to run off? Ketch the train to St. Looey?" He was grinning behind his drooping moustache.

"Now Pa, you know Lainey's not gonna run off. Whatcha doin' here? See my red shoes? Lookit, tossels, pearl buttons, everything. Right down from Kansas City. Just one pair left. Ast your Ma. Ast Miss Ellen . . ."

Addie was bubbling with excitement, her blonde braids were

12

decorated with plaid ribbon bows of the widest, the very widest, ribbon in Marney, and her pale-blue eyes darted to the depot and back as she gabbled.

"Whatcha doin' here?" she insisted. "Huh? Huh?"

"Lord preserve us, Addie," fat Mrs. Bucklin fanned herself with a palm-leaf fan, "give the child a chanct to speak up. You here to meet somebody, Lainey, or you goin' someplace?"

"Bush's coming home," Lainey said and the sound gave her the secret thrill that the knowledge alone had given her since the letter came last week. "He's coming on the Short Line on the 6:18."

"Ol' Bush comin' home," Mot Bucklin tugged at one side of his moustache. "Never did see why he left in the first place. Got the best place in th' county, right there."

"Land ain't ev'thing," Mrs. Bucklin said, "Not when you got to put up with . . ."

"Shhhhh . . . Now, Mama, you know, east, west, home's best."

"Mot you're an ol' fool," Mrs. Bucklin shook her head and her third chin wagged. "I'd not stand it a minute. High nosed, stuck up, earth's not good 'nough . . . Don't tell me! I was raised in Snyder County. Why my ma was a third cousin once removed of . . ."

"Ast Miss Ellen," Addie said, "tell her there's just one pair left." She put her foot out of the democrat wagon and wiggled it enticingly. The white silk tassels glistened. Lainey felt a pang of pure envy.

"It wouldn't do any good," she said. "She'd just tell me it was turkey-gobbler pride."

"Hmph!" Mrs. Bucklin sniffed. "Tell you what, Lainey, whyn't you ride home with us an' spend the night and Mot'll take you over in the mornin', early, to see Bush."

"An' I'll let you wear 'em," Addie burst out, "from right now till bed."

She looked at them, astonished that they would even think she would do such a thing. Miss meeting Bush? Why not for every pair of red shoes in Kansas City . . . the world! She opened her mouth, swallowed hard to keep from being bad mannered, and then found no words to answer.

13

"Go on, ast your Ma. I'll go with you," Addie was climbing out of the democrat.

"Hold your horses," Mot Bucklin grabbed his daughter by one skinny arm. "Lainey ain't said she'd come. With Bush gettin' home an' all . . ." He looked at her keenly and she felt an instant of gratitude to the lean gangling man in the driver's seat. "Some other time, huh, Lainey?"

"Yessir, thank you. I'd like to but Mama . . . Bush . . ." She did not look at Addie.

"Drive on, Mot," Mrs. Bucklin said, fanning herself harder. "They're all tarred with the same brush. Every Saunders I ever did see . . . too good fer . . ."

"But I said you could wear them," Addie screeched, "even tomorrow morning. Even . . ."

Lainey could feel Mama, clear down by the water tower, watching her. "Thank you very much," she said a little hopelessly. If only people wouldn't get mad!

"That's all right, honey. Some other time." Mr. Bucklin drove across the tracks. Addie waved to Lainey, her plaid bows a bright spot of bobbing color. Mrs. Bucklin did not turn. Lainey sighed. She and Addie had so much fun when it was just the two of them but with grown-ups around it never worked right. But to miss meeting Bush . . . Oh, no. She turned and walked back to the depot, taking the ties this time instead of the rails and wondering as she always did why the Short Line put ties too close together for one step and too far for two. By the depot door she could see the men watching Mama walk up and down by the water tank.

"Res'less, ain't she?" Jimp Meeker rubbed his shin with his ankle. "Time Bush got home."

The snicker of laughter made Lainey feel crawly. Pappy Vickers came over to her.

"Be glad to see ol' Bush?"

She nodded, not trusting herself to speak after offending Mrs. Bucklin.

"Well, so'll the rest of us. Place ain't the same 'thout him around."

Pappy Vickers was a part of every trip to Marney. Lainey always saw him at the store where they traded, at the depot, or at the

14

post office or just on the square, squatting on his heels in the shade. He was a master hand at stories, telling of his days on the Santa Fe Trail, or the Injuns he had killed, or the way he had outsmarted the Yankees in the war, or his exploits as a hunter. Every tale held her spellbound. Even Aunt Ellen liked Pappy Vickers, though she called him "Cap'n" as more fitting for one who had fought in the same regiment as her father.

"Cap'n Vickers drinks too much," she said once to Lainey, "and he draws the long bow with those tales of his and his grammar is a caution! But you won't find a better, kinder man in Snyder County. You can depend on Able Vickers!" Coming from Aunt Ellen this was high praise.

"What's ol' Bush doin' way out there, anyway?" Pappy Vickers asked.

"He's been hauling freight out of Oklahoma Station. Only, he calls it Oklahoma City."

"Haulin' freight?" Pappy Vickers rubbed his chin. "Best way to size up a country."

"It's for the Tillery Wagon Yard. They send stuff all over. Kickapoo reservation. Sac and Fox . . . Bush says that's same as they call the Sauks up north but it got changed. And the Potta . . . Potta . . ."

"Pottawatomies, I reckon. Not many o' them left. Not full-bloods."

Wooooo-wooooo-waw-wooooo!

"There she be! Whis'lin' for Bluestone crossin'. You get back to your mama."

"Elaine Sheridan! Get off those tracks! You could be killed!"

Lainey went submissively to stand by Mama. The big diamond stack of the locomotive in the distance filled her with awe. There were tales of children who had been sucked under the wheels and ground to bits.

WOOOO-WOOOO-WAW-WOOOOO!

The hot breath of the engine surged around her, the bell clanging in her ears. A sheet of steam broke from the inward parts of the engine, blinding and choking her. Allegra pulled away and began to run.

15

Then Lainey saw two people in each other's arms, and the familiar pink-voile dress partook of the strangeness of the black broadcloth suit and became the garb of a stranger. Two strangers, standing there in the glory of the sun-touched steam cloud.

She felt dreadfully, terribly alone. Suddenly one of the strangers broke away and ran toward her. He became familiar, beloved.

"There's Lainey! There's my girl!"

In a swooping rush he caught her up and her eyes and her ears, her hands and her nose told her the truth, that Bush was home. Only her heart had doubted, and that but for a moment. Bush was home to stay!

As the men at the depot came crowding around, Bush set Lainey down and took the hands they offered, slapping backs, calling their names. They were full of questions.

"How 'bout it boy? How 'bout that new country? Cain't be much good if they let it go free, can it? Injuns give you any trouble?"

"I got the same scalp I went down with," Bush bent his dark head and the sun turned his hair glossy bronze, like a turkey's wing.

"I had a cousin that went down in '89," Chub Lester said, "but he wouldn't stay. Said the wind like to blowed him to pieces."

"That's right. There's lots of wind there. Caused by folks beggin' to get more land opened up, they tell me."

Mr. Buff, the railroad agent, came by, dragging a limp gray mail sack.

"How was it down there, Bush? Pretty good country?"

"Plenty good," Bush said. "Good enough for anybody."

Mr. Buff wagged his goatee disapprovingly. "You gone back on ol' Mizzou, Bush?"

"Good gosh, no!" Bush exploded, then looked at Allegra in apology. "Sorry, honey. I didn't mean it was any better; I just meant . . . well . . . new country's different."

"Let 'im alone," Pappy Vickers yelped. "You old Pukes, you think this is the onliest place in th' world? Missoury men always have travelled an' they always will. You run acrost 'em any place. They got a likin' for new country."

16

"Plenty of 'em down in the Territories," Bush said.

"There's nothin' like new country," the old man said, and his faded blue eyes sought the horizon, "Why, when I went West . . . little ol' shirt-tail boy . . . startin' with a wagon train up to Independence . . . Ay, the way it makes you feel!"

"That's right, Pappy," Bush said. "It makes you feel sort of free!"

Bush tossed Lainey into the buggy and handed Allegra into the driver's seat.

"Takes a Saunders to drive a Riverview horse," he said. Her face turned as pink as her dress, but before she could turn the buggy Mr. Buff came running out of the depot waving a yellow sheet of paper.

"Hey, Bush! This just came through."

A telegram was rare in Marney. The men on the platform waited as Bush read the message. There was no escaping their curiosity.

"Don't keep us waitin', boy," Pappy Vickers cackled.

Bush folded the telegram, glanced at Allegra. "Well, I don't know why I shouldn't tell you. I asked a friend to send me word. They're opening some more land this fall. The Sac and Fox chiefs signed, and so did the Iowas, and the Shawnees and the Pottawatomies. I guess the Kickapoos are still holding out. But there's a strong chance it'll be opened up in September."

The men drew up around the buggy, their faces serious.

"You honest-to-God think it's good land?" Chub Lester asked.

Before Bush could answer a one-gallused stranger spoke up. "Say, I know a feller that worked for the Sac and Fox Agent one time. Horse an' mule man. He said the dirt down there was out an' out red."

"That's right," Bush said. "I never saw any redder."

" 'Course there's red dirt in Georgia. Cotton country."

"God knows I don't want no cotton," Jimp said, wagging his head. "Work a man to death."

"It's no rest cure," Bush agreed, then he added, "Hundred and sixty acres. If you're man enough to get it."

"Reckon they'll do it by a run like they did in '89?"

"It's a fair enough way. Lot's of sooners then, but maybe they can keep 'em out."

17

"We ought to be getting home," Allegra said shortly. "Ellen's expecting us."

"Huh?" Bush looked at her. "Oh, sure, sure. See you fellows later."

Lainey leaned out of the buggy and waved at Pappy Vickers who lifted his shapeless Confederate campaign hat in reply.

"Can I see the telegram?" she begged. "I never did see one, really."

Bush handed it to her and she admired the loopy writing in purplish pencil.

"Who's Kate?" she asked.

"Kate Tillery. She runs the wagon yard." He folded the paper and put it away.

"You never mentioned you were working for a woman!" Allegra said, scandalized.

"Maybe I forgot to," Bush grinned at Lainey.

"Seems a funny thing to forget. And a very funny thing for a lady to do. Run a wagon yard."

Bush shoved his hat back on his forehead and laughed. "If you could see Kate! And besides, I can tell you one thing," his big brown hand closed over the small gloved one that held the reins, "I didn't know how married I was till I got away from you."

"Let's drive through town," Lainey said, squirming.

"But we're late now. Aunt Ellen . . ."

"Oh, go on if she wants to," Bush said. "I'd like to see the place myself."

Marney had gone home to supper. The square with the court-house in the center was almost deserted. A few lamps burned in the back of the stores making the dim depths more cavernous. Shelley's Dry Goods. Nickell's Merc. Epperson's Grocery. Burke and Blanton's General Store. The last one was the place where Bush worked before he came to Riverview. Bush had told her the story many times of how he was pouring molasses when Allegra Saunders came into the store with the sun shining on her hair and how he had looked at her and gone on pouring and pouring till the gallon jug he was filling overflowed and molasses covered the floor. Old man Blanton made him clean up the mess and docked his wages fifty cents besides. "Not that th' m'lasses are wuth it, but to teach you to stop watchin' th' gals." And the next Saturday Bush had come out to Riverview asking for the job of hired hand and they had been married before the month was out.

There was the lodge hall that Venny Jo McIlroy declared had a skeleton locked up in it. And Topton's Drug Store with the red and green bottles in the window. And there was the bank with Mr. Tom Bridges locking the door. Bush hailed him.

"Howya, Tom!"

The slight, dignified man glanced up, tipped his hat, and walked away.

"You didn't need to do that!" Allegra said, with a smile in her voice.

"Old Tom just can't get over it! A nobody like me to beat his time with the prettiest girl in the county . . ."

"Hush. The way you go on!"

They were talking in riddles in an aggravating grown-up way and Lainey gave her attention to the town. The long wide street was bordered with maples and elms. Behind hedges of lilacs, flowering currants, and golden bell were the homes of Marney built of red brick or white frame trimmed with elaborate wooden curlecues. Many of them needed paint but they had an air of not quite realizing it and managing very well all the same.

On the other road that went down by the river the houses became smaller and smaller until they dwindled down to nothing but shacks at the water's edge. But of the people who lived there Lainey knew nothing. In Marney you were either somebody or nobody; there was no in between.

Just outside the town a patch of sweet clover sent up a heavenly fragrance. A star twinkled in the lavender-gray sky. Lainey would have wished on it if there had been anything left to wish for. She sagged against Bush in deep contentment.

The talk went on across her, building a bridge from the frozen winter day Bush had left to this warm summer evening when he had returned.

"Did Jimdandy bring that colt along? The one that had ringbone?"

"Yes. He's fine now. Sim Petty's looking at him. Did you have a good place to stay down there?"

"Just so-so. But you can get what you can pay for. Anything, almost. I went to the opera up at Guthrie one time."

"Opera? Good heavens! Joe put the creek strip in potatoes."

"Good idea. I wanted to but Ellen was against it and I got tired arguing."

"She said last night she was glad you were coming home. Joe's all right, but . . ."

"I know. She can't boss him around like she can me. Or like she thinks she does."

"Ellen thinks a lot of you and you know it."

"Well, I think a lot of her. It's just that . . ."

The plop-plop of the mare's hoofs in the soft dust filled the silence. Lainey said sleepily, "We've got a Smithwick ham."

"That's fine. Nothing like that in the Territory." Then Bush said, startled, "Does that mean . . ."

"Of course," Allegra answered. "Ellen always has the family to dinner when somebody comes home."

"Oh Lord!" Bush put his head in his hands. Lainey felt him shaking with silent laughter.

"Now, Bush . . ."

"All right. All right."

Lainey thought of the bitter morning that Bush had gone away. He had come to the kitchen to tell her goodbye and she had been eating breakfast and making a dam of the grits to hold back a lake of red-ham gravy. He had kissed her and promised to bring her a present. The biggest present, he said, he had ever brought her. But she had turned her head away from his kiss and stubbornly refused to tell him goodbye until Jimdandy had brought up the buggy and all at once Bush was gone and she had hidden in the closet under the stairs to keep from hearing Trixie's hoofs on the frozen drive taking him away. Now it was all over like a bad dream that leaves only a vague uneasiness in the morning and Bush was home to stay. The present? She wondered about it. Had he forgotten? No, he never forgot. Would it be in the telescope stored in the back of the buggy? Or would it come wrapped in layers

20

of wrappings with her name written on it, "Miss Elaine Sheridan . . ." And when the wrappings were laid back, what would it be?

The long drawn-out whistle of a steamboat on the river sounded. Lainey tried to say, "That's the *Firefly*," but sleep that was rising in her like a tide washed the words away.

She wakened to the sound of angry voices. Twilight had gone and a thin darkness was around them. Up ahead loomed the bulk of Riverview.

"No, I didn't write and tell you how I felt," Allegra was saying, "because I thought you'd get over it. It's just crazy! When you have everything right here to go off to a wilderness!"

"Is that what you think, or what Ellen thinks?"

"I didn't say one word to her about it.'

"Don't you see, this is a chance to get something of our own?"

"Riverview . . ."

"Riverview is Saunders' land. I couldn't own it if I had a dozen deeds." Suddenly the anger went out of Bush's voice and it became eager, pleading. "Allegra you don't know what I'm talking about because you've always been a Saunders . . . a top dog. I can't own Riverview and to me working another man's land is like . . . like stealing another man's wife."

"What a thing to say! You don't need to talk like that."

"But I do need to. It's time I told the truth. Twelve years now and I've been shutting my eyes and my mouth. It's time you knew . . . and Lainey, too . . . that I want my own land." He hammered at his knee and the blows jarred Lainey and it seemed to her that Bush's pain was her own, his anger, his desire. "Allegra, come with me . . ."

"But what about Lainey? Riverview is her home, too. She . . ."

"She'll love it down there. It's great country. New and clean and fresh. And we'll be together, the way we should have been years ago, from the first."

"I . . . I . . ."

Then the choking sobs that stopped Allegra's words lodged in Lainey's throat, too, and they grew so that she could not breathe.

It had to stop! It must stop! She sat up, thrusting herself between Bush and Allegra.

"I'm hungry," she said, pretending an elaborate yawn. "It's way past supper time."

Allegra took up the reins and started Trixie up the drive. The wheels grated on the gravel. As they drove up to the horse block the tall doors swung open and Aunt Ellen stepped out, the double-globed lamp in her hand. Behind her was Uncle Hod, his finger marking his place in his closed book. Back of him, in the shadows, stood Jimdandy and Mattie.

"Welcome home, Bushrod," Aunt Ellen offered her pale cheek for Bush's kiss. "Welcome home to Riverview."

Lainey, stumbling along, clinging to Bush's hand, felt it tighten momentarily. Nothing was settled. It was only stopped for a time. Groping in the thin darkness she found Allegra's hand reaching for her own and together the three of them walked through the open doors of Riverview.

Chapter 3

Through the mist of her dreams Lainey could hear the harp sounds of the river. She stretched luxuriously in the cool morning air then buried her face in her pillow to shut out the morning light. But it was no use; she was awake.

Mouthwatering smells were wafting up the stairs and Lainey sniffed at them, testing each one as a bluetick hound noses the trail. The aroma of the ham, cured by Mr. Smithwick out north of Marney, was distinct and unmistakable. By the middle of the morning the Saunders' kin would be gathering from all over the county to welcome home the traveller, and Riverview was hard at work preparing the best the smokehouse, garden, chickenyard, and kitchen could provide. Only the ham came from outside the borders of the place.

"I hate to admit anybody can beat me curing ham," Aunt Ellen always said as she eased the long mahogany-colored slab into the washboiler, "but the Smithwicks can do it. I wish I had their receipt!"

The faint click of the wire whisk on the ironstone platter told Lainey that Aunt Ellen was making her famous white icing for the Lady Baltimore cake. The egg whites would be stiffened into snowdrifts by that lean, tireless arm, until the platter could be turned upside down. Then a stream of boiling syrup, 'no thicker than a knitting needle,' would be poured on top while the beating went on and on.

"It's the beating does it," Aunt Ellen told disappointed cooks who copied the recipe. She somehow made their failures seem like laziness.

There would be bowls to lick if Lainey went down to the

23

kitchen now. There also would be cod-liver oil to take before breakfast.

But surely nobody would make her take cod-liver oil the first day Bush was home!

And he *was* home. Really and truly. Lainey wiggled her toes in satisfaction and slid over the high edge of the bed. As she stood on the rag rug with her arms wrapped tight around her body she felt a sudden sinking in her stomach.

I won't remember, she told herself. I won't. It was just a dream. But the more she argued the plainer the memory of last night became.

Bush hadn't come home to stay. Mama knew it but she wouldn't tell me. Aunt Ellen knew. So did Uncle Hod. Even Jimdandy and Mattie in the kitchen knew. Everybody but me.

Taking off her cambric nightgown Lainey began to jerk on her clothes. The hem of her dress was turned up and she kissed it, making a wish.

Let it be over. Let it be settled.

She tiptoed down the hall to the cluttered storeroom at the end. Threading her way through the dim shapes of discarded things she was halfway up the long, shaky ladder that led to the tower before she saw Bush standing by the railing, looking out across the Saunders' land.

Working another man's land is like . . . Could he have really said that?

"Hello, there," Bush called. "Come on up."

Lainey scrambled up the ladder and stood beside him.

"Honey, that present I promised I'd bring you . . ."

"I don't care," she said.

"I'm not trying to weasel out. I brought you some things in my telescope. Things girls like, so's you'd have something to show Addie. But what I really meant to give you was . . . this . . ."

He fished in his pants pocket and drew out a small glass bottle, a soda-mint bottle like the one Uncle Hod kept by his plate. It was packed with dirt, red dirt, the color so deep and vivid against Bush's big brown hand that it seemed alive under the shell of glass. Lainey poked it.

24

"Th-thank you," she said, trying to sound enthusiastic.

"Down there in Indian country I heard about giveaways," Bush said. "Indians don't care about ownin' a lot of stuff. Every once in a while when there's a good reason, why, they have a giveaway. Give away pret'neart everything they own."

She nodded, trying to understand. But a bottle of dirt . . . even red dirt . . .

"Say, now, they want to give you a pony but there aren't enough ponies to go 'round to everybody. So they give you a stick instead. That stands for the pony, see, and next time they get a pony they give you one."

"Do they take the stick back?"

"I don't know 'bout that, but this bottle of dirt . . . it's kind of like a pony stick. I scooped it up in the Sac an' Fox country my first trip out."

He put an arm around Lainey and drew her close to him. "I was takin' the team along a hog-back, cross-country, and the wind was blowing like it nearly always does and there I was, up high, and I could see the whole thing. The trees and the grass and the red dirt and the wind that was in my face fresh and free-like because it was blowin' over new country. I hauled up the team and I sat there, watching, and pretty soon it came to me that it was all part of the same thing . . . the dirt and the trees and the grass and the wind and even the sky . . ." He pushed his hand up on his forehead and Lainey knew he was shoving back the hat that wasn't there. "I wish I could say it like some o' those books Hod's got downstairs. But . . . but . . . it was something strong and good and because I was there I was part of it, too. So I got down and filled up this bottle of dirt right then and there and I brought it to you."

He folded the bottle into the palm of her hand. She struggled to understand what he was saying but the words were as slippery and hard to grasp as the bottle itself. She could sense that inside them there was something as strong and live as the red dirt.

"Th-thank you," she said again. Bush smiled.

"Now that's enough about that." He turned abruptly and looked at Riverview spread out before them in the morning sun.

25

"The place looks mighty good," Bush said. "Joe Matthews is a good farmer on the shares . . . or any other way. But you've got to have good land, too. And you won't find sweeter land than this, savin' a little high water, now and then. I know. I've plowed and planted and harvested it. I know."

He said it as a man says goodbye to something he loves.

"Are you going back to the Territory?" Lainey blurted. It was out and she was glad.

"Yes," he looked at her and she saw that his eyes had lost their brown and were green with excitement. "I came back to get you and Mama. When they open up the country this fall I want us to be there, to take up a claim and make a home."

The morning coolness was gone. The sun was hot on Lainey's back. Pigeons wheeled and swooped about them, jealous of this invasion of their tower. A banded blue landed at one corner, watching Bush and Lainey with bright, wary eyes.

"Is it . . . somebody said down there it was a . . . wilderness."

"Hmmmm. Well, some ways you could say that, but I'd say it was more like the Promised Land." He touched her head lightly. "New country promises you things, Lainey. All you've missed any place else, it promises. And you can make it come true if you're willing. For a promise like that Jeb Saunders left Kentucky for Missouri, his folks left Virginia for Kentucky, and back of them, to hear Ellen tell it, they left England for Virginia."

The way he said it she could hear feet marching down the pike. And she would go with them, she, Lainey Sheridan, leaving Missouri for Oklahoma Territory.

"I want to go," she whispered. "I want to go!"

"Do you?" He looked down at her, his voice was calm but he could not keep the excitement out of his eyes. "I want you to make up your own mind. You have a right to know what it'll be like. No towns. No schools. No churches. Not even a house at first. We'll have to live rough. We can't pick our neighbors and some of 'em may be different than you're used to. And it's Indian country."

The small glass bottle was hot in her hand.

"I want to go! Please take me, please!"

26

"Glory be!" Bush shouted, and all that he had held back was in his voice. "Glory be! That's my girl!"

His cry startled the pigeon and it flew up and circled them. And Lainey, unable to look at Bush for fear she could not fulfill the promise she had given him, watched the flight of the banded blue into the safety of the barn loft.

On the way down to breakfast Lainey stopped in the cluttered storeroom and caught Bush's arm. "Suppose Aunt Ellen won't let me go."

He frowned, "If you want to go she can't keep you."

"But she . . ."

"Listen to me, honey, I want you to get some things straight. I blame myself for a lot of this; I should have brought it out in the open, long ago. I just kept hoping . . . But I want you always to remember that your Aunt Ellen loves you. She's a fine woman and she's held this place together for years. Why she held it together with the war going on around it, just her, with nerve, spit, and prayer. She raised your mama and you couldn't ask for better'n that. She's worked harder for the Saunders family than any field hand they ever had and she'll go on working till she drops. But working for people, and even loving them, don't let you own them. If you want to go to the Territory, just take your foot in your hand and go!"

"We had to start without you," Aunt Ellen fretted at the breakfast table. "There's so much to do. Put the children's table over there, Jimdandy."

Jimdandy came backing through the swinging door with a small dining table that was a copy of the large one. None of his children, Jeb Saunders had decreed, should ever have to eat at the second table.

Mattie scurried in, thumped a platter of bacon and eggs on the table and rushed out, slipper heels flapping on the floor.

"Ellen, there's something I want to say," Bush began.

"For goodness sake, this is no time for talk. Mattie, see if those green beans have enough salt in them. And be sure to slice some

27

salt-rising bread for Uncle Alec. No, don't. You never get it thin enough."

Allegra was crumbling a biscuit on her plate, her blue eyes shadowed. Uncle Hod stirred his tea around and around until a whirlpool appeared in the middle of the cup.

"Ellen . . ." Bush said, again.

"In a minute." She disappeared into the pantry, returning with a stack of damask napkins. "I knew I'd put these down someplace. Now," she counted on her fingers, "watermelon pickle. Another jar of cherry preserves. Damson jam. Shall we have comb honey or not? Phronia always wants it." Lainey watched the dark tide of red creeping up Bush's throat. "Blackberry jell. Horace, don't wear out the spoon. Take some more sugar. Apricot . . ."

And then like a sudden storm silence descended over the table. Bush had pushed back his chair and was standing at his place.

"By heaven, Ellen, I've had enough of this!"

"Well, Bushrod." She stood, facing him, tall, spare, and implacable, the line of her jaw tight in her pale face.

"Please," Allegra said, "please . . ."

Lainey chewed on a bite of biscuit that had become impossible to swallow.

"We're leaving Riverview, Ellen. You won't let me tell you decent, the way I wanted to, so here it is. All this foofaraw about a dinner to welcome me home won't make any difference. When they open up new country in Oklahoma Territory this fall I'm going down to take up a claim. And Allegra and Lainey are going with me."

"My sister belongs at Riverview. This is her home!"

"My wife's home is with me. When I married Allegra I came to Riverview because she asked me to."

"And because you had no fit place to take her."

"I don't deny that, but it's water over the dam. Now we're going to make our own home."

"Do you think you have a fit place to take her now? That wilderness! Indian country. Dragging Allegra and Lainey off down there to satisfy your own selfish notions . . ."

28

"I'm not dragging anybody. Lainey told me this morning she wants to go."

Ellen winced but she did not falter. "After you'd talked her into it. A child's choice. She'll hate you for it later."

"Let that be as it may."

"You can't tell me Allegra, my own sister, that I raised from a baby, wants to go down there to that wilderness. You can't tell me that!"

"I'll let her tell you for herself. Allegra?"

Lainey felt a flash of pity for Mama as she looked from husband to sister, then buried her face in her hands.

"I don't know," she whispered. "I don't know what to say."

"You see?" Ellen said accusingly. "You see?"

Then Allegra lowered her hands. As she rose to her feet Lainey saw a taut line around her jaw like Aunt Ellen's, the unmistakable look of the Saunders' kin.

"Ellen, you've been the best sister in the world to me," Allegra said, "but you've taught me too well. All these years you've taught me that the family must come first. Well, Bush and Lainey are *my* family. I'll go with them."

Lainey's shout of joy was checked in her throat by the curious crumpling around Aunt Ellen's mouth. Uncle Hod came over and put his hand on hers.

"Now, Ellen, now, honey . . ."

She moved her hand and clamped her jaw tighter. From down the driveway came the sound of wheels on gravel. The first of the kin was arriving to welcome Bushrod Sheridan home.

"Let me go to the door," Allegra said. "You go lie down for a little. I'll . . ."

Ellen stopped her with a withering look. "I hope I know how to receive guests," she said. She forced her already straight back to a ramrod line and walked toward the dining room door. "You stay here," she said over her shoulder, "with your family."

As the guests arrived the news of Bush's determination to take Allegra and Lainey back to Oklahoma Territory ran through the

29

gathering like **quick**silver. Even in the kitchen where Mattie queened it over the extra help brought along for the occasion there was scandalized muttering. "Po' Miss 'legra . . . po' li'l Lainey!"

Lainey dodged into the dining room to snatch an apple from the carefully arranged fruit bowl. Cousin Martha May was there showing Bert Saunders' bride from Ohio her new pattern of Battenberg.

"It's a shame when you think about Allegra. My dear, she was A Beauty. Tom Bridges was crazy about her; still is for that matter. And Bush was a hired man here on the place. Ellen called him the overseer, but . . ." She caught sight of Lainey. "Elaine, aren't you afraid you'll spoil your dinner, piecing that way?"

Lainey did not answer. If she had she might have been barred from dinner altogether. That old . . . old . . . She went out the front door where Bush was talking to some of the men.

"It'll run over eight hundred thousand acres. Looks like a man ought to get a good hundred'n' sixty out of that. With Guthrie on one side and Oklahoma City not far off there's bound to be railroads . . . sometime."

"Sounds like a good thing, a real good thing," the Saunders men agreed. A good thing for *you*, they meant, mopping their foreheads in the noon heat. A good thing for a Sheridan.

"Nothing sure about it, of course," Bush said. "I may come back with my tail between my legs."

But they knew he didn't believe it. Even Lainey, rubbing the apple juice off her chin, knew that once Bush left Riverview he would never come back.

Lainey went to join the children around the rope swing Jimdandy had strung up to the tallest of the maples. They were taking turns and tall, thin Fielding who was the boss of the children at all these gatherings was pushing the swing. Lainey fell in line with the others.

When it was her turn Fielding said, "Hold tight, I'm gonna run under!"

Up and up she went, feet barely clearing Fielding's blond thatch. Up and up, then back and back. Faster and faster! Higher and higher! At the top of the arc the ropes protested with a jerk and

30

Fielding, leaping high now, caught at the swingboard and gave it a mighty shove. Up and up! Like flying, like dying. Green branches and the gleam of the far-off river. The ropes creaked as the swing hit the end of the arc with a shattering jolt. Up and up and the terrible, wonderful fear that the rope might break or the board slip out. Then down and down, and the anti-climax of "letting the old cat die." But the swing was still going high when the dinner bell clanged and Lainey jumped and ran with the others.

In the hall Ellen Saunders Crump waited for the family to gather. The joy of hospitality was like a halo around her spare frame. To have the family together, and to provide food for them . . . she asked nothing more.

Mattie slid open the dining-room doors; the pageant of the table burst upon them. Ellen had brought out every treasure, cooked up every famed secret recipe, filled every bit of Haviland china, shined every silver spoon. Lainey, swept along in the rush of the children, saw the look she gave to Bush. Direct, challenging, it seemed to say aloud, See what you're taking Allegra and Lainey away from? Can you give them anything like this?

Before Uncle Hod at the head of the table lay the Smithwick ham, ringed about with circles of fried apples, the seed star perfect in each slice. The diamond-marked glaze of the ham sweated brown-sugar jewels. It had been sliced halfway to the bone for quicker serving and the meat gave up a mouth-watering smell. At the other end of the table, in front of Aunt Ellen, was a matching platter of fried chicken. Not a bony piece in the lot! Crusty drumsticks, browned thighs, long breast pieces, delicate white-meated wishbones were heaped together. To look at them was to know that the outside would be crisp, the inside tender and succulent. On a smaller platter was baked hen and dressing.

Up and down both sides of the table were bowls of vegetables; smoking mounds of green beans, cooking since sun-up, icebergs of cole slaw with sour-cream dressing, mashed potatoes piled high and topped with chunks of butter that melted down the sides, cream gravy with brown bits of crackling from the frying chickens, cucumbers sliced into homemade vinegar and put down

31

in layers of onion circles. There was even a dish of tomatoes though Aunt Ellen had not made up her mind completely about trusting "love apples." And in among all the elegance of silver, glass, and china were two big black baking pans where corn pudding bubbled and hissed. Both the pans and the pudding recipe had come from Kentucky with the first wagon-load of Saunders' goods.

And filling in the spaces so that the damask cloth was hardly visible were dishes of cucumber pickle, stuffed mangoes, chow-chow, corn relish, apple butter, strawberry preserves, and two bowls where whole pickled peaches, starred with cloves, floated in thick syrup. Three prints of butter fresh from the spring house still bore a gentle dew upon the sheaf of wheat that decorated them. And at every place along the table lay a plate turned upside down.

Old Uncle Alec asked the blessing in his quavery voice and then there was an earthquake of plates turning over. Uncle Hod picked up the carving knife and began to whet it on the steel. A mere formality for ample amounts of the Smithwick ham had been sliced to start. Wheet-wheet-wheet. He looked critically at the knife edge then placed it on the platter. A stomach rumbled and one of the little girls giggled. Fielding kicked Lainey's shin.

Horace Crump was standing. A quiet, gentle man who had led a cavalry charge into Yankee cannon fire. He was smiling when he spoke but there was a ring in his voice like the ring of the carving knife on the steel.

"Ladies and gentlemen, I wish to propose a toast!" The sunlight from the window gleamed on his glass as he raised it up and held it high.

"To the memory of Jeb Saunders, founder of Riverview. A man who had the courage to leave the comfort and safety of Kentucky for what was then the . . . ah . . . wilderness of Missouri!"

The Saunders' kin looked first at Uncle Hod, and then at Aunt Ellen. They found no answer in her flaming face, but not to honor Jeb Saunders was unthinkable. There was a scraping back of chairs. Even the children stood.

"Jeb Saunders," Uncle Hod shouted, "Drink 'im down!"

The glasses came up from the table in a swooping arch, then

smacked, empty, back onto the table. Somebody began a cheer and the high-ceilinged room rang and the roses in the centerpiece trembled. Then the Saunders' kin sat down, a little embarrassed by their show of emotion, but pleased, too. Hod was a good old boy, and he'd had a lot to put up with. Of course Ellen was the salt of the earth, but she wasn't easy to live with. Not one bit. And Bush was all right, too. Hired hand? What of it? Most of us are hired, one way or another, and if it hadn't been for the way he took hold Riverview wouldn't be the place it is today. Prob'ly sold like most of the places on the river. No, Bush was all right, and he'd make a go of it down there in the Territory if anybody could.

They beamed at each other and at the one-armed man deftly forking out slices of ham to fill the plates started on the endless circle. They did not look at Ellen who sat with her back never touching the chair, every vestige of color now gone from her face.

But Lainey looked at her. She looked and in spite of her gnawing hunger she knew she wouldn't be able to swallow a bite if Aunt Ellen didn't stop looking so . . . so . . .

Chapter 4

They left the Short Line in Kansas City. In the bustling depot where they waited for the Santa Fe to take them on to Oklahoma City, Lainey forgot the way she had cried at leaving Riverview.

"Now, just stop that!" Aunt Ellen rebuked her, finally. "Hold up your shoulders and remember who you are. That'll bring you through." She looked at Bush. "I hope you see . . . I hope you understand what you're doing."

"She'll be all right once we get started," Bush said uneasily.

For days he had done his best to appease Aunt Ellen. He held his tongue at her cutting remarks about the Territory and even relented from his stand of not allowing Allegra to take Riverview furnishings.

"They're as much hers as they are mine," Ellen said, hauling out chairs, beds, and tables. "It all belongs to the family, and Allegra's a Saunders, whether you like it or not."

"It's just Ellen's way," Bush told Lainey. "She can't give in, but she can't see you and Allegra do without. Though what we're going to do with all this stuff . . ."

In the end he went to Mr. Buff and chartered a "Zulu" car from the Santa Fe lines. It would carry household goods and livestock, but somebody must ride with it. Aunt Ellen decided that would be Jimdandy.

The big Negro rolled his eyes back in his head and refused to go. It was only when he realized that Bush was taking some Riverview stock that he agreed to make the trip down. Lainey heard him talking to the bay gelding, Stretcher, "Ol' Jim'll see you th'u. He won't let nothin' hurt you. Wil' country . . . Injuns . . . Jim'll be there . . ."

Together he and Bush went to the horse and mule market at

St. Joe to buy a horse for the Run. Bush said Riverview horses were too highly bred for running in rough country. The idea sounded sensible, but Lainey had a feeling that he just wanted to be on his own in the race. They came back with a tough, close-coupled, black and white horse named Blackjack. With his one glass eye and his spotted hide he looked out of place in the Riverview stables but Jimdandy said he'd outrun anything in sight just for pure cussedness.

The Santa Fe did not leave until 9:30 at night and the Short Line had landed them in Kansas City in mid-afternoon. By six Lainey felt as if she had lived in the depot half her life.

"Let's go look up Jimdandy," Bush said. "I want to see how the stock's ridin'."

Finding Jimdandy and the "Zulu" car in the tangle of tracks, engines, drays, and baggage trucks in the yards took a long time. When Lainey saw the familiar face she felt that she'd drawn a prize out of a grab bag.

"Stock all right?" Bush hailed him.

"They kinda ruckshus at fust, but they all right now, Mist' Bush."

"How you doin'?"

"Well," Jimdandy said, "I wisht I was back home, I do that, but long as I ain't, I figger I'll just enjoy ma'self."

While the men talked about feed and water Lainey climbed into the "Zulu" car and rubbed Stretcher's soft nose and the fawn colored flanks of the Jersey cow. Blackjack rolled his glass eye at her and she did not try to touch him. The household goods in the other end of the car were swaddled in quilts, straw, rag rugs and feather ticks. Everything had a double use. The churn was full of seed corn. The drawers of the Jenny June sewing machine were packed with small tools and onion sets. The walnut wardrobe from the storeroom held bedding and the books Uncle Hod had selected from his library. The parlor organ . . . Aunt Ellen had insisted that they take that . . . was near the front of the car. Lainey worked her hand through the surrounding crating and pressed down one of the pedals. The organ gave a ghostly sigh.

"Once in the dear, dead days beyond recall . . ." she sang softly.

Outside the engines throbbed, whistles screamed, bells clanged, but in the car with the familiar smell of animals she could close her eyes and pretend she was back at Riverview in the big barn.

"We'd better get back to Mama." At Bush's voice Lainey's eyes flew open and she blinked like an owl brought into the sunlight.

"Take care," Bush told Jimdandy. "We'll see you at Oklahoma City. Watch that ornery Blackjack." He put out his hand and after a second Jimdandy took it. Lainey's eyes widened in spite of herself.

"We'll be all right, Mist' Bush. Don' worry. You take care."

Thinking about Bush's shaking hands with Jimdandy made Lainey careless of her walking and she caught her toe in the flange of a rail. Bush waited while she worked her foot back into her slipper.

"Travelling makes things different, doesn't it?"

"You're mighty right." He swung her over a switch-frog. "It's a big world, honey, and it's high time you found that out."

There was more elegance in the Pullman Palace car than Lainey dreamed existed. If only Addie could see her now! There were red plush seats, gold curlicues around the windows, and real oil paintings on the ceiling where the lamps swung. Ice water in an oak barrel at one end of the car gave Lainey an excuse for walking up and down the aisle. But with the miracle of pulling down the beds, everything else was forgotten. She and Mama undressed in the cozy, cramped lower berth, bumping knees and elbows and giggling, then Lainey was boosted into the upper berth to sleep in lonely splendor. The pillow was too fat and puffy and she pushed it away and put her ear down on the mattress. There she caught the rhythm of the wheels, coming up through the car, making a song as they rumbled and rattled.

"Going-to-the-Territory . . . clack, clack . . . Going-to-the-Territory . . . clack, clack . . ."

She went to sleep with a smile on her face.

A breakfast of fried chicken came out of the lunch basket Aunt Ellen had packed. Everybody who left Riverview for a train trip carried fried chicken. It was almost as much a part of the trip as buying a ticket. There were ham sandwiches, too, and devilled eggs, and apples and cookies. Lainey washed it all down with ice water.

After breakfast Bush took Lainey up to the day coach to see some people he had met the night before. It was a come-down after the luxury of the Pullman Palace car, but everyone seemed to be having a good time as they leaned across the aisles talking and swapping food out of lunch baskets.

Bush introduced Lainey around but the names skidded in one ear and out the other. There was a moustached man from St. Joe who knew Uncle Hod and he had just bought a livery stable in Guthrie; a doctor right out of medical school in Philadelphia planning to look over the country and pick a place to practice; a Quaker lady on her way back to the Iowa Mission; a family of Germans from Michigan going down to buy land near their kinfolks, already homesteading south of Edmond, O.T.; a young man sure that he had a fortune in a patent potato peeler.

While Bush stood talking to a man on his way to Darlington to teach at the Indian school, Lainey sat down opposite the Quaker lady. She was a big woman with a face too long to be called pretty. Her small bonnet sat absolutely straight on her iron-gray hair. Her dress with its small gold pin at the collar was brown calico with the smooth texture that comes with dozens of washings and ironings. The same scrubbed cleaness extended to her face and her square-cut hands. She had only one beauty but that was enough. Absolute goodness shone out of her gray eyes.

"We're going to the Sac and Fox country," Lainey said.

"It is a good country. Thee will be happy there."

She nodded as she spoke and the certainty brought Lainey a comfort she had not known she needed. She began to ask the gray-eyed woman questions, even daring to mention her fear of Indians.

"I do not think thee needs to be afraid," the Quaker lady said. "God will take care of thee. And, remember, the Indians are His children, too."

"I forgot about God," Lainey said, then clapped her hand over her mouth.

A faint smile lighted the plain face. "He did not forget about thee."

While they were talking a red-haired man had button-holed Bush. "Ya say you're going down there to farm? That's a mug's game. Lotsa ways to make money in a new country without bustin' sod."

Lainey leaned toward her new friend. "I'll tell you my name. It's Elaine Saunders Sheridan. Elaine from the poem, you know, and Saunders is Mama's family name. And Sheridan is Bush's name. When my Aunt Ellen gets mad she says I'm 'all Sheridan.'"

"My name is Jane Baker."

It was a nice plain name, but to use it was like trying to pick up a round, smooth stone. Lainey decided to say "Miss" so that it might be taken as "Mrs.," in case it really was.

"Miz Baker . . ."

"You may call me Jane," the Quaker lady said. "In the Friends' Meeting we don't use titles."

It struck Lainey that there was a kinship between her and this plain, quiet-spoken lady. Everybody thought she was uppity for calling her own father Bush, but here were a lot of people who didn't even say Mr. or Miss. She liked it.

"Tell me about the mission, Jane."

"Well, it is a small one. The Iowas are not a large tribe. Their chief is named Tohee. He is blind and he lives in the village near us. At our mission I live with William and Sara Gwynne. William farms and Sara and I teach and we all have meetings." She sighed a little. "Sometimes no one attends, but still we have them."

Behind them the red-headed man had turned argumentative.

"I tell you this m'friend, the twin Territories'll make two states a whole lot quicker'n they will one. And think about th' boodle! Two sets o' everything."

But Bush was out-shouting him. "I say it'll be one state. And the best in the Union. Look here . . ."

"Split'er down the Indian Meridian. Leave those biggety bucks an' squaw men have the east side. Plenty left on the west to take care o' white men."

"I don't like that kind of talk," Bush said ominously and got up

38

from his seat. The schoolteacher rose and stepped between the two men.

"Gentlemen! Gentlemen! After all, you're only talking about a theory. Oklahoma Territory and Indian Territory will stand for years. There's no need to get excited about the matter of statehood. Not now, certainly."

A fat trainman waddled up to Bush. "Lady back in the Pullman's gettin' anxious 'bout you."

"Tell her I'll be right along. Now look here . . ." But the red-headed man was stalking off. Bush shook hands with the school-teacher. "Much obliged. Guess I was kind of hot under the collar but I've heard too much talk like that. I say stick together and . . . Anyway, come see us when you're over our way."

"Maybe I will," the schoolteacher said. "I'd like to talk to you some more about this. What I don't understand is why you feel so strongly about it. You talk as if you'd lived in the Territory all your life, and that's impossible. Why, man, you don't even have your claim yet, and you're already wanting to fight about it."

"I guess it does sound funny," Bush mused, shoving his hat back. "I'm Missouri born and bred, but when I got down to the Territory it was like I'd finally got home. Like I'd found something I'd been looking for a long time." He reddened as he realized that the others in the car were listening. "Come on, Lainey. Goodbye, mister. Goodbye, all."

As Lainey stumbled down the swaying aisle, she looked back and saw Jane Baker's bonnet over the high top of the day-coach seat, as steady and unswerving as the North Star.

Outside the train window the panorama of Kansas unrolled. The stories Lainey had heard of the Fifties when Kansas and Missouri burned with war-hate and when anti-slavery and pro-slavery were fighting words, seemed unreal against that placid landscape. Kansas was . . . why, it was quite a lot like Missouri!

The engineer blew for the crossings and the sound floated back to the Pullman Palace car on waves of black smoke. Every now and then the conductor called out stations in his strange garbled language. Gazing out the window Lainey fell to thinking of Pappy

Vickers. He had come to Riverview the day after the big dinner. She had seen him coming with his hitch-and-get-along walk and she and Bush had gone to meet him on the drive.

His faded eyes were snapping and he carried with him the Sharps' rifle he had lifted off a Yankee at the battle of Lonejack.

"I heard down't th' square you were leavin'," he began without preliminary.

"News gets around fast," Bush countered.

"I figgered it was what you was up to when Lainey said you were haulin' freight."

"Yep. A good way to see the country and get paid for it."

The two men squatted in the shade of the maples and Lainey sat down cross-legged beside them, smoothing her dress over her knees.

"Bush, I wanta go 'long with you," Pappy Vickers said. "Now hold on a minute." He held up a hand marked with dark-brown liver spots. It trembled slightly against the sunlight. "You're going into Injun country an' I don't wanta brag but I know Injuns. Only good Injun's a dead Injun. I'm a fair shot. Not what I usedta be, but I can still pick off a mess o' squirrels 'fore breakfast any day. You'll need a man with a gun." Lainey looked away, unable to bear the pleading in the old man's eyes.

"I ain't got chick nor child. Minnie's my sister's child but her and George'd a heap rather have my room than my presence. And I've got the rent money from the house in Marney to stake me. How 'bout it, boy? If ol' Jim Bridger was around he'd give you a recommend."

Bush was digging holes into the ground with a stick. An ant fell into one and struggled to try to climb out.

"Well, Pappy, it's like this," Bush chose his words as carefully as a horse tests a shaky bridge. "It's Indian country, all right, but we don't . . . I don't . . . look for that kind of trouble. We don't aim to fight 'em; we aim to live with 'em. Or 'longside of 'em, anyway."

"Don't fool yourself, boy."

"Times have changed, Pappy, and white men an' Indians have to change, too. I'll have a gun along, but I'm a sight more worried

40

about what kind of seed corn to take." The fire died out of the old man's eyes. He looked tired, almost frail.

"Well," he said with an effort at his old humor, "whatever makes the best whisky, that's the kind to take." He got stiffly to his feet and put out his hand. "No harm in askin', eh Bush?"

"Not a bit," Bush said. "Come down and see us when we get settled. Latchstring's always out." They shook hands warmly.

"I might do that," Pappy Vickers said. "I've got a hankerin' to see new country one more time before I die. G'bye, boy. Take care of yourself."

He stumped away, dust rising in small puffs from his booted feet.

"I swear, I feel as mean as a sheep-killin' dog," Bush had said.

"Arrrrrkansas City, KANsas," the conductor shouted.

Bush looked at his watch.

"Just an hour late. That's good as on time for this part of the country."

Leaning out the window he and Lainey speculated on the people around the depot. The train shuddered as baggage was hauled off and on.

"Can you imagine what this place looked like in '89?" Bush said excitedly. "The day of the first Run? They say you couldn't wedge a flea into the depot, it was so packed."

The engine belched, lurched forward once again and began to pull out of the depot. The cars banged against each other, then settled down.

"Come along," Bush said, and led Lainey into the vestibule. The brightness of the light made her blink. It was almost noon. The uproar of the train made it impossible to talk. She wondered why Bush had brought her out here, but there was no way of asking. All at once he picked her up, her legs dangling, and held her, leaning with him out the vestibule window. Cinders flicked her face. The train rolled heavily onto a bridge across a wide, muddy river with long sand flats on either side.

"Arkansas River," he yelled into her ear.

How bright the sun was! How blue the sky! The train toiled

41

over the bridge, picked up speed, and curved around a bend. Lainey felt the hard thumping of Bush's heart against her as he held her, his face plastered against hers, as far out the window as he could reach. The wind whipped at them. A wild excitement rose in Lainey's throat and she laughed, not knowing why.

"What is it?" she screamed, grabbing at Bush's shoulder.

"This is it!" The wind tore the words out of his mouth. "This is the Territory!"

The land rolled away from the tracks in great, smooth swells. Her eyelashes were battered back, her eyes dry. It was a stretch of endless land, unbroken by house or fence. Even its smell was different. Lainey shivered in the mid-day heat and put her mouth against Bush's ear.

"Oh, Bush," she cried, "I'm glad I came. I'm glad I came!"

Chapter 5

They were a week in Oklahoma City. The lusty, dusty, two-year-old town with its board sidewalks, corrugated iron awnings, the noise of hammers all day and all night and the si-wash, si-wash of saws, was a far cry from Kansas City, or St. Joe or Lainey's memory of her one visit to St. Louis. But she loved it. The stores with their signs askew in the wind, "Guns, Bicycles, Locks," "Cottage Rest, Dinner .20, Lunch .15," "Palace Clothing House," "Dutch Store," "Pettee's Hardware." The small sturdy churches that marched up the hill of sandy Robinson Avenue. The swinging doors downtown that were never still. The Opera House with its kerosene lanterns and curtains of red calico. The tangle of horses, mules, bicycles, even oxen. The occasional flash of color as a blanket Indian went past. And always the tramp of hundreds of hurrying feet.

They had stayed with Kate Tillery, a stocky, weather-beaten woman who looked at the mountain of things unloaded from the "Zulu" car and said, "Whatcha aimin' to do? Start a store? I come to the Run o' '89 with a stove, a skillet, a strawtick, an' a rocker. M'husband made me throw out the rocker."

Mama hadn't liked that one bit. In fact, Mama and Kate hadn't liked each other in spite of how much Bush said they'd be friends. But Kate had been right about loading the wagon.

"You'll never git all that stuff on only one wagon, Bush. Go load up that old Conestoga out in the shed an' I'll send Bud Menifee along to drive it. I c'n spare Bud till you git settled an' maybe you c'n keep him outa faro games for a while."

But even with the second wagon there had been things left over. Kate sent for the second-hand man and bargained with him shrewdly while Allegra stood by, tight-lipped and angry. Lainey felt tears pricking at her eyelids as a slipper chair, a china cabinet,

43

and a love seat with mother-of-pearl insets in the back were hauled off.

The hardest thing of all had been to say goodbye to Jimdandy. If only she could have gone with him, or if he could have stayed with them! At the depot as Allegra gave Jimdandy a box of lunch and Bush handed him five dollars and explained again about the ticket pinned to the inside of his coat, Lainey felt she could see ranged around all the things he had done for her. The swing in the high maple, the riding lessons, the raspberry apples from the far orchard, the guitar plunking in the kitchen, the stories . . . even the horrible "Taley-po" that she begged for and shuddered at . . . All of them were there and she couldn't, she just couldn't give them up. But the conductor bawled, "Boooooard!" and the train pulled out and the links that held her to Riverview stretched and stretched and then snapped as the Santa Fe took Jimdandy around a curve and out of sight.

It was the next day that President Harrison issued the expected proclamation on the opening of the Sac and Fox, the Iowa, the Pottawatomie, and the Absentee Shawnee lands. The Kickapoos had not signed.

"I figgered they wouldn't," Bush said, "wild as March hares, the lot of 'em."

"Plenty without their dab o' land," Kate Tillery said, "but four days off . . . Bush, you better get high behind!"

"We got time," Bush said. "I've made it before in less."

"You wasn't drivin' no covered wagons, nor cluttered up with cows and such." Lainey, listening, knew that Kate would have added "womenfolks" if Mama hadn't appeared around the corner. It seemed as if Kate had done a man's work so long after her husband got killed that she thought she was a man, too.

"We'll make it anyway," Bush said confidently, then he added "With good luck," and touched the wooden box of the wagon for luck.

Their luck had held the first day but the second it broke. The Jersey cow from the Riverview herd fell on the rough ground and broke her leg. Her pitiful bawling filled the empty land with pain and terror. Bush and Mama and Bud and Lainey stood clear of her threshing, asking each other what to do.

"We'll have to shoot her," Bush said. "She'd never get well and besides we can't wait around here."

"But Bush . . ." Allegra said pitifully. "But . . . but . . ."

"Honey, you know animals. You know she'd never make it. We can't leave her here."

"Hey," Bud said, "Lookit over there. Indians."

They rode up on their unsaddled ponies, their coppery faces bright with expectation. They jabbered and pointed and their bright-colored clothes and their wrapped braids seemed fearful and alien to Lainey and she wished she were small enough to put her face against Mama's calico dress.

"They say they'll buy her for meat," Bud interpreted. "They got a camp near."

"How much?"

The Indian held up one finger. Bush held up two. Lainey heard Mama's breath of horror under the moaning of the injured cow.

"I guess it's a deal," Bud said as the Indian dug into a beaded pouch. "But we better drive on. The way they butcher . . . well . . ."

"Bush," Allegra said, "you've got to shoot her. I won't go another step. I won't stand for it."

He looked at her for a minute then nodded. "Tell him, Bud, and you drive on."

They climbed into the wagon and Bud cracked the whip. It was five minutes later that they heard the blast of Bush's gun and the sudden quiet from the cow. Bush caught up with them by a sandy flat.

"Well, that's over with," he said.

"I don't want to talk about it," Allegra answered, stony-faced.

"For a farm-raised girl . . ."

"I don't want to talk about it. And Lainey, don't you ever tell Aunt Ellen."

"Look here, the cow had to be killed. You know it."

"Taking money . . . bargaining . . . with those . . ."

45

"So that's it! Well, let me tell you we're going to need every cent we've got. This wagon . . . that sod-buster . . . And lumber's sky-high. And now we'll have to buy another cow . . . if we can find one."

The anger between the two lasted until the evening camp when they had eaten supper and were sitting by the fire watching the moon rise over the land.

"Makes me think of the night . . ." Bush said.

"I know. When I slipped out to meet you down by the South Branch."

Lainey saw Allegra put out her hand, and Bush take it. The smoke of the campfire drifted and curled and all at once her eyes stung and when she rubbed the smoke out of them her father and mother had gone.

The next night brought them to Captain Creek. As they stopped to let the horses drink and blow bubbles in the cool water Bush came back to talk with Bud.

"Think we can chance drivin' at night?"

"You makin' for that little old bend where Deep Fork crosses the Sac'n' Fox boundary?"

"Yep, I figger there'll be a lot fewer folks make the Run from there than from the Iowa Reservation boundary, what with Guthrie up there, an' all."

Bud nodded, scratching his head. "If it'uz just you'n me I'd say let'er go Gallagher, but with the missus an' Lainey . . ."

"Root hog or die," Lainey blurted out. She had heard Kate use the words and she wasn't just sure what they meant, but they sounded right, and they must have been for Bush and Bud's laughter echoed loudly across the stream and the unplowed land.

"Guess that settles it," Bush said, "Just keep to the trail. I'd hate to stumble into a Kickapoo stomp dance, or whatever they call 'em."

He tramped back to the lead wagon and they heard him crack the long whip. As the team splashed into the water of Captain Creek he yelled back to Bud and Lainey, "Root hog or die!"

Night had come on quickly. There was no gentle lingering twilight here as there was in Missouri. The high grass came up to the sides of the wagon and brushed against the boards with a swish, swish, swish. The stars were bright in the unbroken arch of heaven and presently the moon dimmed their brilliance. There were not many trees, not by Snyder County standards, and what there were grew in clusters around the creeks and draws. Lainey eyed them fearfully for Bud had told her that the Kickapoos had a custom of burying their dead in trees. As she dozed on the wagon seat, drifting in and out of sleep, she dreamed she was back at Riverview and each apple tree in the orchard held a huge, fierce Indian, decked in paint and feathers. She wakened, clutching at Bud.

Then, once again she wakened to see a long line of campfires flickering against the night and through the darkness she heard Bush's triumphant shout,

"Glory be!"

Yawning till her jawbone cracked Lainey realized she must have gone to sleep up on the driver's seat beside Bud last night and he had lifted her back to her bed in the wagon. Her sunbonnet and shoes were beside her but she was wearing all the rest of her clothes. The morning light filtered through the canvas wagon sheet and the rocking, rolling motion had stopped. Voices muted by distance called back and forth. A fire crackled near at hand; water splashed from bucket to pan. And intermingled with these sounds was the far-off whistle of a red-winged blackbird. That meant water, and the water must be Deep Fork! In the dark hours of the night while she had slept they had made it to the boundary of the Sac and Fox country. Root hog or die! Lainey sat up, hugging her knees.

Eee-hee-haw! Ee-hee-haw! Haw-haw-haw! A mule brayed, loud and discontented.

On the edge of the last note a man shouted, "Oooooo, Joe, here's yore mule!"

Laughter came from everywhere and the cry was taken up and repeated a dozen, twenty, fifty times. It was the cry of the land openings, familiar even to Lainey Sheridan, fresh from Missouri. It made her feel initiated to hear it.

47

She put on her shoes, and then her sunbonnet to hide her uncombed hair, and climbed out onto the wagon seat.

The world of last night, of quiet trails and moon-touched land had become a line of wagons, buggies, carts, buckboards, and everything imaginable on wheels that stretched along Deep Fork to the bend, then south along the Sac and Fox boundary. Gold-crowned cottonwoods and ragged willows marked the course of the stream. In the bottom country a clump of trees here and there broke the skyline. Low hills ran up to meet the blue sky, and in the east pink clouds still held the color of the sunrise. The grass was trampled along the boundary, but back off the trail it was thick and green, springing from earth that was incredibly red. Bush's little glass bottle had not lied! Red earth, green grass, blue sky. A raw, bright landscape, as young as the day of Creation.

The morning wind was cold and men moved briskly about their outfits talking among themselves or squatting around small camp-fires where the blue smoke and the smell of frying meat rose together. Lainey saw a few women, long calico skirts swinging, leaning over skillets or reaching into grub boxes at the back of the wagons. But for the most part this was a man's world. She looked for Bush, needing him to reassure her of her rightful place here.

Bush and Allegra were eating breakfast and Bud was up ahead holding Blackjack in place in the line-up for the Run. Bud had used up his homestead rights in '89 . . . promptly losing his claim in a poker game . . . and he would stay with Allegra and Lainey and the wagons. Bush would ride alone. A man on horseback had the best chance, but plenty of wagons and teams and buggies and one span of oxen were in the lineup by the creek.

By the side of the Sheridan wagon stood an ancient wagon with a patched cover lettered, "Nebrasky or Bust . . . We Busted." A weary-eyed woman by the tailgate forked sidemeat out of a skillet to five shivering tow-headed boys. She smacked down a hand that reached for a second piece.

"Let be! Ain't enough to carry us till crops now."

On the other side of the Sheridans a man was standing shaving,

48

squinting into a mirror attached to the horn of his saddle. He was dapper and slender and his velvet-embroidered vest was the fanciest Lainey had ever seen. Catching her eye, he bowed, the razor glinting in his hand. Lainey blushed, jumped down and ran to the fire where Bush handed her a plate of fried ham and some biscuits Bud had baked last night.

Down the trail where they had come last night a steady stream of rigs threw dust into the air. The wind scattered it over the whole line-up and Lainey held one hand over her plate as she ate.

"Good thing we came on in last night," Bush said. "Won't be a place left on the boundary by noon."

"Where are they all coming from?" Allegra marvelled.

"'Most anywhere. Missouri. Iowa. Tennessee. Nebraska. Kentucky. I talked to a New York man last night."

"There must be a thousand people," Lainey said.

"More likely ten thousand. Or twenty. Don't forget this is just a little chunk that you see here. The boundary line runs clear around the four reservations they're opening. With a man and a horse every six feet, or so, and allowin' for wagons and buggies . . ." He shook his head at the impossibility of figuring the number.

"But how do they all get to come? Who says?"

"All you have to do is be twenty-one, or the head of a family, and a citizen of the United States . . . or declare you're goin' to take out papers. And if you served in the war you're entitled to a homestead anyway."

"I wish Pappy Vickers had come," Lainey said. "He served in the war."

"Uh, that's right," Bush said, "but . . ." At Allegra's raised eyebrows he hastily added. "I mean, it's just Union soldiers or sailors." As Bud sauntered up Bush got up to leave, then stopped. "How many do you think are out there?" he asked.

"Countin' in the sooners hid out in the bresh?"

"Countin' everybody," Bush glanced at the Winchester on the wagon seat.

"You didn't tell me there was likely to be trouble," Allegra said.

"For a fire-eatin' family," Bush jibed, "you Saunders stick at

49

the funniest things. Yankies, now, or Redlegs . . . but sooners . . ."

"Good thing to have a persuader along," Bud drawled and Lainey breathed easier. To have Mama and Bush get mad in the unknown country was frightening. "Back in '89 I was ridin' along at a fast clip and I seen a likely piece o' land and I says to my hoss . . . a little dun mare . . . I says, 'That's for us.' I headed over that way and while I was scoutin' around for the pit-and-mound corner marker I come up on a feller standin' right there with an awful lathered-up hoss."

"Oh-oh, he beat you there?" Lainey asked.

"Well, that's what I fust thought, then I took notice that the hoss wasn't winded. I circled around and sure enough, there in the weeds was a pan o' water an' a bar o' soap. That feller made a liar outa that hoss, sure as you're born. But when he seen I was onto him he levelled on me with a gun that looked bigger'n a water barrel and he says to me, 'Whut time is it?' I pulled out my good gold watch . . . the one I showed you, Lainey . . . an' I says, 'One o'clock.' He pulls out his watch and he says, 'It's three o'clock,' an' he showed me the hands and, sure enough, they pointed to three. 'Now that's funny,' I says, 'this watch ain't never been wrong before an' I started with the rest at twelve.' 'When I say it's three o'clock, it's three o'clock,' he says, 'now get yourself outa here but keep in mind you seen me on my claim at three o'clock, if I need ary witness.' "

He stopped as if the story were over but Lainey was sure there was something he was not telling.

"What did you do?"

"Do? I lit a shuck an' got outa there. Arguin' with a man that's got a gun on you is a prime waste o' time." He began to eat, calmly, his eyes twinkly at her discomfiture. Pappy Vickers, or General Sterling Price, she was sure, would have run the dirty sooner off.

Allegra approached with a pan of water and a cake of soap.

"Young lady, don't think for one minute I didn't know you ate breakfast without washing your face. Just because we're in the wilderness is no reason not to live decent. And when you get washed up I'll brush your hair."

50

Lainey washed gingerly, the soap curdling in the cold hard water. With solid licks Allegra brushed the quilt lint out of her hair and re-braided the stubby black braids. It should have made Lainey feel better, but it didn't. The silver-backed brush looked painfully out of place as Allegra thrust it between the spokes of the wagon-wheel. Or maybe it was the uneasy night, or the hurried breakfast. From nowhere at all a lump balled up in her throat. Dust whirled into her eyes. A hound down the line began to howl.

"I don't li-like it," she said to Allegra. "I want to go home."

The words called up tears. Lainey choked on them, hiccoughing over and over, "I want to go home. I . . . want . . . to . . . go . . . home . . ."

"Hush, honey," Allegra pulled her close. "Bush'll hear you. You'll make him feel bad."

She wanted him to feel bad. She wanted to hurt somebody as much as she hurt. She dug in her heels and bawled, "I want to go home."

"Ain't sick, is she?" It was the weary-eyed woman from the next wagon.

"Oh, I don't think so. Just kind of upset."

"I got some calomel. A good course o' calomel."

Lainey's stomach flipped. Calomel was Aunt Ellen's sovereign remedy.

"Thank you, but I think she's just tired. A trip like this is hard on a child."

"It's hard enough on a grown-up woman." The big red-knuckled hands rested on bony hips. "This is sure my last try. I've helped bust sod three times an' I aim to stay here till I rot."

"Where did you live in Nebraska?"

"Up on the Platte. But we wasn't there no time a-tall. Ioway before that. And before that Missoury an' Kansas. I know more about movin' than I do about stayin'." She whirled quickly and gave a back-handed smack at the smallest of the tow-heads. "You, Clem! Allus stuffin'. You think grub grows on trees?"

The child's watery-blue eyes looked up at her; his lips puckered.

"Here, Clem," Allegra covered a biscuit with a slice of ham. "We had some left from breakfast and . . ."

51

The woman pushed down the small, chapped hand.

"We ain't no charity case. We got plenty."

"But I didn't mean . . ."

"We're makin' out just fine. You, Clem, get back where you b'long."

She marched after the child, her back stiff and Allegra put the biscuit back in the pan, her face pink with distress. Lainey had forgotten her tears wondering what had gone wrong and why when Bud came up to them with a tiny dark-haired girl in his arms.

"Musta wandered off. I cain't make head nor tail of what she's sayin'."

She was a doll of a child with bright dark eyes and dark curls, dressed in quaint beautifully embroidered clothes. She was not shy but the words she chattered to Allegra and Lainey as she munched on a biscuit were meaningless.

"Oh, she's darling!" Lainey exclaimed. "I wish we could keep her. She could be my sister."

Allegra fingered the collar of the child's dress.

"We had a French teacher at the seminary. She had some things like this that she brought from home. I wonder . . . but surely not 'way out here." She cocked her head, listening. "Still, it does sound like . . . I'll try, anyway." She spoke slowly, searching for words, "*Avez-vous des* . . . no, no, I mean, *avez-vous une M'ma?*"

"*Oui!*" The child squealed, and began chattering like a blackbird.

"Not so fast," Allegra begged, "*Où est ton cheval et . . . et* . . . Oh, heavens, what is French for covered wagon?"

Lainey listened in awe. "I didn't know you could speak French."

"Not as well as I should. Every lady . . ."

"Violette! Violette! Where 'ave you been? *Ma petite* . . ." A small, moustached man ran up and grabbed the child out of Lainey's arms, with his snapping black eyes there was no need to ask their kinship.

"*Vous êtes très, très méchante!*" He shook and kissed her at the same time. "*Ma chérie! Ma petite chérie!*" She laughed and took him by the ears.

52

"*P'pa, P'pa, Violette très bonne!*"

"We 'ave the good place in the line," he explained to Allegra, "an' we put this little one in the wagon, asleep, while we 'ave *le petit déjeuner*, when we look for her she is gone! Gone!" He flung out his arms in a dramatic gesture, dropping Violette who ran to Allegra. "We are mos' grateful to you, *Madame.*"

"Mama talked French to her," Lainey said. "She learned it at the seminary."

"*Non, non, M'sieu,*" Allegra tried to stem the torrent of French. "Only a little. But I couldn't believe my ears. Out here . . ."

"Ah, *oui*, it ees strange. I myself wonder at it. But my wife, Lili, 'as a kinsman who came to the opening in Keengfeeshaire. He wrote us . . . so we came." His shrug was as French as his waxed moustache. "But I mus' get back to Lili, she ees franteek. She fears the red Indians . . ." He bowed over Allegra's hand and then Lainey's. "*Madame! Mademoiselle!*"

When Bush returned from the boundary Lainey rushed to tell him about Violette. "And Mama talked to her, just like a native."

"Your mama's a wonder. She's going to be a first-rate homesteader."

"I don't know about that," Allegra said soberly, "that little French went a long way, but I failed closer home." She nodded toward the battered wagon. "I meant it in kindness. You heard her say they were short of food." She told him about Clem's biscuit.

"Did you take something from her first?" he asked. Allegra shook her head. "Then she'll never take anything from you. But maybe I can fix it." He walked to the other wagon.

"Howdy, howdy folks."

"Howdy," the woman spoke shortly, skillet in hand.

"You folks got an axe handy? Broke the handle square off mine choppin' into an oak knot. You'd think a feller'd know better!"

The woman eyed him an instant longer, then Lainey saw the shadow of a smile start under the slatted sunbonnet.

"You c'n take that'un over there. 'Longside the wagon."

Bush hefted the axe. "Got a good balance to it."

"My man's a master hand at an axe handle. That there'n's made out of white ash. He worked a week to get it just right."

53

"Reckon he wouldn't want a stranger using it?"

"Go 'long," she shook her sacking apron in an awkward, playful gesture. "We're neighbors, till twelve noon, anyways."

"Well, I sure thank you." Bush came back to Allegra, whistling a little tune.

"May I ask when you broke an axe handle?" she demanded.

"Must have, sometime in my life. But it's not the axe. It's . . ."

"Well, how about chopping some wood, now that you've borrowed it."

Bush squirmed. "I was just fixin' to walk around a little. See who's here."

"They're watching you. You wouldn't want to disappoint your neighbors."

"All right, all right," he turned on Lainey. "Just you stop grinning like a possum-cat or I'll go back and borrow that calomel."

With the axe on his shoulder Bush sauntered to a stand of timber. Allegra climbed into the wagon. Bud was up by Blackjack.

This is my chance, Lainey thought, and stepping light and easy on the trampled grass she walked away from the Sheridan wagons.

Chapter 6

There were more people strung out along the boundary line than Lainey had ever seen in her life. She made her way to the spots where they were thickest, zig-zagging in and out, picking up scraps of talk as strange as Violette's French had been on her ears. "Prove up . . . soldier's preferment . . . indemnified school land . . . head rights . . . surplus land . . . catface brand . . ." She did not try to understand what they meant, liking better the thrill of newness, the bigness of it all, the feeling of being part of a tremendous undertaking. The pull she felt drawing her along the line was the one that brought hundreds of people to the land openings as onlookers. It was a show as big as all outdoors. As big as the Territory itself.

In the midst of a knot of men, Lainey caught a glimpse of the fancy vest of the stranger she had seen shaving that morning. By small, determined pushes and prods she worked her way into the group. He had a little table in front of him, just waist high. His hands moved deftly over it. And beside him was Bud Menifee, his face red, his prized gold watch swinging from his hand.

"Step right up! Step right up, gents. Place your bets. I cover all bets. Any at all. This gold watch? Twenty-five dollars, the gent says, and I say the hand's quicker than the eye. Prove me wrong, gents, prove me wrong. The little shell moves . . . is it here? . . . is it there? Say which gents . . . say which . . ."

The backs of the men closed up solidly in front of Lainey. The gentle persuasive voice droned on. "Step right up, gents, we lift the shell and the gentleman with the watch says she's . . . here. But . . ."

"I'll be hornswoggled!"

A rumble of laughter followed Bud's outburst. Lainey nudged

a gray broadcloth back and a linsey woolsey back, but they were close against her. She wondered what had happened, but something told her not to ask Bud.

From down the line came the sound of singing. The tune was unfamiliar but by the heavy, ringing cadence Lainey was sure it was a hymn. Black-clad men and women stood around in a small, tight circle. The men wore heavy beards, cut square across the bottom, the women small black bonnets. As Lainey came closer the singing stopped and one of the men began to pray in an impassioned voice. The others bowed their heads. Lainey tiptoed past. It seemed impolite to put your feet down flat when people were praying.

Around her others were making way for a man on a black stallion. The horse rolled a reddened eye but the man held him easily, the reins wrapped around one hand, the other loose at his side, near, perilously near, the bulge of a gun at his hip.

"Howdy, Marshall, Howdy!" men spoke to him, and a few called him by name. "Howdy Al."

He lifted his hand in casual greeting but his chilly gray eyes never stopped searching.

"Is that the sheriff?" Lainey asked a woman near her.

"No sheriff in these parts yet awhile. But that's the law just the same. It's Al Colwater, the Deputy U.S. Marshall. Likely enough he'll send somebody to Ft. Smith 'fore this is over."

Lainey felt the marshall's steely gaze sweep over her and she had a wild longing to run. She must find Bush. She must find the Sheridan wagons. She ran this way and that, a hundred wagons were around her but not their own. She was lost, terribly lost. The dust choked her.

"Hey, Sis, whatsa matter?"

It was the part-Indian trader from Tohee. She saw his dark face, his long hair, and bright shirt and behind him she saw a half-dozen Kickapoos in brilliant trappings watching her with dead-black eyes!

Running, running, she heard in the thud of her own feet their dread pursuit. Her feet grew heavy and her throat ached with dust and fear. She dodged behind a scrubby stand of buckbrush and

56

sumac and stumbled heavily against someone standing there. But even as she fell, rolling, to the ground she knew a shuddering relief for the blue eyes, the freckles, the tow-colored hair that stood out in spikes could not possibly belong to a Kickapoo brave.

"Who in tarnation are you?" the boy scowled, "runnin' around like a chicken with its head off."

"Indians!" Lainey picked herself up and pointed through the sumac back to where the Indian men made a bright patch of color against the drab clothes of the others.

"Them?" The scorn was thick in the flat, mid-western voice. "Just a bunch o' Kickapoos, tradin' for ponies. They don't want no girls!"

"But . . . a man I know said they put people up in trees when they die."

"I'd ruther be put up in a tree than stuck down in a hole."

She considered the choice. It didn't sound so bad, put like that. But she couldn't admit she was wrong quite so quickly.

"I'm sorry I bumped into you."

"You didn't hurt. I was just sittin' here, studying 'bout the Run."

"How soon will it be?"

He glanced up at the sun. "Coupla hours, now. I wish I could ride, but Dad won't let me."

"Would the soldiers let you?"

"They don't keer who runs. I couldn't take a claim because I'm not twenty-one, I'm twelve, goin' on thirteen." He jerked off a sumac stem and swished the ground. "But I can beat Dad all to a frazzle ridin' and if he'd just leave me go I could get us a good piece o' land and clean out the sooners . . ."

"They might have guns! A man I know . . ."

"I got a gun, too." He took a long swing at the sumac, then added with a burst of honesty, "It won't fire, but I bet I could chase any sooner off." In a moment despair clouded the clear depths of his blue eyes and he flung the sumac, like a spear, toward Deep Fork. "But Dad won't let me."

A burst of shouting stopped him short.

"Hey! Lookit, over there!"

Across Deep Fork three uniformed men on horseback were

chasing a man who rode Indian fashion on a spotted pony. They were hazing him steadily toward the stream and the clamoring line-up of homeseekers.

"It's the soldiers, chasin' out a sooner!"

The government had burned off the grass, patrolled the area, done everything in its power but still men had slipped past them into the lands to be ahead of the opening. Threats of prison sentence and heavy fines made no difference. They would have the land and have it first.

"Git 'im! Git 'im!" the crowd yelled.

As the chase swung left, Lainey saw the foam fly from the pony's lathered bit. The man who lay along his back had a red beard, and there was a long rent in his blue shirt.

The soldiers drove him closer. They looked strong and powerful in their blue uniforms, riding long-legged cavalry horses with McClelland saddles.

"Git 'im! Chase 'im over here. We'll take care of 'im!"

Everyone was against him! Lainey clenched her fists and prayed for a miracle as the big cavalry horses gained on the pony. "Please," she begged, "please let 'em get away. Please!"

"Git 'im," the boy beside her screamed. "Ride 'im down!"

The narrow margin was closing, closing. Lainey grabbed the boy's arm.

"Three against one's no fair!"

"That don't count, this's a sooner!" He shook her off, cupped his hands and shouted with the others. "Head 'im off! Ride 'im down!"

"No!" Lainey shrieked. "No! No! No!"

Suddenly the pony twisted in his tracks and seemed to double in mid-air. The red-bearded man, lying low along his back, rode him straight at the soldiers. Surprised, they divided, two and one. The pony darted between and headed for the far line of timber. The nearest soldier rose in his stirrups and levelled his gun. Then, abruptly, he settled back in the saddle without firing. The pony and the man disappeared in the distance. The three soldiers rode away, their backs stolid against the catcalls from the crowd.

Curiously, there were a few cheers for the sooner.

"Whew! I'm glad he made it!" Lainey said.

Disgust wrinkled the boy's nose. "Soonerin's no better'n horse

58

stealin'. How'd you like it if he got the claim your folks are waitin' in the line-up for? Or maybe he is your folks! Maybe you're a sooner your-own-self."

She spit like a cat, fury tangling her tongue. "Don't you dare say that! My father's no sooner. He's Bushrod Sheridan an' he's a thousand million times better'n you are, an' I hate you!" She slashed at him with a sumac limb.

"Who cares? Miss Biggety! Miss Run-From-a-Kickapoo!" He danced around her in imitation of a war dance, patting his hand over his mouth to make a blood-curdling noise. "Sooooooner! Sooooooooner!"

"Arch! You, Arch!" A man came panting up, a worried-looking man with a paunch that bulged dangerously over his belted jeans. "What you up to?"

"Nothin'," Arch said. "I was just standin' around."

"Was he devillin' you, little lady?"

The glance between Arch and Lainey was not forgiveness or regret; it was a postponement of settlement until no grown-ups were near. Lainey dropped the sumac limb behind her back.

"Nossir. We were just talking. But I have to be going now. Goodbye." She smiled politely at the baffled man. "Goodbye . . . Arch." For her to know his name when he did not know hers was to have scored against him.

Walking sedately around the sumac clump she forgot that she was lost. It was no surprise to see Bud coming along toward her and not far back of him the Sheridan wagons, and in the line-up Blackjack's black and white haunches. Her step was gay and bouncing. She had had adventures and had come out victorious.

"Hey, gal, where you been? Your mama's plumb crazy," Bud said sternly.

"I've just been walking around," she said, "Just walking around. I don't know why you act like I was half-witted or something."

She went over to Blackjack where Bush was rubbing the horse's legs with Jimdandy's secret liniment. It smelled strongly of witch hazel. Bush slapped the saddle onto the horse, cinched it, took it off, did it over again. He tested every strap and buckle on the heavy stock saddle. The line-up was crowded, now. The knots of people had broken up and strung out along the boundary.

"I'm not going to take that gun," Bush handed Bud the Winchester.

"Well, you might not need it, then again, you might."

"I figger it this way," Bush shoved back his hat, "I've come to the Territory to get a home, not to start trouble. And it's not good sense to carry a gun you're not aimin' to use. Besides, it's heavy." He stirred a pile of things with his booted toe. "Spade, stakes, canteen, grub, oilskins . . . reckon I could get by without those?"

"Don't look like rain," Bud glanced up, "but they'd come in handy to make a shelter. A shelter's a big help if you run into trouble provin' up. Feller in '89 had him a big red umbrella . . . like the ones on vegetable wagons back east in Chicago . . . he set up housekeepin' under it an' lived there three weeks."

Lainey handed Bush the filled canteen. "How much longer till the Run?"

Bud reached for his watch, then grinned ruefully. "Reckon I must of left my watch somewheres."

"You did?" Bush said. "Whereabouts?"

"Under a walnut shell, you might say. Doggone, that feller's the nimblest I ever did see. Son of a . . . gun!"

They saw Allegra coming toward them, her face flushed under the pink, ruffled sunbonnet. Lainey sidled up to Bush, hoping to show she had been there all the time.

"So there you are! I've a good mind to give you a dose of peachtree tea! Where have you been?"

As if it made any difference now that she was found.

"I just went for a walk. Just a walk around." Then she remembered all the things she had seen. "I saw the deputy U.S. marshall. And some Kickapoos. And some people having a prayer meeting. And a boy."

"A boy?" Allegra asked. "What sort of boy?"

"Just a boy. He's twelve, going on thirteen and his name's Arch and his father won't let him ride in the Run."

"I should hope not! What have you done to that clean dress?"

Lainey tried to brush off the red dirt that her fall had ground into the calico.

"Oh, let it go," Allegra said distractedly. "How can you ever keep
60

anything clean out here? Wind and dust! Does the wind ever stop blowing?"

"I don't know, ma'am," Bud drawled. "Only been here two years."

"I saw the sooner," Lainey added to her list.

"I did too! He ought to be in jail. It's a disgrace they let him go."

Bush looked up from the oilskins he was re-folding. "Two sides to everything."

"Bushrod Sheridan! Soonerin's plain stealing. It's against the law."

"There's a good many kinds of law, Allegra. This whole country, now, it was promised to the Indians by treaty . . . 'as long as the grass grows and the water runs.' But it's been opened up, by law."

"Well, my goodness, they were paid for it, weren't they? They didn't have to agree to sell. Besides," she went on, triumphantly, "if you felt that way about it, why'd you come down to take up their land?"

"I guess you've got me there." Bush strapped the oilskins behind the saddle. "But I reckon it's the same reason Jeb Saunders had for taking Riverview off the Osages . . . because I *want* the land."

"But he . . . but they . . ." She gave it up. "How much longer till the Run?"

Lainey, copying Arch's glance, looked up at the sun. "About an hour."

Bush laughed, pulled out his watch. "You're guessing Missouri time, honey. It's later'n that in the Territory. I'd say a half-hour, if the U.S. Army agrees."

As if by pre-arrangement the soldier stationed on the far side of Deep Fork looked at his watch. All up and down the line-up men were looking at their watches. Watches that had timed sermons, ticked out the lives of patients, changed hands in dice games, counted seconds for a cavalry charge, kept time for school sessions and for hangings were balanced in palms where tell-tale sweat glistened along the life line, the heart line, the head line.

A soldier took a pistol from its holster. He raised his arm and the whole line surged forward a step or two "Git back! Git back!" he yelled, lowering the gun; staring at the watch.

Laughter and talk stopped. There was only waiting, waiting, a live thing, coiled and tense. The wind moved restlessly about, shaking the wagon covers and flinging red dust at the mounted men.

"Water! Fresh cool water! Ten cents a dipper." The cry of the hawker was loud or faint at the whim of the wind.

The horses caught the tension from the gripped knees and uneasy hands of their riders. Here and there they reared, pawing and snorting. A pair of matched sorrels turned wild at the smell of the yoke of oxen and lashed out, iron heels splintering a varnished buggy.

Sightseers from Guthrie, Edmond, Oklahoma City, Kingfisher, old settlers with two years or less of experience, stood up in their conveyances to watch the fun. It was nothing, they said, nothing to '89, nothing at all. They opened up picnic lunches and took out fringed napkins, laughing and pointing, but the wind swept their laughter away.

"Ten minutes!"

Lainey's stomach turned to a rock. Allegra pulled her close. She saw Bush shove back his hat, then pull it firmly down onto his forehead again. He leaned forward patting Blackjack's thick arched neck. Low, under her breath she began a pleading chant. "Bushrod Sheridan . . . my father . . . Bushrod Sheridan . . . my father . . ."

"Five minutes!"

Up the line a woman began to cry, high pitched and hysterical. Down the line somebody called for a doctor. Around the soldier time stood still. His arm began to move. Up . . . up . . . dark blue against the bright blue sky. The gun in his hand was pointing straight at the sun that hung, like Joshua's, high in the arch of heaven. Lainey heard the sound of her own uneven breath and felt Allegra trembling against her. Blackjack shook his head and snorted.

"Goodbye . . . Allegra . . . Lainey . . ."

Bush's voice was harsh and strained and he did not turn his head but Lainey felt warmed by it. He had not forgotten.

"Oh God, let him get what he wants, whatever it is!" Allegra whispered, her hands tight on Lainey's shoulders.

"One minute!"

A hush. No breath. No heartbeat. The sightseers quieted. Only the wind, the eternal wind of the Territory dared to move. The soldier's arm straightened, the weight of a thousand eyes pulled on his trigger finger. Down . . . down . . .

The shot!

A clear, short bark of sound that echoed up and down Deep Fork. Repeating a hundred times around the boundaries of the Sac and Fox, the Pottawatomie, the Iowa, and the Shawnee lands. With a shattering roar made up of the Rebel yell, the Choctaw death gobble, the Green Mountain shout, and the wild defiance of every American frontier from Jamestown to the Alamo, the Run of '91 began.

Dirt struck Lainey in the face. She saw Blackjack's black and white haunches leap forward, scramble down into Deep Fork and come lunging up the far side. Bush was gone! Gone in the Run for land, the only wealth, the only possession. A run to the swift, to the strong, to the brave, to the daring. In the September sunshine all the old values returned to earth and hung, glittering, above the Territory. Courage. Speed. Strength. A man and a horse against the world for a woman and a child. For a home. For land . . . land!

Cowboys from the Cherokee Strip, jeans-clad and gun-happy stampeded by.

"Pow-der River! Let'er buck!"

Allegra clutched Lainey but she broke away, standing on the wagon seat. This was a thing to see, to remember forever, to be a part of. Men and horses streamed past. Shouting, screaming, cursing, praying, singing, they splashed into Deep Fork and up the other side. The water the first horses carried slicked the red banks till the second wave of men and horses slipped and struggled and fell, churning the water till it was red as blood. But they clawed up the banks and were gone. Men afoot grabbed the tails of horses to get across and then dug their fingers into the steep banks and climbed out, running. They came and came and there was no end to their coming.

The world had come to take over the Territory.

Chapter 7

They waited for Bush a week and the waiting was the hardest part of all. Perched on the edge of Deep Fork, the water perpetually muddied by endless fordings, surrounded by the untidy refuse of the Run . . . a busted washtub, a splintered chicken coop, a broken plate, rusting tin cans that had held tomatoes or peaches, the charred remains of a hundred campfires . . . they watched the other wagons pull out and leave them.

Only a dozen camps were left by the end of the week. Camping out turned into a tiresome matter with a dreary sameness to the smoke-flavored meals. The joy of not washing retreated as dust ground into Lainey's clothes and skin. There was a rim of red dirt around her nails that could not be removed. Bud turned cranky and took to muttering that he was a freighter, not a wet nurse. Allegra hardly spoke and spent most of her time on the high wagon seat, her skirts gathered about her, watching for Bush.

Left to herself Lainey made up a game. She called it Alike and Different. Wandering up and down Deep Fork as far as Allegra would let her go she catalogued everything she saw as either like something she had known in Missouri or different. Sheep sorrel, pokeberry, pennyroyal, buckbrush, sumac, all these were Alike. But on the Different side were a dozen things she could not name and some the passing homesteaders told her . . . buffalo peas, gramma grass, wild parsnip, tumble weed, prickly pear, and a tough, spiky clump of Spanish bayonet.

Trees were easier. Most of them were Alikes. White oak, red oak, walnut, cottonwood, elm. But then there was the blackjack Bush had told her about that held its brown leaves all winter till the new leaves pushed them off in the spring. And there was a tall graceful tree with waving branches that looked like a hickory but wasn't because the leaves were too narrow. Up in its branches she

64

could see clusters of nuts. It was a black-bearded settler from Texas who told her it was a pecan.

"Come a good frost," he pointed to the nut clusters, "you c'n thrash the branches an' pick'em up by the bushel. Mighty good eatin'. We had 'em down home an' the women folks useta make up a kind of pecan pie with cane syrup that was larrupin'. Candy, too. I rec'clet when we was little shavers we took'em to school to play Hull Gull." He poked around in the leaves and came up with a couple of the nuts, peeled back the outer husk, and putting them between his back teeth cracked down. Then he deftly shelled out the milky kernels and handed them to Lainey. "Here, Sis."

The sweet juicy flavor made her forget what Aunt Ellen said on the subject of swapping gum at school. "They're good!"

"Shore. One reason I picked the Sac 'n' Fox. It's that much like home."

Lainey looked for more nuts but she was too early for frost and too late for the squirrels that raced through the branches. She found another Different in a tree with heart-shaped leaves and thin, rattling pods. "Judas tree," a cross-eyed woman told her. "Bad luck, I'd say. An' we got plenty bad luck already, just bein' here."

"Yes, ma'am." But Lainey made a face at her back.

Cottontail rabbits were Alike, but the lean racy jackrabbits with black-tipped ears were Different. Bud said they could run faster than horses for a stretch. There were lots of red birds, but not one single bluebird. The mockers and the hawks she lumped into Alike but on the Different side was a curious bird with a long tail that opened and closed; she didn't need anybody to tell her it was a scissor tail. The black snake that looped through the grass by the wagon wasn't nearly as long as the one the Sauerbier boy had forked up out of the hay at Riverview, but the coiled patterned horror she glimpsed at the side of the road was Different. She screamed and a man came running from nowhere and whipped the thing to death with an ox goad. "That's old Sudden Death himself, young lady. When you hear him, you git." He turned the quivering coils over with his boot toe and offered to cut off the rattles for her but she backed away, too scared even to thank him. A rattlesnake was too Different.

65

In the Sheridan camp the days dragged out. One . . . two . . . three . . . four . . . and still Bush didn't come. An unmentionable fear haunted Lainey that he had not found a claim and that he would never come back but would ride Blackjack on and on to some distant land.

At noon of the day Bush had been gone a week Bud called Lainey over to see what he had. It was a horned toad, a spiky little lizard with a mottled hide and a triangular head crowned with horns. He was the color of the red dirt on which he stood, panting and poised for flight. This was a Different for sure. Nothing in Missouri had ever had this unblinking, unfrightened, ancient look. Bud scooped him up and held him on his wide palm. "You wanna hold him? He won't hurtcha."

"No!" But Lainey didn't run away. Held between fear and curiosity it came to her that she had seen something like this before. A picture of St. George and the dragon. Here was the dragon, tiny but perfect. At any instant fire might flare from his pinpoint nostrils. He had the charm of Evil from the tales of Grimm and Anderson and the wonderful stories Uncle Hod read out of Malory.

"Watch 'im, now, Ol' Horny likes his back scratched." Bud drew his forefinger down the spikes, slowly, over and over. The angular head drooped, the brilliant eyes dulled, closed. "C'mon, hold out your hand. I dare ya!"

She wanted to and she didn't want to. The palm of her hand tingled at the sight of that strange flesh, but to conquer a dragon is worth doing. She held out her hand, her eyes tight shut. The touch of the horned toad was amazingly light and dry, the scratch of his claws fragile. As she opened her eyes he twisted his head, looking at her with such impudence that she laughed on an indrawn breath.

"I like him! I'm gonna keep him. I'm gonna name him St. George Oklahoma Territory.

"Then you better start ketchin' flies. That's his meat 'n' potatoes."

"I'll put some sorghum in a tin cup. I'll catch a million flies. I'll get a box for his house . . ." She had triumphed.

Bud idled off to the horses and Lainey took up the rhythmic

66

scratching. "You look like you know things," she told St. George O.T. "Like you'd lived here a long time. I bet you're a sign that Bush's on his way back with a good claim." It was easy to believe when you looked at the little lizard, so still he might have been chipped from one of the sandstone rocks. But it was hard to believe other times.

Rumors had run through the stay-behinds and the stragglers like the prairie fires set to smoke out the sooners. Each passerby brought news that was pounced on and passed from wagon to wagon.

"Heard the surveyors got the pick o' the land. Heard they had it filed on before the Run." . . . "Heard some o' the Sac 'n' Fox are agin' the openin'. Heard the Mo-ko-ho-ko's fenced all their land in." . . . "Heard they're openin' the Kickapoo land next. Heard it was a lot better. Wisht I'd waited" . . . "Heard there's a townsite a mile into the Sac 'n' Fox . . . five mile . . . ten mile . . . Heard they had soldiers guardin' it so's nobody could stake it for a claim" . . . "Heard they been standin' in line up to Guthrie two-three days to file. Heard there wasn't nothin' left to eat in the town at no price a-tall!" . . . "Heard the marshall up there come down sick an' there wasn't no law an' things was high, wide, an' fancy" . . . "Heard a feller was leadin' a big passel o' colored folks for a colony" . . . "Heard there was more sooners than in '89. Heard every claim had three on it. Maybe more" . . . "Heard . . . heard . . ."

Truth and rumor like a two-headed calf ran wild. The new country itself was so strange, so different, the ownership of land such an intoxicating thing that nothing seemed impossible. But to all of these tales Allegra had only one question.

"Did you see my husband? Bushrod Sheridan? A big, dark-haired man on a black and white horse?"

"No'm . . . no'm . . . can't say as I did. But he'll be along, don't you worry."

"How can I keep from worrying?" Allegra demanded of Bud and Lainey. "Suppose Blackjack fell on him. I don't trust that horse. That glass eye . . ."

"If he'd been hurt somebody woulda seen him and brought

word. They're thicker'n fleas in there. It's my guess he's gone up to Guthrie to file. I wouldn't look for him under a week." Bud scooped the channel catfish he had caught for supper out of the skillet onto a tin plate warming at the edge of the fire.

"But it's been a week."

Lainey, making a house for St. George O.T. out of an Arm and Hammer soda box, wondered if it would help if she told about the sign she had and showed him to Mama. But the chances were Mama wouldn't like him and demand that she throw him away. Besides, maybe St. George O.T. was just a horned toad after all. Bud said there were millions of them.

Supper was a dismal meal in spite of the crisp, white-meated fish. Nobody talked much and for the first time Allegra didn't insist that a plate of food be kept warm for Bush "just in case." No one stopped by to visit. Another wagon had pulled out today. The rising wind whimpered in the willows. Somewhere in the early dark a coyote yapped.

"Do you suppose Bush didn't get a claim?" Lainey asked, driven by a wish to hurt herself. Hope lighted Allegra's face as she scrubbed at the blackened skillet.

"We could go home," she said. "There'd be some talk but it would die down. We could go back to Riverview!"

Lainey had never thought of going back. Not really. It would be like walking down the tube of a spy glass to the tiny figures at the small end. To ache with homesickness, to long for the tower, the pear tree, the sound of Uncle Hod's voice reading aloud, the sight of Mattie bending over the oven, the touch of Aunt Ellen brushing her hair was one thing . . . But to go back was to pass over a bridge that had been destroyed.

Bud said, "He's got a claim. Bush gits what he goes after."

Lainey saw a slow blush come up Allegra's throat. "Of course. You're right. It's just that a week is . . . is a long time. Come along, Lainey. Time for bed."

Together they made their nightly trip into the bushes, one of the lanterns turned as low as possible between them. Then even that feeble light was blown out and in the dark, as they struggled with buttons, belts, drawstrings, tapes, and dodged branches and winced

68

at the thought of snakes Lainey heard Allegra say in despair: "I'm just not made to be a pioneer! Right now I think a privy is the most wonderful place on earth."

Lainey slept badly that night. The depression that had come over the camp stayed with her and kept her turning and twisting. It must have been late when she awoke because moonlight thinned the darkness and the moon was in its last quarter now. Quiet surrounded the wagons. Even the wind was quiet, though when Lainey put her hand on the wagon sheet she could feel its tremor. And once she opened her eyes she could not close them again.

At last she slipped from under the covers and sat shivering in the September night, her clothes wrapped haphazardly around her. There was nothing to see, nothing to think about. Her right leg cramped and one toe curled backward. From a coop under a homesteader's wagon a rooster crowed, oblivious of time or place. The thin reedy sound made the darkness outside shrink to the size of the Riverview chickenyard.

Stealthily Lainey began to dress, stealthily she crept to the opening, waiting for each noise she made to die out before making the next. Out on the wagon seat her teeth chattered as the wind lifted the bed warmth from about her. Held by the night she stared at a world of black and gray with the moon an icy silver in the western slope of the sky. "On such a night . . ." she whispered, remembering not the words but the throb in her throat when Uncle Hod read them. "On such a night . . ."

Somewhere under the night sky Bush was coming back for them. Somewhere little Violette Gervais curled like a kitten in sleep. And somewhere Jane Baker slept peacefully at the Friends' Mission. Somewhere in this invaded land were the clustered villages of the Sac and Fox, the Iowa, the Shawnee, and the Pottawatomie, who had once owned it all. And somewhere that blue-eyed tow-headed boy, Arch, lived. She'd like to see him again and get a chance to tell him some things! Call her a sooner! But a pang of loneliness came to her as she thought of the surging, tangled mass of the settlers and she knew it would be a miracle if she ever saw him again.

Scrambling down from the wagon she went to the place where

she had hidden the soda box with St. George O.T. inside. In the dim light the box barely showed and she was afraid to pick it up in case he had disappeared or died. But there was the scrambling of tiny clawed feet, a shifting of live weight inside. Did he hate the white walls?

Once Aunt Ellen had put her in a closet as a punishment and she was never able to open that door again without hating. Then there was the baby fox Jimdandy had tried to keep in a pen; it had died without eating or drinking.

Lainey picked the horned toad out and ran her finger over his spiked back, then set him on the sandstone slab Bud used for a cooktable. In a flash he was gone. Another grain of weight was added to her loneliness but she was glad that she had set him free. When you keep something wild in a box or a pen, part of you has to stay in with it.

Lainey stepped softly out of the beaten circle of the campfire, out past the wagons, feeling the grass grow deeper under her feet. The picketed horses lifted their heads. Stretcher blew a snorting inquiry, then they all went back to cropping grass. Away from the wagons the full sweep of the wind came upon her. She lifted her arms and began to run. The moon ran with her, the cold bright stars, and the black horizon. She ran, wheeling, 'round and 'round, the wind tangling her skirts, till she dropped on the grass, and saw the heavens whirling above her. The world moved and circled for her! The stars shone, the moon rose, the water flowed because of Lainey Sheridan. The throbbing, intoxicating vision held her until the whirling slowed and stopped.

"I'd better go back," she said. "I'd better go back right away." The smallness of her voice in the vast night frightened her.

Then under her head the great drum of the prairies began to thud. "Plop-plop, ploppety-plop-plop." A horse coming in, not galloping fast but at a confident, steady gait. "Plop-plop,ploppety-plop-plop." She sat bolt upright, her head to one side.

The sound was coming from the other side of the camp. The wind blew into her parted lips and dried her throat. "Plop-plop, ploppety-plop-plop." It was Blackjack! It was Bush coming home! St. George O.T. had been a sign! She was on her feet running, screaming through the camp, "Bush! It's Bush come back!

70

Bush . . ." Stumbling, falling, she ran on toward the shadowy horseman. "Bush! Bush!"

He was singing. In a loud, unmusical, triumphant roar.

> "'Way down south on Beaver Creek,
> Sing-song-kitty-cantchee-ki-me-O,
> Cotton grows about six feet,
> Sing-song-kitty-cantchee-ki-me-O.
> Kee-mo-ki-mo, Da-ro-mi . . ."

A cloud slid across the moon and off again. White patches gleamed on Blackjack's mottled hide. "Bush! Bush!"

The horse shied. Caught off guard Bush jerked, swore, sawed on the reins, and brought the plunging horse to a standstill. He peered down at her. "Who th' . . . Lainey?"

"It's me! I knew you'd come! I had a sign."

"Lainey! You pret'neart fixed me. What are you doing, out here in the night?"

"Bush . . . did you get a claim?"

He shoved back his hat with a gesture that told her everything. "Glory be! I got the best claim in the whole Territory."

"Is it far? Can we go tonight? Can we start right now?"

"We'll wait till morning. I filed on it up to Guthrie. Stayed on the land a day to fend off claim jumpers . . . spaded up a garden to show . . . then I took out for Guthrie. Stood in line twenty-seven hours . . . cheese 'n' crackers an' canteen water! Ugh! Paid my fourteen dollars; bet the gov'ment I wouldn't starve. Now we got to prove up." Blackjack blew, tiredly. "All right, boy, you called the turn. After the way you ran you've got a right to your say." He reached down and took Lainey's hand. "Come on, honey, time you got back to bed."

He heaved and Lainey scrambled and she was up in front of him in the roomy saddle. The pommel gouged her and Bush's bulk squeezed her but she took comfort in his nearness.

"I'll be glad to see the claim," she said contentedly, and repeated the word for sheer pleasure, "the claim."

"It's a good one. Good grass. Few trees. Bottom land for corn, sandy land for cotton." He clucked at Blackjack and started him toward camp. "I hope there's coffee."

71

She started guiltily; she had dumped out the coffee and washed the pot.

"I had a sign you were coming but I guess I didn't believe it hard enough."

"Remember what I told you? About the present? A stick instead of a pony?"

She nodded. "I remember."

"Well, this is the pony!" his voice was exultant. "The real sure-'nough thing! You c'n throw the stick away. Hundred 'n' sixty acres, and it's all ours! Riverview was the Saunders' place but this is the *Sheridan* place!"

"The Sheridan place." It sounded good.

"I knew it as soon's I saw it. Like it was waiting for me. Like I'd farmed it for years. When I caught sight of that big cottonwood with the catface brand . . . that's the surveyor's mark . . . I jumped down and drove my stake. I had a little trouble with a feller that came up a half hour later, but he went on. Finally."

"Did you see any sooners?"

"I don't know. We all looked 'bout alike. Some folks on the next claim by the name of Hampton gave me some coffee. They've got a boy that said he'd keep an eye on our place when I left for Guthrie."

She felt a wave of dislike for this boy who thought he was so smart! Somebody in camp had stirred up the fire and it blazed high.

"That looks good to me," Bush sighed. "I'm bone tired. Haven't had my clothes off since I left." He nudged Blackjack into a reluctant trot. "Step out, boy, we can't come in draggin' this time. We've got something to show!"

Perched in front with the pommel digging unmercifully at her, Lainey straightened her shoulders, knowing this for the proud moment it was. Mama and Bud waited by the fire but she was with Bush and they had something to show . . . the Sheridan place. She added her slight, shrill soprano to his triumphant bass.

" *'Way down south on Beaver Creek . . .*"

72

Chapter 8

They rolled out of camp before sunup. Tired as he was, Bush was up before any of them, hurrying the loading, stamping out the campfire, refusing to open the trunk so that Allegra and Lainey could have fresh dresses. "Time enough for all that. We've got to get goin'. Claim jumpers everyplace; I won't rest easy till I'm there."

It was strange, after all the waiting, to be actually fording Deep Fork. As the wagons started down the steep slope Lainey began to sing, "Roll, Jordan, Roll," trying to give the song Jimdandy's mellow volume. There was a well-established ford across the stream now and the teams took it quickly. Up the far side and past an overturned buckboard and the camp was out of sight. "I want to get to heaven, just to see old Jordan roll . . ."

The sun came up, a red ball balanced on a red hill. In an hour it had burned the chill out of the air. They turned off the Sac and Fox-Shawneetown road to unmarked country. Where had all the people who lined up on Deep Fork gone to? The countryside was empty. Then Bud began to point out places to her; his eyes accustomed to the long distances from freighting saw what she missed. "Tent up over yonder . . . There's a feller that's got a bresh arbor, right there by that cottonwood; see the smoke? . . . Dogged if there ain't a man plowin'. Aimin' to get a crop o' turnips in, I bet."

A young man on a claybank mare hailed the lead wagon and Lainey climbed down and ran up to join Bush and Allegra.

"You folks going in to Randall?"

"Randall?" Bush looked blank.

"That's what I heard they named it. Man named Randall staked the first lot."

"Oh, the townsite. I heard about that up at Guthrie. Sure, we'll stop."

"Then would you mail this letter for me? Somebody'll be sure to take mail in to Guthrie and I promised my girl I'd write."

"Glad to do it," Bush reached for the fat envelope. "Is she coming out?"

"I hope so," his thin face flushed a little. "I was working in a dry-goods store back in Ohio when a friend of mine wrote me about the land opening. Her folks think I'm crazy."

"Don't you listen to 'em. Best place in the world to get a start."

They drove on. Lainey saw a tiny muscle twitch at the corner of Allegra's mouth. "I hope she likes it the way he does. The way you do," Allegra said.

"Why wouldn't she like it? Young folks . . . young country. Working in a dry-goods store's no life for a man. A hundred 'n' sixty in Oklahoma Territory . . ."

"I know. I know."

The wagon rattled into a deep draw and the team leaned against the harness for the pull up and out. The ground at the top had been burned over a few years back when the country was surveyed and a low second growth of blackjack slashed at the wheels. Clumps of sunflowers waved brightly. Near the top of a long slope they almost overran a small, neat camp. A man with a mattock was struggling with the tough sod, back of him a woman in a blue-and-white-striped dress chopped at the dirt with a hoe. Around them a child darted, gay and quick as a red bird.

"Stop, Bush, stop! It's the French folks!"

The reunion was like that of old friends. Lainey hugged Violette who bounced on her lap. Bush, introduced to Henri Gervais, admired his claim that spread down to the edge of the draw. And while Allegra talked to Lili in careful, halting seminary French, Gervais explained:

"We 'ave some land in what you call the bottom. Some on the slope. On the slope we plant grapes. One year . . . two years . . . a vineyard." He sketched his plans in the air. "Peaches . . . pears . . . apples . . . But not too many apples. Thees ees not the climate. And over here the barn . . ."

74

"Sounds good. Where'll you put your house?"

Henri shrugged. "The 'ouse, it will arrange itself. The vines, the orchards, the barns, they mus' come first."

"Sure, sure. Well, we'd better start. Got a ways to go, yet." Bush picked up the reins shaking his head at Henri's urging that they stay and eat, seconded by Lili's vigorous nods. Lainey unwound Violette's arms from her neck and handed her down to her father. Lili ran to their wagon and came back with a wrapped package that she put in Allegra's hands with a freshet of words.

"I can't understand her; she goes too fast," Allegra appealed to Henri.

"It ees a cutting of grapes, from our home in France. She wishes you to 'ave it because you saved our Violette and because you 'ave spoken to her as a Frenchwoman.

"For me? But . . ." Lainey felt rather than saw Bush's booted foot nudge Allegra's small one. "Well, *merci, Madame* . . . I mean Lili. *Merci beaucoup. Vous êtes trop gentille.*"

"She says it will make good wine and you are welcome and *vive la France et la nouvelle patrie, aussi.*"

They left exchanging goodbyes and promises to visit. Lainey waved to Violette as long as she could see her.

"Nice folks," Bush said. "They'll get along."

"But they're so far from home."

"They're not far from home; they're at home right now. And we'll be, too, 'fore the sun goes down."

Bush covered Allegra's hand with his and Lainey, pretending not to see, reached out from the wagon to snatch at a tall ironweed. "I used to play horse with these, back in Missouri when I was a little girl," she said.

Bush laughed and Allegra smiled. It made her feel good to be near them. The sun was warm now and she leaned back in the seat, playing with the purple blooms that had come off in her hand. Ironweed in Oklahoma Territory was the same as it was in Missouri, too tough for the long green stalks ever to break. It made a wonderful horse, cut off at the roots and ridden bouncing and bucking around the house with the purple blooms for a gaudy tail.

Far to the right three horsemen jogged along. The splashes of purple and red on their clothes blended into the bright morning landscape.

"Indians, prob'ly coming back from the agency," Bush said.

Allegra frowned. "I thought they stayed there all the time."

"Some live near there and some don't. They had the choice of claims before the Run. Mostly they chose together in villages, but some are scattered around, too. How'd you like to have an Indian family for neighbors?"

"You're joking!"

"Not a bit. I heard a family by the name of Halfmoon . . . Sac an' Fox tribe, but they're both Sacs . . . was alloted a quarter near ours. Nice folks."

"But . . . neighbors . . ."

"White people have lived for years in Indian Territory and they got along fine. The Choctaws . . . Chickasaws . . . Cherokees . . . why they have big towns over there, big fine farms, colleges . . . The Civil War was hard on them just the way it was on Snyder County because a whole lot of them were slaveholders, and they fought with the South." Allegra stared, unbelieving. "Didn't you ever hear of Stand Waitie's Cherokee Brigade? Or Tandy Walker's Choctaws? Or Cooper's Indian Regiment?"

"I certainly did not!"

"Well, I did! I heard it from my pa. He was with the Union Army when they got the tar licked out of 'em at Cabin Creek. Nothing like a lickin' to make you remember!"

Lainey squirmed uneasily. She wished Bush would stop talking about his father being with the Union Army. With Missouri divided like it was plenty of nice folks fought in the Union Army, still, in Snyder County . . . But they weren't in Snyder County any more! They were in the Territory and maybe it didn't matter so much.

"I still don't think I want Indians for neighbors!"

Lainey pulled at Bush's sleeve. "A man that came by our camp, he said," she lowered her voice, glancing at the distant horsemen, "that some of them eat . . . dogs."

"No!" Bush said in mock horror. "Did you tell him you ate . . .

76

hogs?" She jerked away, her face hot. If Bush was going to take up with the Indians against her . . .

"When I was haulin' freight through here last winter a norther blew up," Bush continued. "I liked to froze! The wind got so strong the horses couldn't make headway so I took shelter in a stand of timber. There was an Indian camp on the other side and they asked me in. I couldn't talk their lingo so I never did know who they were but they fed me up on some hot stew that sure tasted good. When the wind let up and I started to leave I saw a couple of dogs' heads up on a tree branch. One old woman saw me lookin' at 'em and she pointed to the cook pot. Then she liked to died laughing when I turned green. I never did know for sure . . . they're great ones for a joke like that . . . but . . ."

"Let's sing something," Allegra said hurriedly, "It'll make the time pass."

The slope levelled off. The wagons came to a flat stretch where red sand muffled the sound of the wheels and an aimless little creek wandered this way and that through an edge of coarse green grass. Bush stopped the horses at the edge of the shallow water and Bud drove up beside them.

"That hill over yonder," he said, "would that be the town?"

They stared, their eyes crinkling in the sunlight. A tent city in among the green trees crowned the hill. The tents gleamed white in the sun, a flag atop one of them flashed a signal of color, wagons climbed the slope, and as their eyes gauged the distance they could see the movement of hurrying people. It was a fair sight. "A city set on a hill can not be hid," Bush said slowly, then turned brick red. "That's it. That's Randall, Oklahoma Territory."

They were so taken with the sight that none of them noticed the light buggy till it was right beside them and a young woman in a tan henrietta-cloth dress and a stylish sailor hat called, "Is that the town?"

Bud whipped off his hat. "Yes, ma'am, that's what we reckon."

"I hope they have some kind of stores there. I went to Guthrie to file and my trunk hasn't come yet and I don't have a thing to wear."

"You mean you filed on a claim? In the Run?" Allegra asked, shocked.

"Oh yes," the young woman's eyes sparkled. "Isn't it exciting? I came down to get a teaching job at Edmond but I heard about the Run and I came right over." The sailor hat tilted coquettishly at Bud. "Didn't I see you at the dance?"

"I wish't you had. I didn't know there was any dance."

"Oh my yes! The night before the Run. It was bright moonlight, you know, and some men marked off a place and cleared the stickers and found a fiddler . . . sixty men and four girls! I never danced so hard in my life or had so much fun."

"Lots of fine young men in the Territory," Bush said.

"And lots of old married men," Allegra sounded annoyed.

"Well, I'd better be going," the young woman smiled at Bud, her long lashes tangling in the veil that anchored the sailor hat against the wind. "I'm Emma Turney and my claim's about four miles east. Come see me."

"You come see us," Bush called as the buggy splashed through the shallow water. "That's a girl with git-up-and-git!"

"Of all the giddy, crazy! . . ."

"Pretty as a spotted pup."

"Sixty men and four girls! What kind of a dance is that?"

"I bet she got a good claim."

"Of course she did if all the rest of the men were like you two."

Bush and Bud grinned at each other. Then Bud shouted at his team and splashed past. "See you in Randall," he yelled back and sent the team rattling over the sand.

If Randall was a shining dream city from the plain, it was a brisk reality when the Sheridans reached it. Many of the tents that shone so white in the distance were dingy and patched. The stores Emma Turney hoped to find were nothing but plank counters set up in front of piles of merchandise. Dust rose in a red haze from the churning feet of horses and men. Everywhere was noise, confusion, wrangling, but through and under it all was the kind of excitement Lainey had felt before at the Snyder County Fair.

"I'd like to do some looking around," Bush said, swinging down from the wagon, "I guess you and Lainey'd rather not get out."

"Then you can just guess again." Allegra gathered her skirts and climbed down behind him. "I'm sick and tired of wagons. If that Turney girl can take care of herself I guess Lainey and I can manage."

It was fun to be out of the wagon. Fun to walk past the knots of arguing, shouting men. Fun, even, to stumble over stakes that marked the corners of townsite lots. Men were crowding around an army tent with a sign, "Land Office" where three weary-looking men tried to answer questions, fill out forms, and cope with the shouldering, surging throngs. The air rang with their words.

"It's my lot and you know it! I was there first. Anybody'll say . . ."

"I'll take it to court. I'll spend my last cent . . ."

"I got soldier's rights. Anybody that'll cheat an old soldier'll suck eggs . . ."

"Trade you my wagon, two mules an' a washtub . . ."

"I got a lawyer. He says my case'll stand . . ."

"Fifty dollars cash and not a cent less. Best pair of lots in the townsite . . .

"Sue an' be hanged! I got witnesses that I was on that lot first . . ."

"I got inside information. These lots are right where the railroad . . ."

"It's gonna be a big town. Bigger'n Guthrie . . ."

Further down the row of tents that had become a street, a slight young man in a high starched collar and long black sateen sleeve covers hammered a sign on a tent pole, "Drug Store" and stepped back for an instant to admire it, then hurried behind the counter to wait on the customers already there. "Plenty of quinine," he advised a sallow man. "Take it before meals, much as you can hold on the blade of a knife."

Under a scrawny hackberry tree meals were being served out of a covered wagon. "Loaf of bread an' a pound of meat, an' all the onions you can eat," a man shouted, hammering a pan with an iron spoon. A round cheerful-looking woman put her head out of the opening. "Don't hurry 'em, Ed. That last steer's still a-kickin'."

A harried man ran from one bunch of people to another. "Doc

Harter? Anybody see Doc Harter? Got a feller with a broke leg. Doc Harter?"

It was close to noon and the sun was hot. Allegra pushed her sunbonnet back. "Walking around town bareheaded," she said to Lainey. "Ellen would have a fit."

They skirted around two tents where the rowdy crowd meant liquor was being sold. A fist fight boiled up and a man went down with a thud. A voice shrill with triumph shouted for drinks all around.

A long-legged young man in clothes that were striking because of their dark, sober cut hurried by, saw them, turned and called back, "Church services, Sunday, in the grove down there. Be sure and come and pass the word along."

"Can we come?" Lainey asked her mother.

"We'll try. That's the first thing that's sounded civilized to me."

Nearby a man tried to wait on a dozen customers for nails, hammers, and all manner of hardware while directing the unloading of a wagon of used lumber. He turned down all offers for the boards. "Nossir! I'm going to have the first sure-'nough store in this town. Tore down my store in Kansas and had it hauled down, board by board. I'll set'er up and be open for business before the week's out."

A half dozen Sac and Fox Indians trotted by on wiry ponies. At their head rode an old man with long gray braids wrapped in yarn. His shirt was a bright purple and at his throat and wrists silver buttons flashed in the sun. He rode as if he did not hear the uproar around him. "That's Moses Keokuk, he's one of the head men," Lainey heard. "He had the Big K Ranch before the opening."

The sun burned down; the heat waves shimmered. It was high noon. A week ago this hill had been a beleagured fortress, guarded by soldiers who held off the pressing thousands. Two weeks ago it had stood idle in the sun, a crumbling cabin marking the place where an Indian trader had once had a stock of goods.

"Allegra! Allegra Saunders!" Somewhere behind them a woman called. Allegra jerked her bonnet back into place, but it was knocked askew by the plump woman in the elaborate maroon costume who came running on wobbling spool heels to hug and kiss her.

"Bertha Mebane! I haven't seen you since the seminary!"

They babbled greetings, news, recollections, while Lainey felt forgotten but pleasantly excited as she tried to understand what they were saying. It was like trying to catch the ring on the merry-go-round at the Snyder County Fair.

". . . and the time we hid the watermelon under the bed . . ."

". . . and you in that tennis-flannel nightgown . . ."

". . . so we came down in '89 a month after the Run and Guy went into a bank in Oklahoma City and we have two girls . . ."

"Oh my goodness! This is Lainey, our girl. Elaine, I mean. I married Bushrod Sheridan the year after I finished the seminary."

"Was he the one who . . ."

"No. I didn't even know him then. Bush was overseer at Riverview."

"Oh, that wonderful place, and what times we had there! The foxhunt. And the time the boys put brandy in the punch! And this is Elaine!" The name made Lainey as uncomfortable as the hug but she smiled politely. "I knew your mother, dear, when she wasn't much bigger than you. We slept next bed to each other and your mother was the prettiest girl who ever went to the seminary."

There it was again. The familiar hurt because no one ever went on and said, "And you're just like her." Lainey had thought it belonged to Riverview, but here it was in Randall, Oklahoma Territory.

"And how is Miss Ellen? And Mr. Hod?" Words rushed past. Lainey watched two men struggling profanely to unload a case of type and a printing press.

"So you're going to homestead! Well, I never . . . but we just love the Territory. We came to Randall just to see how things were. Guy thinks the bank may want to . . . Now you just must come to visit us. I've got a million things to tell you but I've got to run. Guy doesn't like to be kept waiting. It's been wonderful seeing you. When I saw that hair I said to Guy, 'That's Allegra Saunders. Nobody in the world has hair like that but . . . You say your name is Sheridan? Now do come to see us. Anytime. Goodbye . . ."

goodbye . . ." There were more kisses and Mrs. Mebane went hurrying down the hill dodging men, horses, and wagons, calling over her shoulder till she was out of sight behind a patched Conestoga wagon.

"Bertha Mebane," Allegra shook her head, dazed. "I just can't believe it. And me in calico and all those clothes in my trunk!"

Bush was standing by the wagon, his watch in his hand. "Time to go. Who in the world was that you were gabbing with?"

"I was not gabbing and she is a dear friend of mine who lives in Oklahoma City and *I want that trunk opened.*"

He wasn't listening. "I've got no idea where Bud is. Checked every place . . ."

"I'm hungry," Lainey complained. "I'm about to starve."

"Here," he handed her a quarter. "There's a food wagon over there."

It was pure adventure to wriggle and push through the crowd with the quarter making a sweaty circle in her hand. At the food wagon the meat was tough, the beans like bullets, the biscuits speckled with saleratus spots and at fifteen cents the meal was higher than a cat's back, but with it came the feeling of lavish living.

The lemonade man with two buckets that each held a chunk of precious ice swimming in water, sugar, and citric acid tempted Lainey, but lemonade, even ice cold, is too quickly gone. Instead she bought two sticks of candy for a penny and started sucking one to a fine point.

Then worming her way through the crowd to the post office she bought a red stamp. High time she was writing to Addie and she twisted the ring Addie had given her at parting so that the seal would be inside and nudge her memory. A fat little Indian boy with eyes like shoe buttons watched her. Without knowing why she put the second stick of candy in his hand. As he licked it, unsmiling, he handed her a milky-white quartz pebble, warm from his chubby hand. She put it in her handkerchief with the stamp, not wanting it, really, but thinking it might be something special. Nearby a man was telling the wonders of the Pott country where he had a claim, behind him a Populist was shouting the glories of

82

his party. Three young women pushed past her and she nearly lost her candy trying to see if it really was paint on their faces. Down the hill a coop of chickens broke as it came off a wagon and the squawking, screeching hens scattered throughout the crowd.

From time to time Lainey went back to the Sheridan wagon; "touching base," she called it. But Bush was not there and neither was Bud. The last time she found Allegra dressed in the elegance of the blue surrah, wrinkles criss-crossing the skirt, and the white straw with the white birds tied on with the spotted veil. Under the veil her face was flushed.

"I got that trunk open myself. I wasn't going to have anybody else turn up and find me walking around town in a sunbonnet!"

It was half-past three before Bush came back. "Well, I finally found Bud. I should have known! He's in a game in a tent down the hill. Couldn't get him out with a prize pole." He shook his head disgustedly. "I told him we'd go on and he can get out to the claim the best he knows how to pick up Kate's wagon. Think you can handle the driving from here?" Allegra nodded. "Then take this team and head for the wagon road. I'll get the other and . . . Say, aren't you kind of dressed up?"

"I'm dressed the way I ought to be, and high time," Allegra answered, chin raised.

"Hmmmm . . . well, I'll tie Blackjack on and get you started."

"I never saw horses I couldn't handle. Just tell me which way to go."

She backed the team and the heavy wagon expertly, plunging ahead into the tangle that filled the space between the tents. She sat straight, the white birds perched bravely on her golden hair, handling the reins with competence. A slender, graceful woman, her fine clothes incongruous against the canvas of the covered wagon, but her courage and determination unmistakable. Laice Saunders must have looked like that, coming from Kentucky to Missouri, and Ellen standing off the Redlegs at Riverview.

"You look . . . pretty." It was the only word Lainey could find.

"Pretty is as pretty does." But Allegra smiled.

A reedy young fellow wabbled out of one of the saloon tents, looked up at Allegra and blinked. "Are there any more at home like you?"

His partner grabbed his arm, took off his own hat and bowed low. "He don't mean no harm, ma'am. He's just kinda off his reservation." He shook the first man by the shoulder. "You durn' fool! Don'tcha know a lady when you see one?"

Allegra ignored them both. Lainey tried to follow her example but she couldn't keep from sneaking a look back to where the two men struggled, the first trying to chase the wagon, the second trying to keep him back.

In and out, through the maze of tents, wagons, teams, children, dogs, and baggage that cluttered the hilltop, Allegra guided the team. The wagon road, when they found it, was crowded with outfits coming in. To get through them took all Allegra's skill.

It was a relief to catch sight of Bush and see him give a signal with his whip for a sharp turn off the road. The uproar of Randall dropped away, the noise of the road faded, then disappeared. The familiar harness rattle and roll of their own wagons were the only remaining sounds. A few turns, a little rise and fall of land, and you could believe Randall no longer existed.

Lainey felt as tired as if she had picked string beans for a week's canning. It was a long time since they had broken camp that morning. A long way back to Deep Fork. Longer still to Riverview. Her bed with the puffy feathertick, and the cool sheets, in the dim high-ceilinged room, floated invitingly before her. She sighed, a long, quivering sound that seemed to come from her slipper soles.

"Why don't you crawl back to the bed in the wagon?" Allegra said.

"I don't want to. I want to be awake when we get there." Lainey sighed again.

"Then put your head down in my lap and try to rest."

The surrah dress was cool and smooth. The nearness to Mama comforting. Kinks along Lainey's backbone straightened out. She settled herself, looking up to the sky where a hawk sailed, tilting his wings this way and that. A hawk or a buzzard could have a good time in Oklahoma Territory. All he'd have to do would be to ride the wind . . . this way . . . that way . . . this way . . .

84

She would not go to sleep! She would not! But if she closed her eyes, just for a minute.

Allegra hummed softly, the vibration carrying along her body to Lainey's ear. Then she began to sing one of Jimdandy's old songs:

> *"The old Ark's a-moverin', a-moverin', a-moverin',*
> *The old Ark's a-moverin' an' Ise gwine along . . ."*

They came to the claim at sunset when the sky was a flaming red with gold bands streaming along the western horizon. They had driven through grass country dotted with small stands of trees, across shallow streams, and over dry gulches. The earth around them was red and in the light of the sunset it seemed like a living thing. The grass was tall around the wheels of the wagon. The sweet evening smell of sun-baked land came to them on a small wind. As far as they could see the country lay, virgin, as it had been for countless years, and as it would never be again.

Bush reined in his team and climbed stiffly out of the wagon. Lainey, wakened by the stop sat up, rubbing her eyes.

"Are we home?"

Bush came toward them. "Yes. We're home. This is the Sheridan place."

He did not shout or point out its excellence. He did not brag on the Territory and what a fine place it was. He just said, once more, "This is the Sheridan place."

They were on a flat-topped hill and from its summit they saw the long downsweep that melted into a grassy plain. Dark clusters of haw bushes dotted the flank of the hill and flycatchers dipped and fluttered around them twittering in the stillness. A quail whistled and another answered. A jackrabbit crouched, frozen, with the light coming pink through his tall ears, then loped down the hill. In the valley the leaves danced on a big cottonwood. Lainey saw Bush's eyes travel till they came to this tree and she knew it must be the one that held the catface brand.

Somewhere in the tall grass down there was the hammered stake that claimed the land for Bushrod Sheridan, but no proving up, no deed on record, could make the land his more than it was at

85

this moment. When I saw it, he had said to Lainey, it was like it was waiting for me, like I'd farmed it for years. A deep joy welling up in her almost painfully made Lainey turn to the west and stare at the red-gold sunset. It was Allegra who broke the silence. Reaching across Lainey toward Bush, her face hidden by the veiling of the white-bird hat, she touched his shoulder almost timidly.

"It's a good place, Bush. It's just . . . fine."

Chapter 9

When Sunday came the Sheridans went to church in Randall. Bush in his black broadcloth store clothes, Allegra in cream silk faille with a puffed and gathered bustle and a hat all quivering loops of blue satin ribbon, and Lainey in a rosebud challis smocked at the shoulders and patent-leather Roman sandals, shining with Vaseline. Not more than a half mile off the claim they began to meet other rigs travelling the same way. Even the countryside had a Sunday look, a quiet, happy, decorous look as if it were glad to rest this Lord's Day from the tumult of the settlement. Only the wind would not rest and, coming from the east, it picked up red dust from the road and tossed it over the church-goers with a kind of casual malice.

"Just look at that!" Allegra shook out her skirt. "And my hat!"

"Now, honey, you always look pretty." Bush slapped his shoulders and brushed down his arms where the dust collected in creases. "And Lainey, here, is as pretty as a picture." He flipped his boots back to a shine with his handkerchief.

There was a way Bush had of making you feel pretty whether you were or not. Lainey took the arm he offered her with a pride that pushed aside the dust-soaked sandals and forgot the petticoat hitched up with a safety-pin. She fingered the garnet cross that had belonged to Aunt Ellen and held her shoulders straight to be worthy of her kin. Together the three of them started for the grove the preacher had selected. A crowd was gathering. All at once the shrill high notes of a trumpet split the air.

"Glory be!" Bush swung around. A man in front of them grabbed for his gun, then let his hand fall sheepishly. A young man with black curly hair was coming through the maze of tents blowing a silver trumpet. Behind him the preacher with Bible in hand invited any and all to come to services. The trumpeter pointed his instrument at the sky and blew till his eyes popped. A drunk shuddered and dove into a tent. Lainey laughed. Going to church in Randall was fun. She began to sing.

> *"From Greenland's icy mountains,*
> *From India's coral strand,*
> *Where Africa's sunny fountains . . ."*

"Lainey, not on the street." The loops of ribbon quivered in reproof.

But this wasn't a real street. Just a strip where the grass was worn off. Saloons and gambling places had "Closed" signs on them. But the explosive energy of Randall could not be bottled up, not even for Sunday. Down the hill the air was peppered with shouting and once with the sound of distant gunfire. Freight haulers guided their teams around the gathering congregation. The ring of hammers and the clatter of lumber being unloaded came and went with the shifting wind.

"Howdy," Bush tipped his hat, dislodging Lainey's hand. "Howdy, Kick. Howdy, Burl. Did you get that sooner put off, Joe? Howdy-do, ma'am. Howdy." Lainey gave up trying to hold his arm and copied, instead, Allegra's polite smile that came and went each time the black hat was lifted.

The grove was a stand of post oak that would not have merited the name in Snyder County. Planks across kegs and boxes made benches, and these were already filled. Women spread quilts to sit on, and babies sprawled across them. Men squatted down on their heels. The pulpit up in front was a tall packing box. Beside it was a portable organ. Two Indians from the Iowa village, west of the Sac and Fox lands, sat cross-legged nearby. Their dark, withdrawn faces set them apart from the rest of the congregation, visiting from quilt to quilt.

"Well, I'll be . . . Howdy, Hamp!" Bush slapped the back of a man ahead of them and a little puff of dust came from his coat. "Howdy, neighbors!"

"Why, Bush! You old . . . Howdy!" Jasper Hampton, his paunch bulging, his pants at a precarious pitch, shook Bush's hand.

Beside him his wife twittered and chirped like a neat brown wren. Between them was the boy, Arch, his bright-blue eyes and tormenting grin just the way they had been the day of the Run. His double cowlicks, front and back, were already rebelling against the last slicking down. Lainey stiffened at the sight of him. There had been a feud between them. She must not be the one to give in.

"Make you acquainted with my family," Bush was saying. "My wife. Our girl, Lainey. I should have been over to your place before now to thank you for lookin' after things."

So this was the biggety boy who said he'd look after the Sheridan place. Lainey should have guessed!

"My land, that wasn't anything at all. Glad to help a neighbor out." Mrs. Hampton's flat, twangy voice came so fast you had to listen closely to catch all the words. "We'd been over to see you before now, but Hamp stuck a nail in his foot, the big, clumsy . . ."

"Now, Mama, it didn't amount to a thing." Jasper Hampton had to interrupt to get a word in edgewise.

"Then Arch went stringin' off and got lost . . ."

"I was not lost. I was just . . ." His protest was lost under the flood of words, but Lainey knew by the flush of red on his face that she had scored against him just by being there and hearing his mother make him out a greenhorn.

". . . and I guess you've been as busy as we've been. But we'll have lots of time from now on. Now we're from Kansas. Out west of Lawrence.

The smile stiffened on Lainey's face. Lawrence, the stronghold of the abolitionists. Lawrence, burned by Quantrill, and Cousin Theo one of Quantrill's men.

"Where did you folks say you were from?"

"They never said," Jasper Hampton managed to get in. "And I told you . . ."

"Now, Hamp . . . He keeps after me for goin' around askin' people where they came from and all, but, my land, I like to know my neighbors and I expect they feel the same."

"We're from Missouri," Allegra said with a ring in her voice. "Snyder County, near Marney."

"Oh." The brown eyes snapped. The wren seemed to ruffle her

89

wings. Lainey hoped Bush would smooth things over but his face was as expressionless as that of the Iowa chief. Jasper Hampton looked at the pulpit as if he were trying to memorize it. Arch examined a scurrying ant. "Well, now," Mary Hampton said at last, "well, now, we're in new country and there's no use bringin' old grudges. Besides, we're neighbors." The word seemed to cover everything with forbearance and comfort.

"That's right," Bush was smiling, "That's sure right, Mrs. Hampton."

"Oh call me Mary. Everybody does, and I don't feel right being so set up." The flow of words that had stopped for an instant was going on as though a stream had come to a damming rock, lapped at it, then covered it forever in cool, deep water.

"These two young'uns must be 'bout of an age." Hamp hitched at his pants and managed to gesture at Arch and Lainey at the same time.

"He's older. He's almost thirteen." Only after Lainey had spoken did she realize that this was giving away she had met Arch before. For some reason she felt she had betrayed them both. The droop of an eyelid promised that Arch would not point out her mistake and in that moment the feud was over, buried in the flood of Mary Hampton's talk.

"We'd better get along and find us a place. My land, I never expected to see so many folks. We're Methodists, but I'd welcome any kind of service and the preacher seemed like a real nice man. Don't know what church he is but we're all tryin' to make the same Promised Land. And look over there! Indians. Now that's real neighborly for them to come, I'd say, wouldn't you?" There was no need to answer, only to nod. Mary Hampton led the way and they followed in single file. Allegra, Bush, Hamp, Lainey, Arch.

Ironweed tickled the back of her neck. "Bet your sooner's here. Big's life."

"I don't care. I hope he made it."

"He sure had him a good horse." It was plain Arch thought that a man who owned a horse like the little paint could not be altogether bad. Lainey took this for an overture.

"Did you have to run anybody off our place?" she asked.

90

He hesitated then shook his head. "Naw. Not really. Fellow came that way an' I was goin' to but Ma talked him into goin' on. Told him she wanted a family to neighbor with an' he was a lone man an' could do better in the Pott country."

"I bet you could have."

"Maybe. Anyway, Dad says Ma's tongue's bettern' a Winchester any day. She talked a fellow into goin' back to jail one time. Took all day but she wore him down."

They were whispering though there was no need, for the hum of talk was all around them as if a swarm of bees had settled in the grove. Just ahead of her Hamp stopped suddenly and Lainey walked into him and Arch into her. They snickered until Allegra frowned and then they were quiet.

After a glance at the crowded seats, Allegra looked in dismay at the ground; the faille silk would never be the same. Mary Hampton pointed to an empty patch halfway down to the pulpit. "How about there? I like to be near enough to hear everything but not too near in case he's a shouter. Look, they've got an organ! My land, I don't know when I've been so glad to get to church. Does this suit you folks?" It was accepted that they would sit together; they were neighbors.

"But we don't have anything to sit on. I never thought . . ."

"Don't bother 'bout that. I brought an extra quilt with me, just in case . . ."

Those three words—just in case—Lainey was to hear over and over. They became a trademark in the neighborhood. Mary Hampton always brought something extra, just in case. And always it came in handy. She spread out two log-cabin quilts now. "That patch's Arch's baby clothes . . . he was the cutest baby . . ." Arch turned his back, squatting on his heels with Bush and Hamp. Mary settled herself with quick, nestling movements looking more than ever like a wren with her brown calico skirts swept around her. Allegra came down beside her, the silk faille billowing like whipped cream. "There . . ." Mary sighed with satisfaction and patted Lainey's hand. "There. I knew we'd get good neighbors. It's the one thing I asked the Lord for. But I didn't know we'd find it out so quick."

"We're the lucky ones," Allegra said and behind her Lainey heard Bush let out his breath as if he'd been holding it a long time. "I've got a pattern for that smocking you liked on Lainey's dress. I can show you, if you want."

"Glory be!" Bush exclaimed. Lainey heard him but she didn't turn around.

And now the young preacher stood up behind his packing-box pulpit. The buzzing dropped to a hum, then became a silence broken only by the wail of a hungry baby quickly hushed. The preacher let them stay that way for a few minutes, knowing, perhaps, that each of them was in some other place, before some other altar. Then he lifted his long arms and seemed to beckon them back to the Sac and Fox country when he said, "Let us pray."

As Lainey bent her head she saw a quick vision of the plain, scrubbed face of Jane Baker. She had said, "He did not forget thee," and it was true. For God was here in this post-oak grove, just as he had been in the church at Marney. Knowing this she prayed within herself in the strong simple phrases Ellen had taught her, "Make me good . . . make me strong . . . make me willing . . . forgive me my sins . . ."

But the preacher's prayer lasted long past hers and the vision faded and she lifted her bent head, little by little, and peered through her closed eyelashes. In Marney she had a secret game of counting kinds of hat trimmings but it wasn't much fun here for there were more sunbonnets than hats. Still there was something different here, something she could not quite place. Looking at the bent heads and remembering Marney and Aunt Ellen and Uncle Hod and Uncle Alec who had sat in front of the Sheridans she suddenly realized what *was* different. There were no white heads in this congregation. Colors ranged from the blue-black of the Iowa chief's clubbed braids to the blond cowlicks on Arch Hampton, but there was no white. This was a young man's country.

"Amen," said the preacher, and the heads lifted. A few scattered Amens echoed from the crowd.

"I guess we're not the only Methodists," Mary Hampton whispered.

92

Then the preacher's wife sat down at the portable organ and a freckled man with a voice like a Jersey bull announced that he would line out the hymns and they would start with "Beulah Land." But he reckoned without the congregation for even in hymn-singing the settlers did not like to be dictated to, and without waiting for him to give the first line they swung out together in a surging lift of song, "I've reached the land of corn and wine . . ." Their voices drowned the organ and left the freckled man standing open-mouthed. This was their own song and they sang it with fervor and assurance. "O Beulah land, sweet Beulah land, as on thy highest banks I stand . . ."

When that was finished a high sweet soprano from the back of the plank seats started, "Bringing in the sheaves, bringing in the sheaves, we shall come rejoicing . . ." and they were all singing again, the freckled man joining in with the others, beating time with a stubby forefinger that nobody regarded. Then "Onward Christian Soldiers," with a thundering chorus that shook the leaves on the post oaks. Lainey heard Arch's voice crack on the third phrase but he caught up and went on with the rest. A woman near the front, her face half-hidden by a slatted sunbonnet, raised her hand and asked for "Sweet Hour of Prayer." They sang it softly and there were husky notes here and there, and across the breadth of three quilts Lainey saw the sudden shine of tears on the leathery cheek of a woman with a brood of children around her. They might have gone from one song to another all day but the young preacher raised his hand, the organ wheezed to a stop, and the people waited as he opened the Bible that lay before him on the packing-box pulpit.

"Now faith is the substance of things hoped for, the evidence of things not seen," he read in a strong, clear voice, his face taking light from the words. "By faith Abraham when he was called to go out into a place which he should receive for an inheritance obeyed; and he went out, not knowing whither he went . . ." He read on, calling the great roll of faith as Paul wrote it to the Hebrews, his voice mounting with each name. Then he looked up from the Bible directly at the waiting people. "But now they desire a better country . . ." And closing the Bible he began to preach.

Mary Hampton jumped up from the ground and began folding up the quilts. "Wasn't that fine? Just wonderful. I declare I feel I've had a blessing. And now you folks come right along and eat dinner with us."

"Oh, I don't think we ought to . . ."

"Why of course you will. We wouldn't count it Sunday unless we had somebody to break bread with us."

Lainey touched the faille sleeve. "Please, Mama, please."

"I got a pony," Arch said. "Name of Dumps. She's all mine, too! Raised her on a bottle."

"Please. Please."

Bush and Hamp stood back, allowing this to be women's business. The scattering congregation pushed around them. "Well, I . . ."

Mary Hampton was already leading the way to their wagon, quilts over her arm. "Now you come right along. I brought plenty, Just in case . . ."

For the next eight months the Sheridans lived in the wagon. As the year turned toward winter Bush took the wagon box off its wheels, banked it with dirt and with boards from the sawmill at Tohee built a canvas-covered extension on the side for Lainey. Using slabbed boards, with the bark still on he put up a cook shack with the monkey stove inside and some packing boxes as tables and chairs. Lainey had almost forgotten what the things from Riverview looked like. She had seen them briefly when Bud Menifee had finally turned up at the claim, shamefaced and broke, and helped Bush unload the wagons. They had emptied the wagon going back to Kate Tillery's and had taken the biggest pieces of furniture out of the Sheridan wagon. These were stacked on a platform of crossed poles, covered with prairie hay and topped with a patched wagon sheet.

Some of the things had been traded in Randall for groceries that were freighted out from Guthrie. The freighters' charge of twenty-five cents a hundred pounds sent the cost of food sky high. The Run of '91 was too late in the year to raise much garden and the homesteaders were hard put to make out till spring. Turnips did pretty well and some folks came through on a diet of turnips and rabbit and flour gravy. Kaffir corn was the best crop, growing head high in the patches of newly broken sod. It was meant for stock feed, but it could be headed and the grain parched and boiled for "coffee," or ground and made into a mush. A thin, sweetish-sour syrup could be made from the stalk.

The Sheridans were luckier than most people because of the stubborn generosity of Ellen Crump. But by the end of the winter the Riverview rations were getting low and the money sack looked limper and sadder each time Allegra took it out of the feather pillow. So they traded what they had for what they needed. The long pier glass went for a cross-grained brindle cow that could be milked only by snubbing her to a tree. A walnut dressing table, meant for Lainey, went for a coop of hens. A cut-glass berry bowl with six saucers brought a case of canned tomatoes and a keg of jelly.

The wagon sheet that was sparkling white when they left Kate Tillery's weathered to a mottled gray. It was better, Bush and Lainey told each other, for now it didn't hurt your eyes when the sun hit. But in the new country there was little need for pretending. Everybody was in the same fix. The homes that dotted the quarter sections were as varied as the people who lived in them. Plenty of folks still kept house in wagons. A few burrowed into the clay and made dugouts, whitewashing the walls, and putting cheese-cloth on the ceilings, and living in a perpetual shower of red-clay nuggets. Those who had pioneered in western Kansas and Nebraska built soddies. There were some small, square log houses built from whatever timber the land provided. Occasionally a settler from the South built two of these and connected them with a dog-run. Tents were a common sight. Brush arbors for stock were everywhere. Scattered among these dwellings were the reed-mat houses and bark shelters of the Sac and Fox, and the solid houses of the Indians who had taken the white man's ways and built homes on their removal in the 70s and 80s. Serving as their center were the stately red-brick buildings of the Sac and Fox Agency and Boarding School.

But houses and food were of small account. Even people didn't matter much that first year. The important thing was breaking the sod. Before it could be planted it must be plowed. The tough mat of grass roots that had covered it for centuries had to be ripped apart and the young tree sprouts grubbed out by hand. This was not just hard work, such as most of the settlers had known before they came; it was a battle that only the strong could win.

Already some families were leaving. Bush shook his head when he saw a loaded wagon go slowly by. To him this was a personal struggle between himself and the land and he could no more have left it than he could have turned his back on a man who attacked his honor. Night after night he came back to the wagon camp, sweat soaked, dirt caked, too tired to speak, and the next morning he was out before sun-up to start again. Yet he loved the thing he fought and once in Randall he knocked down a disgruntled settler who cursed the "mis'able red hard-scrabble." Work and short rations trimmed him down to lean tough muscle. He let his beard grow, for shaving in the hard water was uncomfortable. His brown skin took on a deeper brown. By the time the first year had run its course he looked like a different man.

Lainey changed, too. Her legs were growing faster and without Aunt Ellen's patient needlework most of her skirts were cutting high water. She kept her braids, but the wind whipped them so that Allegra pinned them around her head in a small wreath. Her face, too, was a darker tan, for she wore sunbonnets only when directly told to, and her green-brown eyes seemed larger. There were more disturbing changes that had come to her body, but dressing and undressing in the canvas lean-to she could pretend not to notice them. Only from Addie Bucklin would she have asked questions and Addie had faded to a querulous, "why-don't-you-write" that wandered occasionally to the claim.

In October Lainey was twelve. Her cake was a slab of hot gingerbread. There were presents from Riverview and somehow Mary Hampton found out and brought a string of chinaberry beads. At first Lainey had been pleased to be twelve, but by now the pleasure had dimmed. It meant, "You're too big to climb trees. Keep your skirts down. Sit up straight. Keep your knees together. You're twelve years old!"

Of the three of them Allegra changed the least. Clinging to the standards instilled in her by Ellen she had come through the months better than most. By miracles of washing in limited water, and ironing with sad irons that cooled in the wind faster than you could heat them, by brushing her hair through four verses and six choruses of "Lorena" and rubbing tallow on her hands and never, never walking in the sun without a bonnet, she had managed. Nobody knew what it cost her but she paid the price, her back straight, her head high. Now in April they had moved the monkey stove outside the cook shack because of the heat and looking at herself in a mirror she hung on a blackjack limb Allegra shook her head.

"If anybody'd ever told me I'd do this, I wouldn't have believed 'em."

"Do what?" Lainey stirred the mush on the stove.

"Oh . . . live in a wagon . . . wear calico weeks on end . . . cook outdoors . . . eat off a box . . ." She waved her hand to include a hundred other things, unsaid but unforgotten. "It's funny to me," she loosed the coil of her hair and let it slide around her shoulders, "the way you've taken to cooking. Back at Riverview with everything to do with and Mattie and Ellen to teach you we couldn't drag you to the kitchen. Now, with that little bitty old stove and dirt blowing and nothing fit to cook . . ."

How could you explain that in the Riverview kitchen cooking was a mystery for grown-ups hedged about with rules and receipts and proper ways of doing things while on the claim it was free and easy . . . like playing house with acorn cups and china chips.

"There's lots to cook. Rabbit and quail . . . and rabbit."

"Ugh! Sometimes I feel like I'm turnin' to a cottontail."

"And mush. But I saw the bottom of the sack this time. And it's the last one."

"We'll try some boiled kaffir. Mary Hampton says it's pretty good with syrup."

There was no mention of the stores in Randall where meal could be bought. There were few trips to town these days and when anything broke or ran out they patched, mended, or changed plans. Nobody talked to Lainey about money but she knew they were short of cash. The money sack hardly made a lump in the feather pillow.

Allegra coiled her hair around her head, taking the hairpins out of her mouth, one by one. Watching, Lainey thought she had never read a fairy story that began, "Once there was a princess with short black hair and green eyes . . ."

"When I think about all those dresses. Not even out of the trunk!"

"'member how we dressed up at first?" Lainey smiled at the greenhorn she had been.

"I still think it was right. A lady should be properly dressed in the afternoon."

"But out here . . ."

"Still, if somebody came by. Or like the time I met Bertha Mebane."

Lainey put the top on the kettle. "When we get the house . . ."

"'When we get the house,'" Allegra mimicked, an edge on her voice. "That's all I hear. You and Bush seem to think the wind will stop blowing, the dirt will turn black and the place will get civilized all because we move into . . . that." She pointed to the house that squatted, roofless, on the flat-topped hill.

In the short stretches of time he snatched from grubbing sprouts or breaking sod Bush had built the house. It was a hodge-podge of a place, starting with lumber freighted in from Guthrie . . . that took most of the money . . . changing to cottonwood siding from the sawmill at Ingram, too green and already curling at the edges, and ending with native oak with the bark on. To make up for these differences there was a door with store-bought hardware and the greatest luxury of all, two full-sized glass windows. On the outside a ladder went up to the strap-hinged slab "window" that was the opening to Lainey's room under the unfinished roof.

The house waited now for the red-oak shingles. Bush had rived them out with a froe, soaked them in rain water and feather-edged them with a jacknife. It was work that could be done by lantern light so Allegra dug into the boxes and brought out some of the books Uncle Hod sent along. *Thaddeus of Warsaw, Lorna Doone,* and a thin volume of the poems of Edgar Allan Poe. She read aloud by the lantern light with Lainey tucked up beside her and though she couldn't read like Uncle Hod the magic of the words took hold and the new country became a stronghold in Poland or a moor in England, or the sad sweet music of the poems seemed one with the night wind and the flickering of the lantern. And the pile of shingles grew.

"It's a good location," Lainey chose Bush's words. "We'll get the breeze."

"Oh my heavens! If there was just some place to get *out* of the breeze. The wind hasn't stopped blowing one minute since we got here. Not one!"

The wind was part of living in Oklahoma Territory. Nothing could be put down that wasn't weighted. The first time they had done the wash, Lainey and Allegra put things on the grass to bleach, the way Mattie did. By noon some of the clothes were on the next claim and some of them were never found. Allegra hated the wind and blamed it for everything. But Lainey loved it.

The wind was a companion if you'd let it be. It was always there and always changing. Sometimes fierce and cruel, whipping the sparse trees, piling up black thunderheads, blasting out rain that struck the face like stones. Sometimes, out of the south, it was gentle and tender, whispering half-guessed secrets. Sometimes it roared from the north with a knifing cold that cut to the very bone. Or it could be full of fun and foolishness, rolling up great bundles of tumbleweed and chasing them across the claim, then, tired of the game, piling them into gulches. Or spinning up dust devils that danced across the land to climb straight in the air and disappear in the sun. The secret was to go with the wind and not to fight it.

"I like the wind," Lainey said, stirring the fire to cover her words.

The snapping of the fire and the plopping of the mush went on and it was a full minute before Lainey turned around to find Allegra standing, one hand still at the coil of her hair, the other at the throat of her dress, her wedding ring glinting in the sun.

"Mama? Mama?" There was no question she needed to ask, only a need to be answered.

Allegra gave her head a little shake and thrust in the last hairpin. "What did you say?"

She tried to frame a proper question but found none. "Dinner's ready. That's all. Want me to call Bush?" She reached for the polished cow horn, longing to blow it.

"Never mind. He'll come when he's ready. I think I'll go lie down awhile."

To lie down in the middle of the day with your hair fresh combed and dinner smoking on the stove! Puzzled, squinting in the noon sun Lainey watched Allegra go toward the wagon. Once there she stopped and turned back.

"Lainey, do you remember . . . But I guess you wouldn't."

"Remember what?"

"Nothing. I just got to thinking." She reached one hand behind her for the rib of the wagon cover. "I didn't mean all I said . . . about this place. The house is going to be fine. And I never had a better friend than Mary Hampton. Not anywhere." She stopped and seemed to listen before she went on. "It's just that I feel bad today. The heat so early, and all. That's all it is. That's . . . all." She went inside the wagon and Lainey heard the bed creak beneath her.

The mush was plop-plopping too fast. Moving it back from the fire Lainey burned her hand and tears stung her eyelids as she sucked at the place. With a long stick she lifted the kettle off the stove and put it on the ground. There, let it get cold! Nobody cared. If she burned her hand or caught fire and burned clear up nobody would care at all. Bush wouldn't come in from the field and Mama wouldn't get up from her bed. Probably even Hamptons wouldn't come to her funeral!

She sat down on a box and invited sorrow. Each disappointment that marched past grew bigger and blacker until it seemed that nothing nice had ever happened to her. Not one single thing. That she would be lonesome on the claim was something she hadn't expected. But she was, lonesome with a kind of aching sickness that went on and on without a promise of relief. Bush was too worn out with the bitter work of sod-busting for companionship and Allegra was absorbed in cooking without a kitchen and washing with almost no water. The neighbors, struggling to get set for

100

winter, had little time for more than a friendly hail as they went past. No one to talk to, no one to see, no one to care what happened to her.

The remembrance of Riverview was sharp and painful to Lainey now. There were always people there and things to do. Each season brought its special events. Planting garden, sticking peas, sewing strips for rag rugs, canning, setting hens, airing the Confederate uniforms, washing carpets, making cider, making apple butter, butchering, making sausage, making soap . . . each came in its own time. And then the pattern of work was starred by celebrations. Birthdays, Christmas, Last Day of School, the Horse Show, the Snyder County Fair, Fourth of July, Sunday School Picnic, and the gatherings of the Saunders' kin. In the Territory there was no pattern for work or play and the days seemed without importance.

"If I just had somebody," she whispered forlornly, rubbing her eyes with her knuckles, "Like Addie . . . or somebody . . ."

"Hey! I'm hungry." Bush flipped a pebble at her. "You're woolgathering."

To cover her feelings she began to scold him for letting dinner spoil.

"I was talkin' hoss with Henry Halfmoon," he admitted. "He says there's a good fishing hole on Big Sandy. But I'm not going fishing. Nothing's going to toll me off this place till I get that field clear of sprouts. Where's Allegra?"

He was over at the wagon before Lainey finished telling him about Mama and the way she acted. Lainey dished up and sat waiting while the food cooled. When at last they both came to eat Allegra sat pushing her food on her plate without lifting a fork but Bush talked and laughed and ate and praised the sorry meal beyond all reason. Then he wiped his beard and announced he was going to work on the house.

"I've piddled around long enough. Time it was finished."

He hardly had time to gather his tools before Lainey heard him up on the roof pounding shingles as if he were killing snakes, singing at the top of his voice.

101

> " 'Way down south on Beaver Creek,
> Sing-song-kitty-cantchee-ki-me-O . . .'"

"Men are funny," Allegra dried the last dish and spread the towel on a haw bush.

"I think they're hateful." Lainey swished the dishrag around the pan.

"You're just put out because Bush was late. I think I'll go back and lie down."

Lainey poured the dishwater in the trench that led to the garden patch. A scum of soft soap stayed on top of the ground. Suppose Mama was sick? Suppose she died? Scraps of things overheard floated back to her. "Galloping consumption . . . died in a week." "Just a pimple but it ate the nose away and the side of his face." "She went into a decline. Just turned her face away and died."

A cold fear wrapped itself around her heart and would not let go. If anything happened to Mama . . . or Bush . . .

Chapter 10

As the days went on Lainey's loneliness became more acute. She would not leave the camp but stayed in the narrow area of wagon, cook shack, and garden, dogging Allegra's footsteps, asking questions, pulling things out of the packed boxes, and trying to cook dishes far beyond her own capacity or that of the monkey stove. One night after she had gone to bed in the lean-to she heard Allegra talking to Bush.

"If she'd just leave me alone! Go somewhere, anywhere. She . . . she breathes down my neck. I don't have a moment's peace, and the way I feel . . ."

"There's talk of starting a school," Bush said, "if we just had a schoolhouse. A man over west said he'd teach for a dollar a month per pupil."

"I'd pay twice that! I think I'll lose my mind with all that silly girl talk!"

"Now, honey . . ."

Lainey pulled the pillow over her head, too hurt even to cry. Her own mother . . . The next morning after the work was done she announced that she was going for a walk, half hoping that Mama would forbid it and prove the things she heard last night weren't true. But Allegra said emphatically that it would be a good idea and fixed her a snack of biscuit and bacon to take along.

She left the camp, her eyes downcast, and her feet kicking sullenly at the bunch grass, but it was hard to stay mad. The day was warm, the sun bright, and the sky a deep blue. The wind that tickled the cottonwoods into shivering delight teased Lainey until she lifted her head and half-smiled at a mocking bird perched on the topmost branch of a dead tree, his song rippling through every birdcall he had ever heard.

103

How did he do it? She wondered, and tried a few whistles in answer, but the mocker was so much better at it than she was that she left him to his singing while she watched two tumble-bugs rolling a ball over and over and over on their way to some mysterious hiding place. A horned toad darted from one clump of grass to another. Snake spit bubbled at a joint of a juicy stalk. A striped lizard watched her from a rock. The Territory *could* be nice, she thought, if you just had somebody to enjoy it with you.

She came to a dry gulch, a split in the ground like a great knife slash, and being unfamiliar with the country she took one step too many toward the edge and the earth crumbled beneath her feet. She hurtled to the bottom in one jarring thud. There she stood up, unhurt, but shaken, dirt stained, and indignant at the treachery.

Red walls rose about her like a narrow prison. On either side the dirt had caved in so that the sod shelved out with nothing to support it. That was what had betrayed her. The roots of the grasses dangled, four, five, six feet long. No wonder Bush was worn out with breaking sod! On one side of the gulch near the top a curious streak of white clay ran as straight as a chalk mark on a school blackboard. Lainey took off her shoes to empty out the dirt, then removed her stockings and dug her toes in the sand.

A few yards away a tree stump choked the gulch, its roots writhing into snaky tangles that held leaves and trash of all kinds. Lainey squeezed past the stump and found a stretch littered with round red rocks, some of them big as her head, some that fit into the circle of her thumb and finger.

She turned one rock over with her big toe. A hairline crack ran along the underside. With a bigger rock she pounded and the rock split open. Tiny jewels filled a cavity in the center! Hardly breathing Lainey picked up the split halves and ran her fingers over the sharp edges of the crystals and into the glistening fairy cave in the middle. She cracked another rock, found the same hidden wealth. Another and another. Her hands hurt from hammering but her heart danced with the riches she found. She arranged them in a glittering semi-circle and sat down to gloat over the treasure. Around her were hundreds more red rocks and inside each one was a gleaming wealth of jewels for Lainey Sheridan to set free!

But the rocks were too heavy to carry back to the wagon. She must find a place to hide them. As she dug into the leaves and trash around the tree stump, leaving one rock here and another there, Lainey became aware of one spot between her shoulder blades that itched and burned. The feeling of being watched slid over her whole body. Slowly she looked around, turning her head so gradually that her neck muscles twitched. Nothing. Nothing at all.

She split a few more rocks but the joy was gone. Wealth had turned into a burden. She selected one small rock, so evenly split she could put it back together to show Mama . . . No, not Mama . . . just Bush. Then she knelt to put on her stockings and shoes. The feeling of being watched returned, stronger than ever. Lainey jammed her shoes onto bare feet, took her stockings and ran. Up the bank, clawing at clay, hanging on roots, pulling over the top by a stand of Johnson grass, she ran all the way to the wagon chased by a fear she did not dare to turn and see.

The further she got from the gulch the less valuable the treasure she had found became. That night she proffered Bush the rock, not even opening it out.

"Yep, lots of 'em around." A yawn blurred his words. "Sparkly stuff inside."

The next day she went back, taking great care not to be followed. Down in the bottom of the gulch the tarnish Bush's words had put on the jewels disappeared. They were her treasure and they were waiting for Lainey Sheridan. The stone in her pocket clinked as she tiptoed on the sand. Near the tree stump there were barefoot tracks. Were they her own? Then Lainey heard a faint rustle, a nestling sound, like a mouse in a drawer of papers. The rock clutched in her hand, part weapon and part talisman, she rushed the tree stump. This time she would find out!

Crouched on the other side, moving no more than the red earth itself, a girl watched her with eyes as bright and shiny as a new-split lump of coal. Hair as black and shiny as her eyes hung over her shoulders in braids. Lainey could see the rapid beat of the

105

pulse in her throat, and knew that the Indian girl was as scared as she was.

"Hello," Lainey dropped the rock to the sand. "You live around here?"

She could have counted ten before an answer came. Then a slim brown finger pointed down the gulch. "Live . . . there."

The dry gulch, Lainey realized ran from the Sheridans' claim on down to the allotment Henry Halfmoon and his family had from their tribal government. Then this must be . . . "Are you Half-moon's girl? Bush . . . my father, Bushrod Sheridan . . . told me they had a girl but I didn't think . . . that is . . . I . . . Say, were you here yesterday? I thought somebody was watching me."

The Indian girl's cheeks turned a coppery red. "I here. I watch. My mother says that's . . ." She gave it up, shook her head.

"I know. Aunt Ellen's always telling me a lady shouldn't stare, but, shoot, how else can you ever see anything. Anyway, a cat can look at a king."

Laughter sparkled in the black eyes. "Me . . . cat? You . . . king?"

Then they were both laughing. Lainey Sheridan and Annie Halfmoon walked down the dry gulch together to share its wonders with each other.

After that they met every day, giggled, ate whatever snack either one could take without being noticed, and time began to fly for Lainey. She heard the plans for the subscription school with hidden resentment knowing that they would break into her fun with Annie. That neither one was certain of the other's language made very little difference to them. Words, they found, were not as important as the grown-ups made out. They broke dozens more of the round red rocks and arranged them in elaborate patterns on the sand. They made dishes out of the white streak of clay, explaining to each other that this was for little girls and they were just fooling. And they made up The Game. It was a combination, part Snyder County "Pick Up Sticks" and part an Algonquin gambling game that had travelled to Oklahoma Territory by way of the southward trek of the Sac and Fox . . . Minnesota, Iowa, Kansas.

106

Then one day Annie did not come. Lainey wandered up and down half the morning, but the trill of the tongue that was their signal was unanswered. Day after day Lainey went to the gulch, but Annie did not return. Then, on a day when Allegra decided to hitch Stretcher to the buckboard Bush had traded for, and drive over to Hamptons', Lainey pretended to have a cold as an excuse for staying home. But as soon as Mama was out of sight she walked the length of the gulch, and took the faint trail to the Halfmoon house. She walked fast so that there would be no time to change her mind.

The clearing around the log house was small and it looked as if it might go back to woods at any moment. Lainey walked through a garden patch where some beans and squash were growing. There was a small barn of slabbed timber and at the far side of the clearing a bark-roofed shelter with a stone fireplace in the center to which, Annie told her, the family moved in the hot summertime.

From the edge of the garden patch Lainey eyed the house. There was no sign of life there. In a pole corral back of the barn two paint ponies nuzzled some corncobs in the dust. An assortment of lean, savage-looking dogs sprawled by the door of the house. If only Annie would just happen to come out the door! Lainey waited, counting, "Five, ten, fifteen, twenty . . ." Well, that was no good. Wetting her lips she gave the trill. The dogs leaped up, barking shrilly, charging down the garden path then running back to the cabin as if they carried a message of a great attack. Then the door of the cabin opened and a woman came out. She shouted at the dogs and they came, fawning, to her. When she ignored them they retired, muttering, to their place around the door.

The Sac woman came down the path toward Lainey, her full dark-blue skirt swinging as she walked. Her hair was parted in the middle and greased till it shone blue black. Around her neck dozens of strands of beads made a bright bib of color. She looked at Lainey without speaking and the things Lainey had planned to say fled from her.

"I'm Lainey Sheridan," she stammered, "from over on the next claim. I came to see Annie. Maybe she didn't tell you we're friends, but we are. That is, can she come over, sometime. My mother . . ." She was babbling and she knew it but she could not stop. "Can Annie come to see me?"

"Annie's gone." It was as if a deep-toned bell had struck twice. "Gone?"

"Gone to gov'ment school." There was no change in the woman's face but the loneliness in her voice could not be mistaken.

"Oh. Well . . . tell her . . ." There was nothing to say, now, but the silence was not embarrassing as it had been before. Each of them knew the other missed Annie and wanted her back. "I guess I'll go home, then. Goodbye."

"Goodbye," the Sac woman nodded gravely. "You come back. Sometime."

"Oh yes, thank you," Lainey said, then added her part of the ritual. "You come see us."

When Lainey got back from Halfmoons' place she found Mama already in camp. Mary Hampton was not at home. She had gone with Hamp and the man who was going to teach the school to see about some prospective pupils from over by Taney. It was settled that they would have the school; the Hamptons were giving the land and the parents of the pupils were contributing the labor and materials for the schoolhouse. Bush had stopped work on the house to help get the schoolhouse started.

"I thought he wanted the house now," Lainey said. "First the sod to get busted, and then he was all worked up about the house and now . . ."

"First things first," Allegra smiled. "We want you to have an education and some friends . . ."

"And you want to get me out from underfoot!" It came out, sharply, cruelly, and shame bit Lainey as soon as she heard her own words. But there they were; she would not take them back.

"There are some things that you can't understand till you've been through them," Allegra said quietly. "I shouldn't have said that, but . . . well, you shouldn't have been listening."

Allegra spent more and more time in the wagon. She was sewing on something. Lainey found snippets of white cloth here and

108

there and short ends of pink and blue embroidery thread. It must be a surprise for Allegra hid it whenever anyone came near. The spring had turned into summer and it was hot, hot as it never got in Missouri with a burning, golden heat but the nights were cool for the wind never failed them.

Lainey was in the cook shack setting some bread to rise when she saw Arch come up with his pony, Dumps, hitched to the wooden sled, and the Hamptons' water barrel bumping along on top.

"Ma's sent me to Buffalo Springs after water," he said to Bush. "She said for me to take your barrel along too. And Ma said would Lainey like to go? I'll look after her."

"I'll look after myself," Lainey came out of the cook shack, tossing her head.

"Some spring water would taste good," Bush said, glancing at the wagon. "No need to disturb your mama, Lainey, go get your bonnet and go. You haven't been off the place in a week."

It was the part of a neighbor to share in Oklahoma Territory. The Hamptons never went for water, drove to Randall, or cut a pie melon without including the Sheridans. Mary neighbored with everybody, and Hamp was always the first one at a roof-raising or a well-digging, or any kind of a gathering where help was needed. He had built far more than his share of the schoolhouse, considering that he gave the land. In fact, Mary had confided to Allegra in Lainey's hearing, Hamp would just naturally rather do somebody else's work than his own.

Lainey put some pieces of stewed rabbit and some cornbread in a salt sack and put on her pink ruffled sunbonnet. The brown one was more practical but this was a trip! Bush and Arch had both water barrels on the sled, a homemade contraption with long runners that slid over the thick grass. Dumps was too fat and short-legged for the real work of sod-busting so hauling water was her main work. She stamped her right front hoof and rattled the harness to show she was ready to go.

"Past two o'clock," Bush considered the sun. "Be sure you get back by dark."

"We'll be back by then, easy. C'mon, Slowpoke." Arch jerked

109

her bonnet strings and Lainey was glad she had chosen the pink one. "Giddap, Dumps."

It was a perfect day for travelling. The grass was dotted with crimson poppy mallow, blue spiderwort, and the golden plumes of wild mustard. The green and white of snow-on-the-mountain marked the low spots and the delicate lace of tumbleweed decorated the tops of the hills. Wispy clouds raced across the sky as the south wind chased them.

The way to Buffalo Springs was well marked. It moseyed along, taking the easiest route. As they left the Sheridan place Lainey's worries about Mama slipped from her. A trip can cure almost anything, she thought, and jumped off the sled to walk with Arch at Dumps' head. A dove whickered up from beside them.

"They make good eatin' in the fall," Arch said, "back in Kansas . . ."

"Do you want to go back?"

"Nah! Do you?"

It was a fair question, but Lainey knew she would answer it different ways at different times. "I like it here," she said slowly, "more than I don't like it."

He nodded, understanding. "Reckon they'll start school up again?"

"I guess so. But we'll sure have another teacher."

They laughed, remembering the lanky, loud-talking fellow who had started the short-lived summer subscription school. Old Slackpants the boys called him. He was long on licking and short on learning and when the second month's pay was collected he vanished. The angry patrons gathered at Hamptons'.

"Should have known when he got his money in ad-vance."

"And I paid for four! No discount for numbers."

"Guess we'd better name it Jackrabbit School. He sure skedaddled outa here like a jackrabbit."

"Who'd think a teacher would skip out like that? A teacher!"

The settlers had come to the new country believing in education. A schoolhouse was the first thing they had built after their own shelters. They were shaken as they would not have been at any other failure. A preacher, a judge, might have been forgiven; a

110

teacher, never. They planned warily for someone to take his place. A committee of Ab Pritchard, Bush and Hamp . . . though Mary was expected to do the work . . . would act as the school board. Jackrabbit School District . . . the name stuck in spite of Mary's pleading for Union or Pretty Prairie, or Morning Star or anything else . . . would open in the fall. They would not be caught napping this time.

The trail wandered through Pritchard's place and across the edge of Doggett's. Bill Doggett, struggling with a grasshopper plow, hailed them.

"Goin' after water? I hear Jurd Morehouse's got the trail blocked. Don't mess with him. He's half crazy, what with claim jumpers haulin' him into court."

"We'll watch out."

They went on, the trail angling toward Wellmans'. Dumps cropped a mouthful of grass. Lainey jumped off the sled to pick some wild roses, then she ran to catch up with Arch who was standing in front of a pile of thorny brush that blocked the trail. From the top a piece of wagon sheet fluttered, lettered on it in large black letters was, NO TRESPASIN. They stared at the sign.

"What'll we do?" Lainey said. "Go back home?"

"Nope. Ma'd skin me alive. We'll zig a little 'n' zag a little."

"Look," Lainey nudged him. A man was standing under a tall elm tree some thirty feet from the brush pile, a shotgun in the crook of his arm.

"Howdy," Arch called, lifting his arm. There was no reply.

"Cranky devil!" Arch brooded as they went on. "Man can do what he wants to with his own land, I reckon, but he ought to say 'Howdy.'"

The land dropped down gradually and Jurd Morehouse was out of sight. Arch guided Dumps by some inner sense of direction and picked up the trail on the other side of the Morehouse claim. The sun was halfway down the sky. They hurried to get to the springs.

111

Buffalo Springs was at the bottom of a deep cut in the red sandstone. The soil around it was thin but a few runty, twisted post oaks had managed to get a roothold on the trail to the bottom, shading the way down to the crystal-clear water that gushed out of the rock wall. Delicate maidenhair ferns waved above the water and streamers of coontail moss curled and straightened in the current. Below the springs a natural pool had been enlarged and dammed by some nameless traveller. The water swirled into it, then calmed into mirrored smoothness. Minnows darted in the sunlit patches and when the sled approached unseen frogs hit the water with a series of splashes like a descending scale.

Homesteaders drove for miles to fill their barrels at the springs. Women who had made one bucket of water do for a day's cooking, washing, and drinking, took off their shoes and stockings and stood ankle-deep in the stream that overflowed the pool. Children held water fights and launched bark boats that wrecked in the weeds around the bend where the stream dived underground.

Arch held back on the barrels so that the sled might not override Dumps' heels. He let her drink from the stream, then hitched her to one of the oaks on the trail above.

Lainey climbed to a sandstone ledge patterned with scalloped lichens. Purling, whispering, chuckling water-talk came up to her. All her life she had lived within the sound of the river and she had not known that she missed it until now.

Arch was in no hurry to fill the barrels. It was rare for Mary to give him time off from the man's work he did and his young bones soaked up the leisure. He squatted by the water, catching minnows and crawdads with cupped hands, skipping flat stones across the smooth pool. Then he climbed the face of the springs, digging into the smooth, mossy rocks with his fingernails and the welt of his boots. For a long time he was out of sight; then Lainey heard the tell-tale, scrape-scrape-scrape of a knife-blade on sandstone. Arch was carving initials. She tip-toed up the trail, appearing above him.

"Fools' names and fools' faces . . ."

He jumped, planting his foot solidly on the letters in the stone. No shoving or teasing could make him move.

"Clara Doggett? Esterene Pritchard? Grace Wellman? Dotty Sullavan? That's it! That's who it is! I can see an 'S.' Just wait till I tell her."

"You hush up!"

"Wait till I tell her! Wait till I tell her!" Lainey gloated, dancing up and down just out of reach. Arch grabbed at her, doubling back her wrist.

"Will . . . you . . . shut . . . your . . . mouth?" He punctuated the words with shakes that rattled her teeth. Then he dropped her arm and gave her a shove.

"Ouch!" She ran stumbling down the trail, rubbing her wrist. He ran past her and when she caught up to him he was opening the salt sack.

"Let's eat," he said briefly. It was an easy way to make peace. Their mouths were too full for talking. They washed down the snack with gulps of water.

This led to a game of lying belly-down on the edge of the pool and seeing which one could stay under water the longer. Lainey came up first, gasping and sputtering, to find Arch's blond head half under, his arm groping in the pool. She grabbed the slack of his pants and he came up, front cowlick plastered on his forehead. He shook her off and went down again. This time he came up wet to the shoulder, a blackened spoon in his dripping hand.

"Saw it the first time," he choked. "Betcha it's solid silver."

Water streamed from his shirtsleeve into her lap. A silver spoon! Magic in the words. Crusted with tarnish, bent by the tumbling waters, it looked as if it might have been in Buffalo Springs a hundred years.

With fine sand from the bottom of the pool they scrubbed and

113

polished. The sun's rays slanted through the trees and the light around the springs turned golden. A terrapin waddled through the shallows, a fox squirrel peered from a young pecan tree. Dumps whinnied insistently. The thin, soft metal began to shine, initials on the handle curled and twisted into each other. An E and a P. An M, or was it W?

"Who d'ya s'pose?"

"Nobody in the Run. Been there too long."

"Not Indians." They stood up, knees wet from kneeling on the sand.

"Bush said the Spanish were here. And the French."

The gleam of the silver was history. Unknown, unknowable. Lainey ran her finger around the fiddleback handle. She wanted it more than she had wanted anything for a long time. But Arch had seen it, brought it up. She put it in his hand. A big hand, brown and broad-fingered. A man's hand on a boy's wrist. The spoon looked frail, delicate.

"Here," Arch said, "I don't want it. You take it."

She shook her head. "Finders keepers."

A mustang trotted around the bend. The man on his back was likely a Mexican Kickapoo. He rode without a saddle, a striped blanket folded across the horse. The mustang began to buck and snort, backing away from the water. "Ho . . . ho . . . ho . . ." The Indian talked him down, brought him to the stream, but he refused to drink. The Indian jerked his chin at Arch and they talked together out of Lainey's hearing. Then the mustang reared and took off up the trail in a thunder of unshod hoofs.

"What'd he say?" Lainey demanded.

"Nothin' much. We got to get these barrels filled." Arch grabbed one bucket, thrust the other at Lainey.

"But he must of said something?"

"You talk too much. Get to work. Want to be here all night?"

Startled, she looked for the sun. It was not there although its golden light still filled the west. The shadows around the pool were purple. The cool had turned to chill. The fox squirrel was gone. The terrapin had closed his shell. As she dipped and poured she became aware of the silence. Only the water talked on.

"Guess we're ready." Lainey went with Arch to bring down Dumps, unwilling to stay alone by the springs. The sunset was fading, now, a cast of lavender in the blue sky.

"Bush said be home 'fore dark." Lainey hoped Arch would say she was wrong.

He nodded. "Yeah. I know."

It was better on the trail once they started. Insects shrilled. A bat darted in wide arcs. Dumps stopped fidgeting and pulled steadily. Lainey began enjoying the trip again. Their disobedience put just enough edge on the evening to make it fun. But Arch stayed cranky. As they took the turnout around Morehouses' he unbent a little.

"Star light, star bright," Lainey chanted, pointing to a tiny gleam in the gray arch above them. "Make your wish."

"I got a wish." Arch said. "I sure got a wish."

"If you tell it won't come true."

"I won't tell." His hand tangled in Dumps' mane looked white instead of brown.

"Don't be in such a fidge. Bush may ra'r an' pitch, but he won't be really mad. And your folks will just think you stayed to supper at our place." All this sounded so easy that it delighted her and she refused to hurry, tormenting the boy with small delays. When she sat down to get a rock out of her shoe he blew up.

"Ketch me takin' you anywhere, again! Just ketch me!"

"I guess you wish I was Dotty Sullavan. I saw you holdin' hands with her at the literary." It was an out and out lie but she had a need to hurt him.

"Get that shoe and come on!"

"If you don't like the way I act, I'll get home by myself!" She made as if to go in the opposite direction. He caught up with her, took her arm.

"Lainey, please come on. And hurry!"

"Why . . . all right." She walked at Dumps' shoulder, matching her stride to Arch's. Trees and bushes grew into strange shapes in the dusk. A riderless horse tore by at a full gallop.

"Now what in the world started him up?"

Arch shook his head. Dumps nickered. The sled grated over a

strip of bare ground. A whippoorwill complained, another answered. It was much, much darker.

"Back home it's light a long time after sundown. I used to play out. An' Jimdandy told me stories." Lainey shuddered, recalling "Taley-Po." The spot between her shoulder blades began to burn the way it had the day before she found Annie. She started to say so, turned her words into a cough. She sneaked a look over her shoulder, found Arch watching her.

"What'd you see? What're you lookin' for?"

"Nothin'. Nothin' a-tall." They plodded on. A screech ended in a strangled gurgle.

"Screech owl," Arch said.

"Oh." If she went on for ten steps she could look back. Eight. Nine. Ten. Better make it twenty. Something's back there, walking the way we walk. Fast or slow. Eighteen. Nineteen. Twenty. The sled grated over bare ground.

"Whoa!" The white blur of Arch's face turned. "Lainey, I'm . . . lost."

"Lost?" She shifted her weight from one tired foot to the other.

"We've been at this place before. Dumps knew it. She tried to pull away but I turned her. Now she's lost, too.

"They'll come and get us. Bush will come."

He shook his head. "I said I'd take care of you."

"Why can't we just stop right here? Sit down and rest. It'll be mornin'. Sometime."

"Because . . ." his hand found hers in the tangle of Dumps' mane. Big, broadfingered hand, she knew just what it looked like. Tensed to a fist in a schoolground fight. Wagging an insult at Old Slackpants' back. Around a hoe handle. Around a silver spoon. "That Kickapoo . . . what he told me . . . There's a panther loose."

Panther. The word took shape in the night, slit-eyed, crouching.

"They found tracks around the springs," he continued. "And the Iowas been losin' stock. The Quaker folks up at the mission lost a hog."

That would be Jane Baker! Jane with her bonnet and her smooth-combed hair. Jane who was not afraid. She heard the calm voice

116

saying above the noise of the train, "God did not forget thee."
Tell Him to hurry, Jane. Hurry . . . Hurry.

"I thought I heard something behind us a while back. A funny feeling . . ."

"And the way it got so quiet at the springs. And the way Dumps took on."

"And that horse running by."

They added these things together and found they were frightened.

"It's Dumps he's after. If it is a panther, I mean. They don't jump people. Often." Then they heard a sound behind them like a heavy body brushing through high grass.

"Let's go on. Let's keep walking." Fear is a ring you can't walk out of. It moves with you, narrowing. Lainey felt sweat in the palm of Arch's hand.

"Whose initials were they? Back at the springs? I won't tell."

Five steps, ten steps before he answered. "Yours, silly. Yours and mine."

S is for Sheridan, not Sullavan. Not Dotty with her glib talk and her red curls. A.H. and L.S. She could see it, carved on the rock. Or did he put E.S.? She did not ask, liking to have something to think about while her feet moved heavily and the night settled like a black shawl.

Dumps took them down the side of a gully. The barrels shifted. "What're we haulin' this water all over creation for?" Arch demanded. "We can get more tomorrow."

Tomorrow. There would be a tomorrow. Arch was planning on it. They each took a side and tipped the barrels. A rushing miniature cataract. Then silence. The thirsty red earth drank the water. Arch shoved the barrels to the ground and unharnessed Dumps from the sled. "Faster this way. She'd have a better chance."

They walked on, the pony between them. They might have turned her loose, or even tied her to a tree to take her chances but neither of them thought of that. Arch had raised her on a bottle, broken her to harness, taught her tricks. The noises behind them were closer. Yards closer.

"I'm scared," Lainey croaked. "Are you scared?"

117

"No. Yes. I dunno." Walk, walk, walk, through the brushing grass. Lift your feet high against a tangling vine. A stumble might be your last. "I'll get you home. I promise." She heard him and believed but the way was long, the night dark. Walk, walk, walk. "Lainey, I want you to have this. I meant to give it to you first time I saw it." He pushed the silver spoon into her hand.

"Thank you." Always say thank you. Always and always. Aunt Ellen's face came to her. Aunt Ellen would not be afraid. She had stood off the Redlegs and brought Riverview through the war. "I'll keep it, forever."

"Remember the Run? An' the time I called you a sooner?" He was trying to help her and she must do her best. She pushed back the night and the panther and the tiredness that was a tangling snare on her legs.

"Remember the first day of school an' Burl puttin' a horny toad in Bluebell's lunch bucket?"

"An' the bales of hay for seats in the back?"

"An' Pink's blowgun?"

"Can you spell Mississippi that crazy way?"

"Sure. M-i crooked letter, crooked letter-i-crooked letter, crooked letter-i-hump back, hump back-i!" They laughed, a shaky sound in the darkness.

She stumbled over bunched grass and fell, scrambling to her feet again.

"Lainey! Are you all right?"

"I'm all right." But when I fall down again I won't get up. I'll lie there and rest. I've got to rest. Got to. I'll close my eyes; I can walk in my sleep. People do.

"Somethin's up ahead!"

She came wide, quivering awake, straining into the dark. A black mass blocked the way, a dim white fluttering at the top, barely visible in the starlight.

"I'll be dog!" It was Arch's natural, everyday voice. "That's that durn' brush pile of Jurd Morehouse's. Dumps brought us back to it!" He rubbed the pony's head. "Good girl! Good girl!" Then they all three came to sharp listening attention. "He's treed!" Arch whispered. "In that big elum where Jurd stood."

118

There was something final and decisive in the act as if the panther had let them go long enough. The big barn cat at Riverview playing with a crippled mouse . . . Lainey tried to rub the image from her mind with her knuckles but it burned there. Burning eyes looking down from the elm.

> *"Tiger, tiger, burning bright,*
> *In the forests of the night . . ."*

She heard herself say it as Uncle Hod had in the back downstairs sitting room while he read from a leather-bound book. The delicious chill of the words in that safe haven! Nothing like this. Nothing.

"What're you sayin'?" Arch whispered as if the panther might overhear.

"Just a poem. Uncle Hod . . ." Too hard to explain, she repeated,

> *"Tiger, tiger, burning bright.*
> *In the forests of the night."*

"That's it!" Arch smacked Dumps on the shoulder. "Burning bright! We'll set fire to the brush pile." She waited in confused wonder as he turned out his pockets handing her the contents. String. Knife. Top. Lump of sticky stuff, probably beeswax. Chalk. More string. "Ma don't let me carry matches, but I think . . . Two of 'em!"

At his direction Lainey shredded an edge of the wagon sheet sign while Arch crouched on the ground shaving a dry stick to bits. "Hurry . . . hurry . . ."

He made a nest of the threads and the shaved wood, shaping it with his fingers. Lainey held her breath while he drew the match twice along his tightened pants leg. The third time it sputtered, spurted flame. Into the center of the nest, the threads caught and carried the fire to the shaved wood. They fed the flame, their mingled breath fanning it. Twigs, leaves, small branches. A point of light in the darkness. Arch held a spray of last year's blackjack leaves, dry as powder, over the fire and it caught. He threw it toward the center of the brush pile, defying the darkness, daring

119

the panther. The fire crackled; the flames licked at the brush. In the light Lainey saw Arch's face in what seemed like the first time for weeks. His face was dirty, a line around his mouth where he had licked his lips, but triumph burned there now.

"We did it! We did it!" He caught her by the shoulders, then took up a rock and whizzed it across the flames at the elm tree that towered outside the circle of light. "Now you ol' devil! Now you ol' hog stealer! Now you ol' ol' . . . We did it!"

They capered in the dancing light, their shadows huge on the grass. What it was they had done neither one asked. To be unafraid after terror, if even for a little while, was enough. Nothing could stop them now! Not even the assault of Jurd Morehouse, charging down with his gun, cursing as he came.

"Blasted claim jumpers. I'll kill ya, plague take ya!"

Arch stood up to him, shouting over his shouts till the gun came to a wavering halt.

"Bush Sheridan's gal? An' Hamp's boy? What're you doin' here? Settin' fire to my prop'ty?"

But there was Blackjack galloping toward them and Bush with his arms around Lainey till she could hardly breathe. "Lainey! I thought you were gone for sure!" She felt tears cold on his cheeks and wondered and there was no time to do anything but answer him as he ran his hands over her. "Are you all right? All right? Lainey! Are you all right? Your mother's half crazy!"

"I'm all right." She pulled back, a little embarrassed. "Arch took care of me." For the first time Bush looked at the others.

"What happened? Did you find 'em, Jurd?"

"First I knew was when I saw the fire. They coulda burnt me out. Settin' fire to my prop'ty." His little red-rimmed eyes were suspicious still.

Arch said, "We set the fire because of the panther."

"Panther?" Bush cried.

"Painter?" Jurd Morehouse snorted. "Ain't no painters 'round here. Couple o' cowardly calfs, 'fraid of their shadders."

"Don't you call me no cowardly calf," Arch stormed.

"Take it easy, boy," Bush said. "Where'd you see the panther?"

"We didn't see it," Lainey answered for him. "But it was there. We heard it."

"A Kickapoo we met at the springs said there was one around. They saw tracks and some stock was missin'. Hog killed up at the mission. And . . ." The story sounded weak, even childish. The men looked at each other across Arch's head.

"It was there! It was!" Lainey pounded on Bush's arm. "The way Dumps acted, an' it jumped in the tree. Right over there!" She pointed to the tall elm waving in the night wind. Bush picked up a blazing branch from the brush pile and walked over to the tree. He circled it, holding the branch high. Came back shaking his head.

"Not a thing there. Not even claw marks on the bark."

"Painter!" Jurd Morehouse sneered. "Coon or polecat. Settin' fire to my prop'ty. I oughta take yore pants down an' . . ."

"Shut up," Bush said. "The way I look at it if you hadn't blocked the trail it wouldn't have happened. As for the panther . . . it's easy to hear things . . . nights 'n' all." Plainly he did not believe them. "Where'd you leave the sled and the barrels?"

"Over there," Arch pointed. "I'll get 'em tomorrow."

"No use to make another trip. I'll get 'em now." He took another branch from the fire and held it high for the wind to freshen the blaze.

Jurd Morehouse trailed him, muttering, "Claim jumpers . . . my prop'ty . . . claim jumpers."

Arch and Lainey went, too. It was easier to go along than to stand in silent disgrace.

"I don't care," Lainey kept saying, "I don't care." Arch said nothing.

Ahead they saw the barrels and the abandoned sled in the wavering light of the torch. Bush set the barrels on the sled, brought the torch down, dropped to his knees. They saw him lean close to the ground and heard him whistle. Together they ran toward him.

There, on the ground, where the water from the barrels had soaked into the bare earth of the gully, were the tracks of a panther. The pad marks were round, soft, unmistakable, inches across.

They were deep, as if the big cat had stood there, considering, watching his quarry.

Bush straightened, his face ashen above his beard. "By heaven!"

"I told you," Lainey cried. "You wouldn't believe us."

Jurd Morehouse scratched his head.

"I'm sorry, honey. I'm bound to say I thought you made it up. Not meaning to, just scared an' all. Boy, I sure beg your pardon." Bush put out his hand to Arch.

"That's all right," Arch wiped his hand on his pants leg before he put it in Bush's. "We fooled around the springs when we shouldn't have. Got a late start. But it wasn't any polecat made us late. No four-legged one, anyway."

He looked pointedly at where Jurd Morehouse had been standing but the man had gone. They saw him pass the flaming brush pile, a distorted shadow in the leaping light.

"It was a dirty trick, all right, to block the trail, I got a notion to . . . But you're both safe. That's enough for right now. Still I'd better let the neighbors know." He raised his gun and fired three times, the hunter's signal that the lost is found. "Let's get home."

Putting Arch on Blackjack and Lainey behind the saddle Bush insisted on walking behind Dumps and the sled. The weariness she had held off by gritting her teeth came over Lainey in a smothering wave. Little by little she leaned forward until, as they climbed the hill by Pritchards' she rested against Arch's bony back. Her face turned cheek down on his shoulder-blade. One hand held to the cantle of the saddle, the other clutched the silver spoon. She would keep it forever and ever.

Chapter 12

Bush took Lainey and Arch to the Friends' Mission to see the panther. One of the young men in the village had shot him when he sneaked back to his kill. It would be a good thing for them, Bush said, to see in daylight the thing that had tracked them in the dark. Besides, it would give Lainey a chance to visit with the Quaker lady she had met on the train.

They had a time getting started from Hamptons' because Mary wanted to talk school-board business. She favored the application of a Miss Christine Swenson of Minneapolis who was staying with her brother in Guthrie. Thirty dollars a month was plenty for a woman and they might have to pay a man thirty-five. And then if things didn't work out there was the brother to fall back on so the girl wouldn't be stranded on their hands. She was nineteen, had a year of experience, and . . . At last Bush drove off with Mary still talking, waving his whip in goodbye.

"I'm sorry," he apologized to Arch, "but we have quite a ways to go and my wife's skittish alone on the claim. Since the panther, and all."

"That's all right. I know Ma," Arch ran his hand through his water-slicked hair. "Sometimes I think that's the reason Dad finds so much to do 'way from home. To keep from gettin' his ears bent."

Lainey gasped at hearing him say what she and Bush had agreed on in private.

"Never was a better woman than your mother," Bush said. "But she does find . . . considerable to say."

The roads were better marked now. Little trails to and from claims joined the old road from the Sac and Fox Agency to Shawneetown and their many travellers helped broaden and deepen the track that had been used before only by freight haulers

123

and Indians on ponies. They had a snack of cheese and crackers and bologna by the roadside and a little after noon they went up a twisting trail that finally led them to the Friends' Mission. It was a small log house, the yard swept neat and bare. The door was open but no one was in sight.

"Likely school's in session. We'll hitch and go 'round back."

"Somebody dodged in the brush back there." Arch half-rose from his seat.

"Some o' these bucks c'n be fractious customers," Bush said. "Better let me do any talkin' that has to be done." They got out of the buckboard and circled the house.

There was the panther hanging from a pole set in the crotch of two trees. Its heavy paws were lashed to the pole with rawhide; its black-tipped tail brushed the dust. The flat-skulled head was turned toward them. Death had carved an evil grin on the mask. This was the phantom turned real, the nightmare come true. Lainey and Arch stopped in their tracks.

"Well, we came a long ways to look at the plague-taked thing. Let's see it."

Bush strode over to the panther but the other two did not join him. Well enough for him to talk, to run his hands over the heavy shoulders, to finger the sheathed claws and measure the length of the back! He had not walked in the dark with the yellow eyes burning between his shoulders, or heard the rustling footpads of the tracker.

Two Indians suddenly appeared. One of them, a slight young man, was hardly as tall as Arch. The other was older and paunchy. The young man carried a gun with a blue-black barrel; it was easy to guess he was the hunter.

"I'd like to buy the hide," Bush said. Neither man acted as if he had heard. "I said, I'd like to buy the hide, here, when you get it tanned."

The two men looked at one another. Muttering, hissing words and then a little laugh turned Bush's ears red.

"I don't savvy your talk, but I'd like to buy the hide. The panther hide." He spoke with great distinctness as to a child or a deaf old man.

Talk went back and forth. The young man turned his back. The older man said, "He say, 'Man kill him, get him. You want, you kill.'"

The red ran down Bush's neck and disappeared under his collar. He took a step forward. The older man looked at him stolidly; the young man turned around without seeming to move. "Look here, you . . ." Then he stopped and swallowed. "I guess you're right at that."

"If I'd had a gun," Arch said suddenly. "If I'd just had a gun . . ."

"Better you didn't," Bush grunted. "Half-killed he'd be a plain devil."

"He got him with one shot. Next time I'll have me a gun." The boy brushed past and ran his hands down the yellowish-gray flanks. "You old sinner!"

The young man spoke to his companion, propped his gun against a tree and took a skinning knife out of his belt. He cut a tuft of black hairs from the tail and handed them to Arch.

"He say you did good to get 'way from him on trail. He say this hair good medicine," the older man interpreted.

"Thanks!" Arch put the tuft in his shirt pocket. "How'd he know about me?"

The question died on the air.

"Indian grapevine," Bush said a little sourly. "I've heard about it before."

The young man gestured with the skinning knife above the white belly fur. Lainey felt her dinner push at her throat. She hated the panther but she did not want to see the sleek hide laid open.

"I guess I'll go find Jane Baker." Nobody answered. Three more Indians had appeared. Behind her Lainey heard the wheet-wheet-wheet of a knife on a whetstone.

The log house was a refuge. Inside it things were safe, well ordered. A woman's world in which Lainey had a place. Jane Baker was sitting straight backed on a backless bench. Except for the lack of the bonnet she might have come right off the Sante Fe, months ago. Brown dress, white collar, gold pin, plain face shining with soap and welcome. She stood up but the five little Indian girls sitting on a bench in front of her went on chanting, "B-A, bay, B-E, bee, bay, bee, bi, bo, bum."

"I am glad to see thee." At Riverview Lainey would have been

125

smothered in a hug and a kiss. Jane's welcome needed no such extravagance. "Does thee like the new country?"

"I love it! I'm just crazy about it!" Lainey hesitated, pulled her talk in to match Jane's sedate speech. "I like it. Bush got a claim ten miles out of Randall. We're still living in the wagon, but . . ." She went on and on. The need to talk had been built up over weeks and months. The Indian girls stopped their chanting and listened, round-eyed.

"My goodness, I've sure talked a lot!" All at once Lainey was conscious of her voice filling the house, bouncing back from the corners. "Tell me about your school."

"This is my school. We were in a tent for a while but now we have a house. And these are my pupils."

"Do you have many more?"

"This is all," Jane said serenely, "but there will be more later."

The smallest girl asked a question and Jane nodded. They all scampered to the door, looking back and laughing. The smallest called something over her shoulder.

"She says to thank you for turning school out."

"Oh. I didn't mean to."

"It's all right. They come and go. I may not see them now for several days."

"I don't see why you stay, just for five. And if they don't care."

"I have a concern," Jane said. "It is up to me to keep the school open. In God's good time they will come, but only if I do my part. Sarah Gwynne works with the women and Will Gwynne is teaching the men to farm. I work best with children, so that is what I do."

"I'd like to be just like you," Lainey said in a rush of admiration.

Jane considered, straightening the row of books on the shelf by her desk. "I don't believe thee would. Thee only thinks thee would."

"But you know things. How they're going to come out and all. Like about the school."

"Faith is easy to some, hard to others. I think thee will always want to go and find out."

Lainey turned this over in her mind. They sat in companionable silence. Bush put his head in at the door. "Quaker meetin'?"

126

"Very nearly. I have been a poor neighbor, enjoying Lainey and not coming out to greet thee. And this young man."

Arch was introduced and Lainey told the story of the panther. Jane brought out a plate of molasses cookies, wafer thin and crisp. While Lainey and Arch crunched on the cookies Bush talked politics and statehood. There was too much talk going around, he said, about making the twin Territories into two states. One strong state, Indian and white men together, was his hope.

"Ours, too," Jane agreed, "but it may take a long time. Indians . . . white men . . . there is much to be forgotten."

"Well, it's been good to talk, but we'd better go now. Come on Lainey, Arch."

"Thee must come back. Don't wait for a panther."

"I still think I'd like to be like you," Lainey said.

Jane Baker's smile was as bright as the gold pin at her collar.

"Well, goodbye," Bush took up the reins. "Let 'em put it to a vote. We'll show 'em one state's the way we want it." The bay horse shook himself. "Goodbye. Take care."

It was a farewell that had grown up in the new country. Friends were far apart, messages uncertain, sickness, accident, violent death, frequent.

"Take care," they called from the buckboard. "Come see us. Take care."

"Come back," Jane called. "Take care and come back."

The calls met, twining in the air, making a link between the hurrying buckboard and the woman standing in the bare swept yard of the Mission. "Take care . . ."

Lainey sat at the table with her feet hooked under the chair rungs and bit her pencil. A half hour ago she had written, "Randall, Oklahoma Territory, Dear Addie," She could begin, "School starts in three weeks and our teacher, Miss Swenson, is real nice." But Addie hated school and thought teachers were invented to plague pupils. Or, "A panther almost caught us when we went for water." But Mama had forbidden that for fear it might get back to Aunt Ellen and worry her. Or, "I have a new green dress." But, to be honest, she didn't. Mama had cut it out, basted it up, and now it hung under a sheet in the corner.

It was the heat. You had to get used to the heat, everybody said. Heat did not come on gradually as it had back home. It leaped at you, full strength after a mild, pleasant springtime. Heat came up with the sun, reached what you thought was a peak at noon, then soared to a higher, gasping, unthinkable peak at three in the afternoon. It cracked the ground, dried the sweat, burned the skin. Streams disappeared, crawdad houses fell apart, heat waves shimmered up from bare red earth. Only the cotton thrived.

All over the new country in what patches they had been able to break men planted cotton. The plants had sprung up, a stout green army. And now the sun pried open the heavy green bolls and the cotton spilled out. Men grinned to each other as they met in Randall, "Bale to the acre!" they said. "A cash crop!" A gin was built at Randall and it ran night and day.

Some said the cotton was to blame for the chills and fever that plagued the settlers. No matter, put quinine on the table; take it every meal. Bale to the acre! A cash crop! Cotton takes labor. There was no help to be hired and no money to pay wages. So whole families took to the field. Lainey went with Bush carrying her cotton sack. By noon her fingers were sore, pricked by the needle-sharp boll ends; the cotton sack weighed like a dead man.

"She shan't go back," Allegra said when they came in to dinner. "It's not fit work."

"Any work's fit that's honest," Bush said. "But she can quit if it's too hard."

Aching back, sore fingers, blasting, battering heat! A curious pride mushroomed in Lainey. "I'll go back. I like it. If I just had some gloves."

The afternoon went quicker than the morning. The second day was easier than the first. On the last Lainey sang in the field, "I been workin' on the railroad . . ." She went to town on the cotton wagon, and stayed by Bush as the sharp-eyed buyer plucked at the fiber. Long? Short? Middlin'? When Bush got his check he gave her a dollar.

"Wish it was more. I'm proud of you."

Lainey bit on the pencil again, making a pattern of tooth marks. She might begin, "My friend, Annie Halfmoon, came home from

128

government school for a while. We had a lot of fun." She pictured Addie's face. Indians in Snyder County were the scalp-lifters of history or the sorry stragglers that occasionally drifted in from the reservations in Kansas. Addie could never understand about Annie's laughter, her skill at The Game, the way she shared her dish of Tom Fuller. Lainey put down the pencil. Words trapped you when you tried to write things out.

She went outside where Allegra sat shelling black-eyed peas. She worked slowly, rocking the armless rocker as her hands moved in the long green pods. Everything Allegra did was slowed, leisurely now. Like the red earth she drowsed in the heat. She had not hurried since they moved into the house the first day of June.

That day had been almost cool. Hamptons came over to help with the moving-in and Mary brought the first rose from the bush she transplanted from Kansas. As the men carried the familiar furniture into the house Allegra ran to greet each piece. Her hands smoothed the dust from the walnut, maple, and cherry surfaces. She washed the thin china and rubbed the silver back to a shine. "This was Grandmother Jent's chair. This table came from Kentucky. Aunt Maris Saunders gave Ellen this cake plate. There is my graduation fan!"

When the parlor organ came in she stopped unpacking dishes and made Bush and Hamp move every piece of furniture until she had it just right, so that the light from the glass window fell on the keys, but so the draft from the door would not hurt the tone. Then she sat down on an upended packing box and touched the keys. Singly, at first, as if she feared they might have suffered some change. Then in chords that sang out sweet and mellow. She began to play. Parts of showy "pieces" learned at the seminary. Verses of hymns. Bits of love songs. Phrases from marching songs of the war. She played as a starving man might eat, confronted by a banquet. It was past noon before she stopped.

"Glory be!" Bush put his hands on her shoulders. "This is really home, now."

"My land, that was wonderful," Mary Hampton said wistfully. "I wish Pritchards could have heard it. And Doggetts. And . . ."

"And Wellmans and Sullavans and Jurd Morehouse!" Hamp

jibed. "Leave it to Mary. She'll make a neighborhood of us yet."

"Maybe, sometime later," Allegra said, turning back to the organ.

Lainey dated the change in Allegra from the day the organ came into the house. She was more contented, took pride in arranging the Riverview things in their new, strange surroundings, and even neglected to scold the wind. The sickness that had worried Lainey had gone. It was true that now and again Mama had a way of straightening up and catching her breath as if she had a crick in her back, but nobody dies of a crick. Some of the things Addie Bucklin had told her came back now and again but Addie was not reliable and those things could never, never be true of Bush and Mama.

They finished the peas and Allegra handed Lainey the kettle. "Put 'em on to cook. Gash some salt pork and throw in one or two red pepper pods and some salt." She rocked back, fanned herself with the empty pan. "Back home I'd be taking a nap."

It was too hot to sleep in the daytime. Too hot to work. Too hot to do anything but endure. The chickens drooped, their beaks open. A black-and-green striped lizard scuttled up the cottonwood siding. The smell of grass and trees baking in the sun came in on the hot wind. Lainey hurried to finish the peas and get out of the house. Her room, above, was like an oven. She would sleep out of doors but for fear of snakes. At least it was cool at night. The days would have been unbearable without the relief that the night wind brought.

She sat down on the ground by Allegra's chair. Her mother's hand touched her head and rested there. It was a rare caress and Lainey held very still to enjoy it. Then a fear crept into her joy and she froze. Something was going to happen.

"I . . . I don't know how to say this," Allegra started. Lainey stared at the ground. An ant was crawling there. If she willed him to stop . . . "I ought to tell you . . ." If she had been shot for silence Lainey could not have spoken. The ant crawled busily over a piece of foxtail grass. All at once the strained voice stopped, Allegra stood up, peered down the road. "If we were back home I'd declare that was Pappy Vickers!"

Lainey bounced from the ground, released. Up the road came an

130

old man who walked with a familiar hitch-and-a-get-along. "It is Pappy Vickers! It is!" She was off like a shot, screaming a welcome. She had never been so glad to see anybody. Never. Never.

"By doggies! Lainey Sheridan! I'd about give out!"

The old man smelled of dust, Snyder County tobacco, and age. When she grabbed him she was astonished to find her face came above his shoulder; which meant she had really grown. Allegra hurried from the house her arms outstretched.

"Cap'n Vickers!" The title gave him standing as an honored guest. "Welcome to the Territory."

"Dog take that Bush Sheridan!" the old man growled. "What's he mean bringin' the prettiest gal in Snyder County plumb out here?"

Allegra smiled and blushed. "Now, Pappy! When did you get here?"

"Got to Guthrie yesterday. Call that a capital? Not much like ole Jeff City! Then I took the stage to your town o' Randall. Wild and wooly an' full o' fleas, ain't it? Feller there told me Bush lived just a whoop an' a holler beyond so I started footin' it."

"Randall's a good town, Pappy, it's settled down a lot since we first got here." Lainey said.

Pappy Vickers collapsed in the rocking chair outside the house, drank two dippers of water and sloshed the third over his pink pate. "Hotter'n the hinges!"

"It's cool at night," Lainey fanned him with his Confederate hat, "and this heat isn't so bad because it's a dry heat."

"Stop talking like Bush," Allegra said. "Hot's hot. Now, Pappy, tell me the news."

Pappy Vickers settled back.

Ellen was fine, saw her Sat'dy buyin' some pink foofaraw at the store. Hod was down at the post office askin' about some books he'd ordered. Jim Saunders' mare got the blue ribbon at the Horse Show. Drucy Peery had the lung fever; lot of it around this year. Shep Batten finally got in as County Clerk. Miz Conyers died. Mot Bucklin bought the Owens' forty, south of the river. Give Mot time and he'd own the county, even if the county'd never own Mot. Mary Gribble got at outs with the Cumberland Presbyterians and went over to the Campbellites. On and on he talked and the red dirt darkened, the blasting heat lifted, the wind gentled. Snyder County appeared.

"Didn't Ellen send any word?" Allegra asked as Pappy stopped for a dipper of water.

"She didn't know I was comin'. Nobody did. An' I'd take it as a favor if you didn't mention it when you write. I don't want George an' Minnie knowin' where I am."

"But they'll worry . . ."

"I'm not beholdin' to those two an' you know it. Minnie's my own sister's child but she ain't got the sense of a addled egg. And George'd sell the handles off his mother's coffin for an extra dollar." There was no disputing what he said. All Snyder County knew Minnie wasn't overly bright and that George had married her for the rocky-hill farm she had from her mother. He only allowed Pappy to stay there because of the small sum of rent money he drew. "I'm gonna take up some o' this free land and stay."

"The land's already all taken up," Lainey said. "And claim jumpers . . ."

"Go stir the peas and put on the coffee," Allegra broke in. "Then blow the horn for Bush. He won't want to miss a word of this."

So Pappy Vickers came to the Territory. No more was said about his taking up land. In time Lainey realized that he had never meant to, but only needed something to tell himself. Bush helped him build a half-dugout near the dry gulch that ran between the Sheridan and the Halfmoon land. Remembering his tales of Indian fighting Lainey was fearful of the location, but Pappy seemed to have forgotten that the only good Injun was a dead Injun and he spent hours sitting in the bark shelter, or on the sunny side of the house, making talk with Henry and his kin.

He roamed the countryside, bringing in some game now and then, though it was not as plentiful as it had been at first. Wild turkey and deer were hard to find and the quail had been slaughtered by the wagonload to sell, illegally, and help hard-pushed settlers over the hump of the winter. Only the rabbits were still plentiful. Pappy sat on the banks of the streams and fished and dozed; the streams were no longer as clear as they had been before the sod-buster plows ripped the covering grass off the land. The

132

water ran red after every rain. But Pappy found fish enough and his rent money bought meal and salt, sidemeat and coffee and tobacco. When he tired of his own cooking he ate with the Sheridans. Once in a while he helped out with the work, but this was regarded as a favor.

"Pappy earns his keep twice over," Bush said, "just bein' around and knowing the names of folks in Snyder County. It's like a tonic to Allegra to hear him."

But he did more than that. To Lainey he took the place of Aunt Ellen with her stories of the family, and Uncle Hod with his reading aloud. He talked to her by the hour of the Border Wars . . . those bitter raids between Kansas and Missouri over slavery and abolition. He talked about the coming of the war, itself, and how brother fought brother and wounds were made that would be years healing. He talked about General Sterling Price, beloved leader of the Missouri Confederacy, and the battles of Westport, Wilson's Creek, Lone Jack, and Independence. He told tales of his capture and how he had been sent to a far-off prison and had eaten rats to eke out his rations. And back of the war he told her of the great days of the Oregon Trail and the Santa Fe Trail and the California Trail when Jim Bridger and Kit Carson and John Charles Fremont . . . that was Tom Benton's son-in-law . . . were pushing the western country clear to the sea. Listening to his old voice she felt the same urgency, the same moving onward that she had when Bush had told her about coming to the Territory. A mighty army of which she was a part.

Then all at once the cotton was in, and it was time for school. Now, besides Pappy Vickers, Lainey had Miss Swenson, the new teacher. She was cool and clean as the fjords of her native Sweden. The first thing she did after greeting the twenty-eight pupils . . . all grades . . . was to have them scrub the schoolhouse. Some of the parents grumbled that this was not in the Three Rs, but they were soon won over. Christina Swenson was a born teacher and even with all the books different and not enough benches . . . some still sat on bales of prairie hay . . . and no blackboard, the pupils of Jackrabbit School learned their lessons.

Every day the teacher's desk was crowded with offerings. Puffballs full of "snuff," red rocks shaped like roses, wild flowers

133

crammed into fruit jars, arrowheads, fox grapes, a baby rabbit in a cigar box. Miss Swenson ate noon lunch with the pupils and often "swapped." She boarded with Wellmans and Lainey, seeing Mrs. Wellman's good lightbread and butter go for soggy saleratus-speckled biscuit sopped in bacon grease, or rocky chunks of cornbread, wondered why Miss Swenson did it.

The schoolboard decided it was well satisfied. Miss Swenson had only one fault. She liked to spend weekends with her brother at Guthrie. What Mary Hampton had considered an asset turned into a liability. A teacher should be on hand for every literary, and really ought to teach Sunday School, too. But the school was doing well and next year they'd need a bigger schoolhouse. September, October, November . . .

Next year! Bush coming home from the board meeting let Blackjack slow down to a walk as he planned on more and more cotton and renting land from Henry Halfmoon. Next year! Allegra, waiting up for Bush put wood in the stove against the November chill, and sat back to dream of a boy named Saunders Sheridan who would, somehow, take them all home to Riverview.

Next year! Lainey curled into a ball in the chilly little room under the roof wondered if being fourteen meant being grown-up. And if it did would she ever have a fellow? Dotty Sullavan had quit school at fourteen and was known to be going to dances with a wild bunch over near Ranse. The neighbors said Dotty would get into trouble but so far her only trouble was keeping her fellows straight. It made you wonder about all the things Mama and Aunt Ellen said.

Next year! Men in territorial offices and in far-off Washington pondered the problem of the Cherokee Outlet . . . that twelve thousand square miles known as the Strip. Should it be opened to settlement as the land-hungry boomers demanded, or kept to lease to the great cattle ranches?

Next year! Only Pappy Vickers dreamed no dreams, made no plans. Under the buffalo robe in the bunk of the half-dugout he heard Blackjack go by and dozed, waked, dozed, listened to the coyotes, and dozed again, content to be once more in new country.

134

Chapter 13

The morning started with frost that sparkled on the brown grass and brought the last of the pecans showering down, but by noon the sun was warm to the back. It was early afternoon when Curly Pritchard, Ab Pritchard's young brother, came riding, lickety-cut, up the road to the Sheridan place.

"That boy's going to ruin that horse," Bush grumbled, walking out to meet him. Lainey came along noticing only the way the thin November sunlight picked up the red gleam in Curly's hair, and his new blue shirt picked up the color of his eyes. As she came closer she saw the sure sign of the courting male . . . Curly was growing a moustache.

"Get down, Curly, come in an' eat with us."

"No, suh, thanks," Curly drawled, the sweet talk of the South on his tongue. "Sis just sent me out on the rounds to ask you-all over t'night. She's sure it'll happen tonight."

"Well, now, that's mighty friendly, but I got no idea what you're talking about. What's going to happen? Where?"

"I reckon I did get it tangled up, but the way she goes on I thought ev'body in the Territory knew Sis brought her night-bloomin' cereus with her from back home. This is the night it'll bloom and she wants the neighbors to come see it." He winked at Lainey. "Yore feller'll be there."

Lainey turned hot and cold. Only last night she had wondered if she would ever have a fellow and now it was coming true. A flower that bloomed in November was no more miracle than this. She longed to ask, Who do you mean, my fellow? But she didn't.

"It's the first time the plague-taked thing's bloomed so late. Mostly it's been summer. One time Sis wouldn't let Ab change

135

farms till it bloomed an' he was outa work half a year. She sets a heap o' store by it. Doggetts are comin' an' Hamptons an' Sullavans, an' Sis said for me to ask Jurd, but Ab said blamed if he'd have him in the house 'count of him blockin' the trail again. There's some folks Sis knows from Randall, an' the preacher, an' Novaks and some new folks . . ."

"I'd sure like to come," Bush said, "but Mrs. Sheridan's not feeling so good."

"That's too bad," Curly looked at the ground.

"Can't we go? Please? I've never seen a night-blooming whatchamaycallit." Lainey jumped up and down while Bush considered.

"Well, Curly, some of us'll be there. You c'n count on that. And thanks."

"That's fine. Now I've just got Wellmans' left. Sis said for me to ask the teacher, special." Any way you figured the route it was unreasonable for Curly to go last to Wellmans'. And why, Lainey wondered, did his face redden so?

"Now that's too bad," Bush said. "Wellmans drove her in to Randall to take the stage to Guthrie."

"Oh." It had a flat, dull sound to it. "Well, I'll mosey 'round that way and leave word with them." Curly seemed to have lost all his zest. "Sis thought teacher might like it. It's a real cur'osity." He gathered up his reins and rode on, his goodbye coming back thinly over the autumn wind.

"So that's the way the land lays! Curly's struck on the teacher!" Lainey was outraged. Miss Swenson in a homesteader's cabin! Besides Curly was just out of school himself.

"He's eighteen," Bush said. "Old as I was. She could do worse."

"Besides, she's got a fellow back in Minneapolis. Grace Wellman told me."

"Your mama had a fellow, too. Ask her about Tom Bridges."

The bank in Marney was Bridges' bank. The biggest house with the most stained-glass windows, the most carved wooden scroll work and over-lapped fish-scale shingles was Bridges' house.

"He'd have been your pa, if your mama hadn't kicked over the traces. Sorry?"

136

She grabbed him around the waist, squeezing hard. She wanted to say, I love you better than anybody in the world. Instead she said, "I hate Tom Bridges!"

He laughed, pulled her braids and went in the house. She stayed out a little longer, hugging herself and thinking about what Curly had said.

But things worked out the way Lainey had been afraid they might. Mama lifted her eyebrows at the suggestion of going. Bush said he would put a chair in the wagon and heat the sad irons against the chill. It wasn't the cold, she said, let him take Lainey and leave her at home. No, he would ask Hamptons to take Lainey and he would stay home himself. No, no, he must go, though what a grown man wanted to see a plant bloom for . . . It wasn't the plant; it was the sociability. Of course if he thought more of sociability than he did of her . . . Then Bush blew up. He was going and Lainey was going with him and Allegra could stay home with her ideas of what was right and proper the rest of her life!

There was no door to slam but Allegra ran into the space that held their bed and jerked the calico curtain with the same effect.

"By heaven! I . . ." Bush's nostrils showed a white line. He stalked out the door.

The stove heat beat on Lainey but she shivered. She put her face down on her knees and tried not to feel or see or hear.

Allegra's sobbing and the crash of Bush's axe crept past her fingers in her ears. She tiptoed to the door. The wind felt good against her face. She ran out of the yard and down the road. As she ran one part of her saw the tracks of Curly's horse, a nick in the right front shoe, repeated over and over and over. Curly was struck on Miss Swenson but he mustn't marry her. When you get married strange things happen to you. She, Lainey, would never marry. Never. Never. Her heels bounced on the words. Her unguided feet brought her to Pappy Vickers' place. The stovepipe crooked out the window like a welcoming arm.

She pushed on the door that had never known a lock. Pappy started up from his doze. "Howdy, Lainey, anything wrong up at the house?"

She was crying in great lung-tearing sobs. It had been a long time since she had cried and it was at once a pain and a relief. The old man led her over to the bunk. The buffalo robe scratched her face. His thin blue-veined hand stroked her head and he made little foolish clucking noises like a hen talking to its chicks. Her sobs died down to hiccoughs, then stopped altogether.

"They said awful things to each other. Just awful!" Tears came back, choking her. Pappy Vickers nodded like the Chinese idol a missionary had sent Uncle Hod.

"Good thing for both of 'em."

"Good thing?" She sat up, shocked tearless.

"That's right. Your mama's not feelin' so good right now." He hesitated, looked hard at Lainey. "She hasn't talked to you about . . . anything?"

Lainey shook her head, remembering the day Pappy had come but hurrying away from the memory as fast as she could. "She was sick but she's not now. She said she was all right."

"Well, she is all right. But you got to make 'llowances. And Bush he's so dog' determined that the Territory's pure heaven that it rubs him the wrong way when it turns out to have some failin's. D'ya see?"

Lainey shook her head again. "You don't know how mad they were!"

Pappy went over to the monkey stove, put in a stick of wood and pulled the coffee pot to the middle of the stove. "Remember that cider back in Snyder County?"

Her mouth went watery and she stood once more by the cider press hearing the mumble of bees and yellow jackets, watching the apples pour down the chute, tasting the clear, amber juice. "I remember."

Pappy Vickers got down two tin cups and measured sugar into each. "Come cider-makin' time, some folks, namin' no names, would fill up a few jugs an' let 'em set. The cider'd get to workin' in there an', wham!" he cracked his palms together and she jumped. "Out came the cork!"

Lainey smiled, a wan watery smile.

"Folks, now, they're a good deal like cider. Married folks,

138

'specially. They can stay sweet just so long. Then, wham!" he cracked his palms and this time she laughed.

He poured coffee and handed her a cup. She was not allowed to drink it at home and the dark hot brew made her shudder, but she finished her cup.

"Now," he said, as she gulped down the last of the coffee, "you go on back to the house and if I don't miss my guess you'll find those two sweeter'n honeycomb. As for the doin's tonight, you an' Bush take out and tell Allegra I'll be over to set."

Lainey came slowly into the house with her arms full of stove wood from the new-split pile. Bush was standing by the mirror, trimming his beard. Allegra was at the organ, playing. The house was warm and spicy with the smell of gingerbread.

"I've been down to Pappy Vickers'."

"That's nice," Allegra leaned toward the music, studying the notes.

"He says tell you he'll be over to spend the evening."

Allegra tried the passage once again. "That's nice. Now go press your challis and get down the ironstone platter for the gingerbread and be sure you remember to tell Mrs. Pritchard I'm sorry I couldn't come."

"Yes, ma'am." She went outside and climbed the ladder to her room. Rooting around for the challis a dull spot of anger began to burn in her. Pappy Vickers was right; they were sweeter'n honeycomb. She listened, heard Bush say something in a low voice and Mama laugh. But what about her, Lainey? They didn't care how she felt or what happened to her. I'll never marry, she shook the challis dress. Never have a fellow even. Never!

The gingerbread on the ironstone platter felt warm on Lainey's lap. She lifted the tea towel that covered it and breathed deep of the spicy fragrance. Nobody ever came to a gathering in the new country empty-handed. Wives showed off their cooking skill and young men who batched it brought hard candy or store-boughten canned peaches, or some other treat from Randall. The hostess always acted surprised at each offering.

Rigs were close hitched around the double log house with the

139

dog-run. Sullavans new green Studebaker spring wagon . . . that showed where their cotton money went. The preacher's bay horse with three white stockings. Novaks' old covered wagon in which they had made the Run. Two fancy red-wheeled buggies meant that some of Curly's bachelor friends had arrived. Bush backed the buckboard into the space between Hamptons' buggy and Wellmans'. Dumps, standing saddled, nickered at them.

The lamps had been lighted in both parts of the house, even though it was not yet clear dark. Women moved back and forth setting a table in the dog-run. Children were everywhere. The older pupils from Jackrabbit School had up a game of Hide and Seek. Dotty Sullavan ran slowly by looking over her shoulder at Chick MaGruder. The men gathered around the front door. Their talk rumbled.

Politics and crops. Crops and politics.

They bounced back and forth names they hadn't known a year ago. Dennis Flynn. Tom Ferguson. Hooley Bell. Pleasant Porter. William H. Murray. Rolly McIntosh. Frank Frantz. The politics of the Territory were as varied as its people. Democrats. Republicans. Populists. Farmer's Alliance. Followers of Sockless Jerry Simpson and believers in the Single Tax system might have adjoining claims. But the prime topic was statehood. On that they were united. Oklahoma Territory, not yet dry behind the ears was bawling for full statehood. To these men in the Sac and Fox country, close to the Indian Meridian, it was a touchy matter. One state, not two!

"Well, if it ain't Bush Sheridan!" Ab Pritchard plowed through the men to welcome them. His wife, Sis, bobbing along behind. The hounds that were Ab's greatest treasure set up a barking. "You, Jude! Trumpet! Spot! You wuthless, rabbit-chasin' biscuit eaters!" The barking went on. The dogs surged about his feet, lapping at his hands, their curved tails like small sickles. "Be quiet, you!" Ab roared. "Where's the missus, Bush?"

"She's not feelin' so good. But she sent along a little something."

Sis Pritchard threw up her short fat arms. "Land o' Goshen! You folks shouldn'ta done that!" She took the ironstone platter from Lainey.

140

And now Bush would go off with the men and Mrs. Pritchard take the gingerbread over to the dog-run where the women were and Lainey would be expected to join in the game of Hide and Seek. Panic seized her. How could she ever become one of the party?

"Curly says your plant's about to bloom," she snatched at this to put off the minute.

"Thinks more o' that plant'n she does o' me," Ab grumbled.

"Now, Ab, don't bring that up." A delighted chuckle came from under the double chin.

"I'll leave it to Bush! Here we was, comin' down to the Territory, Sis drivin' one wagon an' me the other. We come to one o' those dang dry-bed rivers. I looks upstream and here comes a wall o' water. Flash flood!" He pantomimed the action and the dogs went wild. "I whupped up my Maude mule but it was comin' too fast. I turned loose the dogs an' made a run back for Sis. There she set, holdin' her dratted plant. 'Jump,' I yells, the water sloshin' at the hubs, 'Jump, you fool, jump!' 'I won't leave my plant' she says. 'Jump,' I says, an' about that time a big ol' cottonwood come tearin' downstream an' took me 'long with it. I figgered Sis was a goner."

"What happened?" Lainey begged as Ab stopped talking to shift his tobacco.

"Well, little lady, that cottonwood carried me more'n a mile 'fore I could get clear. Finally I clumb out an' walked back an' there set Sis, high an' dry, holdin' onto her plant."

They looked at each other and shook with laughter at their recollection. "I jest figgered," Sis wiped her eyes, "that I'd never get me another night-bloomin' cereus, but a woman that can pick as much cotton as I can c'n allus get another man!"

Their laughter set off again and Bush and Lainey joined in.

"I sure want to see that plant!"

"You will!" Ab shepherded Bush to the knot of men. "Like I say, Sis . . ."

"Now, you run play," Sis Pritchard said to Lainey. "I'll put this with the rest."

Oh, why had she ever come? "I'll carry it for you."

141

"Well, somebody else's drivin' in . . . You put it on the table . . . Miz Hampton . . ." Sis Pritchard thrust the dear familiarity of the ironstone platter at Lainey and hurried away. The chorus of barking rose again. Lainey sidled up to the dog-run. No one paid any attention to her. A smell of vinegar and dill from a dish of homemade pickles tickled her nose. She moved from one foot to the other and back again.

Mary Hampton, slicing homemade lightbread, looked up, "That you Lainey?"

"Yes, ma'am."

"My land, don't stand there gawkin'! Go on and play."

"This gingerbread. Mama sent it."

"Sent it?" A sharp-nosed woman sniffed, "Why didn't she come herself?"

"She isn't feeling so good."

Lifted eyebrows. Whispers. Lainey set her teeth.

"Some folks just have to be different," the sharp-nosed woman said. "Delicate."

Mary Hampton put down her knife, "It's a good thing some folks are different when there's so many that're just plain hateful."

Into the uncomfortable silence Ab Pritchard roared, " 'Jump' I says, 'Jump!' "

"That's the tenth time I've heard that this evenin'," the sharp-nosed woman was glad to change the subject.

"Anybody know if teacher's comin'?"

"She went up to Guthrie," Mrs. Wellman arranged molasses taffy on a plate.

"Pore Curly! And him with new red suspenders!" They laughed, unfeelingly, glad of a chance to see a man discomfitted in this man's world.

"I thought Curly had a girl in Little Rock."

"I heard teacher had a fellow back home."

"Territory makes 'em skittish. They come West an' get new ideas."

"Lainey, are you still over there?"

"Yes, ma'am."

"Well, go on out and play!"

142

"Yes, ma'am."

It was an order, not to be disobeyed. She made a place for the gingerbread and went as slowly as she dared to the place where the Hide-and-Seek game was going on. A maple tree was the base. The dusk had turned to dark with the promise of a moon making a glow on the horizon. The wind felt cold to Lainey but most of the players had thrown their coats in a pile on the ground. Bluebell Shimer was It. "Fi', ten, fifteen, twenny . . ." Dotty Sullavan stood in the lamplight from the door and twitched her hips and out of the dark Curly Pritchard joined in the game. They vanished together. Curly who was struck on Miss Swenson! Never, Lainey promised herself, never, never! "Eighty-fi', ninety, ninety-fi', one hundred! Bushel-a wheat, bushel-a rye, all that ain't hid, holler 'I.' " Then, without giving the laggards a chance, "Bushel-a wheat, bushel-a clover, all that ain't hid, cain't hide over!"

A giggle and a scuffle from the shadows. That Curly! And that Dotty! The game grew frenzied. Lainey would have given anything she owned, anything at all, to be in it but she could not join. She stood at the edge of the players and watched. Bluebell would not give the Home-Free call. She brushed past Lainey on a round of searching. This misery was punishment for the anger she had felt at Bush and Mama. This was what she deserved for talking to Pappy Vickers. For leaving Mama at home.

Out of the dark Arch, Red, and Bucky pelted toward the base yelling taunts at Bluebell. Arch grabbed Lainey's arm as he ran by. She jerked like a rag doll, found her feet and tore along behind him. "One, two, three for me!" They smacked home base.

"No fair!" Bluebell screeched. "You were outa bounds. An' Lainey wasn't playin'."

"I was, too!" Lainey screeched back. "I've been playin' all the time." She felt alive, warm, immensely able. She jumped up and down, jerked off her coat and flung it onto the pile. Your fellow'll be there, Curly had said, was it Arch he meant? Was it? She tried to find him in the milling players but he was gone.

Glenn Novak, first caught, was It. He began counting. "Fi', ten, fifteen, twenny." Lainey ran with the pack. The wild mock-fear of the game and the sharp night air raised their spirits to a frantic

143

pitch. They ran and shouted and screamed and hid and clutched, Lainey the wildest, the loudest of them all. A new girl, whose family had just moved to the neighborhood last week and taken over the Ellitch claim, stood irresolute on the edge of the game. Why didn't she join in? There was nothing, nothing at all to be afraid of. Lainey ran past and grabbed her hand. "I know a good place to hide." The grateful clutch of her hand was reward enough.

The moon rose, huge, yellow, and a little lopsided. The shadows on it might be a rabbit as Annie said, or the Man in the Moon. The flare of a match at a pipe broke the darkness around the men. From the house drifted the smell of coffee.

"Come an' get it or we'll throw it out!" Ab Pritchard boomed.

It was a noble spread. Vinegar pies, dried apple pies, dried peach pies, pumpkin pies, pickles, preserves, cheese and crackers, sliced bologna, lightbread, butter, hard candy, and a big bowl of parched field corn, buttered and salted.

"Fall to," Ab Pritchard urged. "If you go hungry it's your own fault."

But no one in the neighborhood wanted to take the responsibility of being the first to start. Sis Pritchard appealed to the preacher. "Reverend Gordon, will you oblige?"

As his hand came up the heads bowed. The dog-run was quiet except for the hissing of coffee boiling over in the kitchen. "Oh Lord, we thank Thee for this food. Bless the hands that have prepared it. Bless this new country which Thou has given into our care and help us to be worthy of it. Amen."

The shortness of it startled them, but the fervor touched their hearts. There was a chorus of Amens.

"Now, Reverend," Sis Pritchard said, "let me help you to some pie. I know it's all good 'cause I never made a bit!" The men laughed, but the women waited to see which piece he would select. Sis Pritchard's knife hovered over each.

"You tempt me, but serving in the Mission field made a dyspeptic out of me. I'll have to forego the pie. But a slice of that gingerbread, now . . ."

Lainey thought she would burst with pride.

The women and girls began to serve the men and boys. It was a

144

point of honor not to take from your own dish, no matter how much you wanted to. The women and girls filled their own plates and ate slowly, enjoying the taste of somebody else's cooking. There were homes where meals might be skimpy tomorrow, but no one begrudged the lavish spread tonight. They were proud to share with each other. The bowls were down to scraps; children wandered around the table filching bits. The women got up and scraped up the dishes over Sis Pritchard's half-hearted protests. Mary Hampton washed and three women dried.

As the last spoons were sorted out Sis Pritchard herded all of them into the big square room. They had almost forgotten why they had come. The Pritchards' furniture had been moved out. An upturned keg was in the middle of the room with an oil lamp hanging over it. It felt good to get in out of the night chill. Lainey ran out to get her coat, wormed her way back into the room.

The men ranged themselves around the wall. The women sat on the floor on quilts they had brought in the wagons. The unmarried couples sought the shadows at the back. The boys and girls sat in front of the women, and the babies and little children filled every crevice. The new girl . . . Doris Shipp was her name and one of her eyes didn't quite track with the other . . . sat on one side of Lainey. On the other side were two little Pritchards and a Wellman. Then Arch, Red, and Bucky. Talk that had begun to buzz died down as Sis Pritchard backed into the doorway carrying a blue and white granite kettle in which the night-blooming cereus grew. She threaded her way among the people and with infinite care set the kettle on the keg.

The neighborhood stared at the plant. They saw a spindling, branching growth, thick gray-green leaves, with spines up and down the branches. An ugly plant, not to be compared with a Boston fern, or a Christmas cactus, or a Hen and Chickens . . . none of them would have given it houseroom. But Sis Pritchard had brought it from back home and dared a flood to keep it. They peered at the plant and then at her.

"I reckon this seems kind of foolish to you-all," she pushed a strand of hair away with the back of her hand. "But maybe you won't think I'm plumb crazy after you see it bloom. The bud

145

that'll come out first is there," her stubby finger pointed to a drooping white-edged green oval on one of the branches. "I've had this plant a long time . . . got it from a peddler that said it came from Mexico . . . an' every time I see it bloom it seems like I'm seein' a . . . miracle." She stopped, embarrassed by what she had said and the shake in her own voice. " 'Scuse me, Reverend, if I'm talkin' outa turn."

"There's lots of miracles," came from back by the wall. "I'll not dispute that this is one."

"Well. Anyway, I drug you-all out and this here's my plant. You can sing or talk while you're waitin' if you want, but it seems better if we just set."

And so the waiting began. Some of the men lighted pipes and blue waves of smoke curled upward as they hit the heat of the lamp. Lainey watched them, grateful that they moved for she was going to die just sitting still. Simply die. The wind coming through the cracks in the wall made the lamp flame sputter and the snaky branches of the plant seem to twist in the light.

Wait. Just wait. Sis Pritchard could have asked anything else of the neighbors and they could have done it easier. They were not accustomed to sitting, doing nothing. They twitched, sneezed, whispered, coughed, made tiptoed trips to see about the horses or the children who had gone to sleep on pallets in the kitchen. At last the silence overcame them and they sat and waited, the need gone to move or to make a sound. The plant was the important thing. As if it were a heathen idol and they worshippers, their eyes and thoughts clung to it. Lainey found she could not look away. The plant took different shapes before her.

Then there was a stir beside her and without looking she became aware that Arch was sitting there. The Pritchard children had disappeared, the little Wellman girl crawled over to her mother. She leaned her weight back on her arm, hand braced on the floor, and knew that Arch's hand, braced like hers was only inches away. The strange, ugly plant cast a spell about her. She felt and saw with her whole being. The white edge on the green bud looked larger. Was it?

"It moved!" came a whisper behind her.

"Shhhhhhh. Shhhhhhhh!"

The bud quivered. In the dark, in the shadow of her own body, Arch's hand moved against hers. They did not look at each other; their faces were set, intent, staring at the mysterious plant that had come from God-knows-where and God-knows-why down to the Territory for them to watch. How long had the bud lain, green and fleshy in the branch, to rise and bloom tonight?

Breathing quickened in the room. A child wailed in its sleep.

"Shhhhhh. Shhhhhhh!"

The night-blooming cereus was the center of all their hopes and dreams. It was high prices for cotton and a red silk dress; it was a trip back home and a baby that would live through the second summer; it was high-stepping horses and an unmortgaged farm. They leaned forward and their faces were strained, tense.

The length of Arch's arm was against Lainey's; their shoulders touched. Her eyes ached from staring at the bud and something was beating unbearably inside her. A throbbing, an aching, as the flower ached to escape the bud.

It moved! It turned. The green fleshy bud tore itself open, the movement slow, as if it were in exquisite pain. Long white petals unfolded, short center petals rose. Slowly, slowly, breathe lightly, this moment will never come again! Perfume spilled into the air and ran down the coiling smoke to the walls of the room. A heavy sweet, sensual odor.

With one last, perfect motion the cereus came to full bloom.

"Show's over," Ab Pritchard said. "Sis, how 'bout some more cawfee?"

Lainey turned one way, Arch the other. She did not want to meet his eyes. Bill Doggett opened the door to the dog-run and the chill air set the lamp swinging. The neighbors began to talk of trivial things.

Sis Pritchard carried the plant away, refusing all offers of help. The women gathered up pans and bowls and sleepy children and urged their men to their hitched rigs. Young couples paired off. Dotty Sullavan turned sulky as her mother ordered her into the green Studebaker wagon.

"Don't go now! The night's still a pup," Ab Pritchard begged.

"There's another bud or two; they'll open at two-three in th' morning. Make a night of it."

No one heeded him. There was work to be done, stock to be tended, distance to be covered. They said all these things, but the real, the secret truth, was that no one wanted to watch a miracle repeated. They wanted to be gone, now, with the sight of the night-blooming cereus locked within them. Thanks and goodbyes were subdued. The neighbors rode off over the frosty, moon-touched land, calling in afterthought, "Good night . . . come see us . . . take care . . . good night."

In the buckboard Lainey set the ironstone platter between her and Bush. She wanted to be separate, as alone as possible. The evening had been part misery and part delight. She remembered the way Curly had said her fellow would be there. Was it Arch? She considered all that had happened between her and Arch tonight and the plain and familiar became strange and full of hidden meaning. Had he touched her hand first? Or had she touched his?

"You're mighty quiet," Bush said. "Tired?"

"No. I'm not tired."

But she might have been for she had come a long way since that afternoon when Curly Pritchard had ridden up to the Sheridan place. Further than the Santa Fe had brought her on the road to the Territory; further even than the night-blooming cereus had come from the Mexican desert.

148

Chapter 14

"I'm going to be the Main Angel," Lainey announced at supper. She had hugged the news to herself ever since Miss Swenson told her just as school let out. Now she flourished it like a bright banner over the remains of the pumpkin pudding they had had for dessert. "It's the most important part in the play. Or almost."

It was disturbing that Bush reached for the pudding and Mama poured more coffee.

"It's the Christmas program. I have to have a costume. With wings."

"Maybe you could grow some," Bush poured milk over the scraps of pudding.

"You make 'em with wire and cover it with cheesecloth. Miss Swenson showed me how. In Minneapolis all the angels had wings but here only the Main Angel. That's me."

"Uh-huh. Bush, we're nearly out of coffee."

She tried one more time to make them understand. "I'm the one that says, 'Fear not for behold I bring you good tidings of great joy.'" A paralyzing thought stopped her. "I can have a costume, can't I? And wings? I promised Miss Swenson!"

Bush frowned. "Lainey, your mama's got more to do than work on costumes."

"Now, Bush," Allegra got up wearily and began to gather up the dishes. "Don't look like that, Lainey. That nightgown of mine with ruffles will make over into a nice robe. It's the wings that have me bothered."

The costume became the only thing in life. Lainy hurried home from school and skipped through her chores to rip, cut, and baste. The nightgown, with its ruffles removed and wound on a stick for further use, made a fine robe, but the wings taxed the

149

whole family. Baling wire was too heavy, unravelled chicken wire too light. At last Allegra sent Bush to the woods to cut lengths of grapevine, soaked them to make them pliable, shaped and covered them with cheesecloth. "I remembered Ellen said they used grapevines for hoops during the war." The cheesecloth had been used to make smearcase and smelled a little of sour milk no matter how many times Lainey washed and bleached it. Bush, who would not be serious, said not to mind, it'd never be smelled on a galloping horse. Pappy Vickers added his part by peeling tinfoil from his chewing tobacco and shaping it into stars to spangle the wings.

And wherever she went, whatever she did the words Lainey was to speak sang within her. Fear not . . . fear not . . . fear not . . . good tidings of great joy . . .

"Look at Lainey, talkin' to herself," Bluebell Shimer snickered.

"Rather talk to myself than talk to you anytime," Doris Shipp defended. Since the night the cereus had opened Doris had been Lainey's shadow. It was nice to have a best friend but once in a while it was a little tiresome, for Doris would allow no other girls near. "Just you 'n' me," she said over and over. "Just us."

At school things were at fever heat. Lessons were almost abandoned. The Christmas program would use every pupil in Jackrabbit School. Rehearsals went on until everyone knew everybody else's part. At recess games were forgotten and the pupils stood in small bunches "hearing" each other in recitations, dialogues, songs, declamations, and the climax of the program, the play.

The entire district was expected to come. Miss Swenson worried for fear there might not be room for the curtain made of unbleached muslin sheets borrowed from a half-dozen families. But a play without a curtain was unthinkable; besides the two pupils who could not memorize even a simple piece had parts as curtain pullers.

After the program they would have the tree. It was not just for the school but for the whole neighborhood. Parents would put presents for children on it, husbands and wives for each other and fellows for their girls. Daisy Pritchard said Curly had a great big box for teacher. Presents from fellows were carefully graded

150

as to what they might mean. An autograph album could be given to anybody. A box of chocolates . . . hard as bullets . . . was a sign you were "goin' together." A manicure set, or a comb-and-brush set was about like announcing an engagement. Knitted sleeve holders and embroidered collar bags were favorite presents from the girls. When the presents had been stripped from the tree there would come the treat. Hard candy was expected, an orange hoped for. It was the yearly orange for some. The entire school yearned toward Christmas Eve.

On Saturday afternoon, three days before Christmas Eve, Allegra said the costume was all done but the hem. She'd finish that when Bush got out of the house. He was going to Randall to do some trading. Lainey ran to the chicken pen for the last eggs to send along and packed two pats of butter in a tin bucket. Bush had a list of things to get and she was hopeful at its length. But the only glance she got was not encouraging, "10 yds. cot. flan." A Christmas present out of cotton flannel didn't sound like much.

Pappy Vickers announced that he was going along. "Got to lay in my Christmas cheer."

"Watch out for that stuff they sell at the Red Dog. It's skull buster for sure."

"Watch out yourself," Pappy Vickers strutted to the door. "I was weaned on Taos lightnin'."

"You're sure it's all right for me to go?" Bush turned to Allegra.

"Of course. I've got the Main Angel to stay with me," Allegra smiled so that Lainey would know it was only teasing. "We need things, and we may not get in for awhile."

"Guess I ought to take advantage of this weather. Warm as spring, pret'neart."

"Looks like a green Christmas."

"Green Christmas, fat graveyard." Pappy Vickers was mournful.

"Shush, man! That's for back home. In the Territory we're gonna live forever."

"Then le's get started. Gonna live that long I crave excitement."

"Lissen. Last time you craved excitement I had to pull you outa two fights."

"Same feller both times," Pappy Vickers said. "Durn-fool

151

Yankee. Next time he'll know bettern to run down Jeb Stuart."

Bush went to the door. Came back. "You sure?"

"I'm sure. And don't forget."

"I'm not likely to. If he's out on a call I'll leave word."

Lainey pricked up her ears. It was too close to Christmas to be nosey, but that sounded like Dr. Harter. She shuddered, tasting the tonic he had sent her.

"I won't take any more of that nasty stuff!"

They both turned on her.

"Who said anything about *you?*"

"Little pitchers . . . You're too big for that."

"Well, I won't take it!" As long as they hadn't told her, she needn't *know.* . . . Resolutely, as she had done ever since Pappy Vickers came, she pushed the truth from her mind.

With Allegra she watched the buckboard with the two men down the road. It wasn't out of sight before the Pritchards rattled by, waving and calling back.

"Daisy said some of their folks were campin' over on Deep Fork waitin' for the Kickapoo country to open up. They're the ones with so many kids."

"Children," Allegra corrected. "Kids are little goats."

"I wish I had a sister."

"You do?"

"Well, you did. You had Aunt Ellen."

"That's right. I couldn't have gotten along without her when Mama died."

"How did she die?"

"In childbirth," Allegra said absently, then caught herself. "Now whatever made me say a thing like that to you?"

"How do you mean? The way she died? How?"

"We've got to get at that costume."

"But you said . . ."

"Do you want that costume or don't you?"

The white robe slid coolly over Lainey's gray-flannel petticoat and flowed down over her stout shoes. She wished she had taken her Saturday bath before trying it on. As she stepped onto the empty woodbox so Allegra could get at the hem, the wings pulled heavily at her shoulders. Could she fly? Why not? In dreams it was easy.

"Turn," Allegra directed through a mouthful of pins. Lainey faced around toward the window.

"Somebody's coming!"

"Stand still!"

"It's Arch. Oh, my goodness, he'll see me." She jumped off the box.

"He'll see you in the play. It's just the hem."

"I don't care." She was skinning out of the robe, pins scratching her face.

"All my hem marks! Now I'll have to do everything over." Allegra got up heavily. "Come in."

Behind the bed curtain Lainey struggled into her dress.

"Howdy, Miz Sheridan." Arch stood in the doorway, not quite in or quite out.

"Come in and stay awhile. How's your folks?"

"They're fine." He moved an inch further in token obedience, then settled back by the door jamb. "Dad went over to Ruckers' to help put up their barn. Ma went along. Said it'd be her Christmas present to get off the claim." Lainey came in. "Hello."

"Hello." She had buttoned her dress wrong and it came out uneven at the waist.

"I thought I'd go in to Randall."

"Now that's a shame. Little earlier and you could have gone with Bush and Cap'n Vickers."

The south wind puffed at the door and the dying fire in the stove made the room too warm and stuffy. The sun was bright in a cloudless sky.

Arch looked out and back. "Back home we'd be sleddin'."

"I know," Allegra said. "It doesn't seem right. Christmas and all."

"Weather breeder," Arch prophesied.

"When I was a young lady," Allegra said dreamily, "a young man used to come and take me out in the winter in a little cutter built like a swan. He drove a blooded mare."

Tom Bridges, Lainey thought to herself.

"I saw Halfmoons down the road a piece." Arch volunteered, "Headin' for the agency to bring their girl home for Christmas."

Annie home! Now she could trill and somebody would answer. She had told Arch and no one else about their friendship. It was his way of letting her know.

"Well, I better be goin'." He said it without moving.

"Stay and have some supper with us," Allegra said. "Go some other time."

"Nope. Got to go today." Arch twirled his hat on one finger, looking at it as if he had never seen it before. Abruptly, he said, "Red's a pretty color. I always like red."

Lainey sensed something was expected of her. "Red's nice."

"But there's green. Green's pretty, too."

"Green's nice."

His hat flipped off his finger, he leaned over to get it, came up frowning. "One's bound to be nicer'n the other. Prettier."

She could find nothing to say. Red? Green? Red? Green?

"I like red," Allegra put in, "for a girl with dark hair. A real brunette."

Relief showed on Arch's face. "That's right. I've heard Ma say that, too. Well, I got to be goin'." This time he went.

"What was he talking about? Sounded crazy to me," Lainey said.

"Christmas talk, maybe. I saw autograph books with red and green covers in the drug store last time I was in Randall."

Warm blood rushed to Lainey's face. To have her name called at the tree with a present from a boy! And from the drug store. She thought of the frame building on the edge of the hill with its smell of strange things in glass jars, its rows of hundreds of patent remedies. Lately Mr. Link had put in a line of presents in a glass counter, right back by the green curtain that separated Dr. Harter's office from the store. Every girl in Jackrabbit School knew each gift there and what it cost.

"You'd better not count on it; I might be wrong." Allegra picked up the costume, pulled out a few pins, put it down on the table. "I believe I'll lie down awhile."

"We'll hem it after supper."

The aimless peace of a house without a man settled on the

154

place. No hurry to get up a hot meal . . . cold meat and biscuits for the two of them. No need to clear up the clutter of sewing . . . leave the black-handled scissors on the floor, the saucer of pins on the table, the tape measure looped from the chair to the floor. Allegra's breathing became heavy, evenly spaced. Lainey pulled the silk crazy quilt over her, then dug back of the organ for her store of Christmas presents.

The dust cap, made for Mama, was finished at last. It had a grayish tinge taken from her hands as she worked on the French knots. Ought to be washed, but she was afraid to try. She had bought Bush a shaving mug with part of her cotton money, forgetting he had let his beard grow. Never mind, it was hand-painted and he could use it for coffee. For Pappy Vickers there was a brightly varnished pipe to replace the smelly old thing he smoked. Now Arch. Should she or shouldn't she? The thought of putting something on the tree for him if Mama was wrong was too terrible. Besides, she'd spent all her money. Lainey put the presents back and went outdoors.

The south wind was soft on her face, and she tossed her coat inside, reaching instead for the gray crocheted shawl Mama kept behind the door. It was much too nice a day to stay in the house. A day like this, when by all rights it should be cold, was like a Christmas present. Mare's tails clouds had streaked the sky since Arch had come. It would take him a long time to get to Randall riding on short-legged Dumps. A crow flapped over; its caw-caw-caw drifting back after it was out of sight. Annie coming home! Doris was fine but she was always after you to promise things. Never to eat lunch with anybody else. Always to save a seat. Never to have secrets. It wore you down. Lainey crossed the road, strolled through the field where the corn had been, across the strip of pasture to the dry gulch. The house was further from the gulch than the wagon. A quarter mile at least. And uphill besides.

Due north a line of dark clouds pushed over the horizon. They looked the way Pappy Vickers said the mountains did, lifting from the plains and towering in the distance.

At the bottom of the gulch Lainey made initials in the sand with the toe of her shoe, A.H., L.S. Then she drew a heart around them

155

and quickly scratched the whole thing out. Suppose somebody saw her? The rattle of far-off wheels brought her scrambling to the top of the gulch as the Doggett buggy went by. Everybody in the world was going some place on the Saturday before Christmas but Lainey Sheridan.

She wandered down the gulch feeling sorry for herself. The tree stump held a new clutter of trash, the round red rocks were there, but they had lost their power to make her feel rich and mysterious. Lainey chunked one over the top and listened for the thud.

The line of clouds in the north rose higher, pushed by blacker clouds behind them; they spread across the sky, dark and threatening against the sunlight. A froth of white edged their line of advance.

The south wind dropped to a whisper as the Princess Elaine walked down the dry gulch, her velvet and ermine train heavy behind her, the gleaming gold crown balanced on her head. Her thronging subjects rushed forward, begging her not to go into the terrible danger that lay beyond the tree stump. I'm too old for this; it's silly. But I'll just finish it up this time. She walked forward grandly, proudly. A knight in golden armor and a golden helmet with a white plume knelt at her feet. "Stay, Elaine the Fair, and I will go in thy stead." He cast his helmet on the sand. It was Arch!

Lainey stopped, baffled. How had it come about? She had never seen the knight's face before and the Princess Elaine belonged at Riverview while Arch was part and parcel of the Territory. As she stood puzzling the light changed. The racing clouds had swallowed up the sun. The sky was a rolling mass of black and gray. Snatched back from the court of Elaine the Fair, Lainey could only stand and listen, aware, suddenly, of the death of the south wind.

Out of the north, a dark cave from which the clouds poured endlessly forth, came a faint humming. It grew until the air vibrated like an untuned harp. Lainey crouched on the side of the gulch and waited. Louder and louder came the humming until it

156

was a roar and Lainey Sheridan and the red earth cowered together as the great compass of the wind swung 'round.

South. Southwest. West. West by north. North. North!

With a shriek of triumph the norther took the Sac and Fox country.

The last blue streak of sky went under. An unnatural twilight covered the land. The temperature began to drop. Cold fingers probed at the crocheted shawl and found the shivering girl beneath it. For the first time Lainey knew and shared Allegra's hatred of the wind.

Clutching the shawl around her, Lainey climbed out of the shelter of the gulch. As she reached the top the full force of the norther struck her in the face and forced the breath back in her lungs. Clinging there, face down, gasping, she waited for a lull. None came. The noise of the wind grew stronger with a high-pitched screaming edge. Lainey got to her feet and tried to run but there was no running. Only breathless staggering. A few steps, then a turn around to breathe. The icy wind cut like fire deep into her lungs. Sand stung her face. The hill was impossibly high and the house on the top squatted in the face of the norther. 'Get the breeze,' Bush said, but he hadn't bargained for this. Bush!

Bushrod Sheridan, my father . . . Bushrod Sheridan, my father . . . Bent double Lainey fought the wind borrowing strength from his name. Things had come between them lately . . . the claim, Mama's illness, even Arch . . . Now the norther blew them all away. Bushrod Sheridan, my father . . .

Lainey's face was numb and her feet like stumps. Dead corn stalks tripped her. Through the field, now, and past the turnout for Pappy Vickers' place. She could go to the half-dugout and get out of the wind, get warm under the buffalo robe. But a nameless urgency drove her up, up the hill instead. No light in the house? How could Mama sleep through all this? It would wake the dead. Don't think about death. Don't think about the whip of the sand. Tie the shawl over your face. Breath-wet wool smells like winter wash-day at Riverview with long underwear steaming in the kitchen. Safe warm kitchen. Safe strong brick walls.

157

Lainey stumbled into the shelter the little house made and caught her breath; resting against the door she fumbled for the latch. Her numbed fingers stopped as she heard a shuddering groan from inside, then she jerked at the door, fighting the wind and her own terror.

"Mama! Mama!"

The darkness indoors was thicker and more terrifying than the darkness outside. She had fought her way up the hill for shelter but it was not here. This was a secret chamber where something animal writhed on the floor and cried out.

"Mama!" Lainey screamed.

From some far crevice where she lay trapped by pain Allegra heard the terror in her child's voice and answered.

"Lainey! Thank God you've come. Get a light." She stopped, panting. "The tape measure. I tripped on the tape measure. Oh. Oh. Oh."

Lainey found the matches, spilled them, blew on her fingers, heard the dragging breath from the floor behind her, gritted her teeth and struck a match. The lamp wick took fire and the chimney turned hot in her fingers. The light grew and the dread place into which she had stumbled became home. The stove. The table. The safe. The organ. But the bed was empty and Mama was on the floor, her face white, her lips bloodless.

"Go get somebody. Anybody. I didn't think it would be this soon. Oh! Bush, Bush!" A wordless cry choked off as Allegra bit down on her hand. The room was cold yet Lainey saw sweat shining on her mother's face.

"I'll get some wood. I'll fix the fire."

Anything to get away.

"Don't leave me. Don't leave me. Don't!"

Lainey caught the writhing hands and tried to hold them. Allegra pulled half up, then lay back down again.

"Mama, is it . . . is it . . ."

"I tried to tell you," Allegra gasped, "the day Cap'n Vickers came. But I couldn't. I didn't know how. Do you know? Did somebody else?"

"Addie told me. About babies." It was true, then. The things that came before. Then this. The sight of Addie's perspiring face and every word she whispered came back to Lainey. But this was Mama and she needed help.

"I didn't want you to be here. I didn't want you to have to know. Bush was going to take you over to Hamptons'. Dr. Harter was coming. Oh. Oh." She set her jaw, stopped the scream in her throat.

"It's all right. I mean, I'm not scared. Can you get up to the bed?"

They struggled together. Allegra who looked so light, so delicate, was heavy and awkward. Leaning heavily on Lainey, her hands pressed against her body, she stumbled to the bed and collapsed.

"I'll start the fire." But the woodbox was empty. The day had been so fair Lainey had not thought to bring in wood. She edged around the house to the woodpile, head down against the norther. Arms filled with wood she struggled back. The wind shook her violently, turned her around, and she blundered into the chicken-yard fence. She was heading toward the pasture! On her hands and knees Lainey fought down panic. Dropping half the wood she crawled with one hand on the chicken-yard fence till she found the slat gate that was opposite the rear of the house, stood up and made a dash that brought her smashing against the back wall. Behind her in the screaming dark the cow bawled pitifully. "I'm sorry," she snivelled, then the weak little words enraged her and she yelled into the teeth of the wind, "Root hog or die!"

In the house Lainey dumped the wood and stopped to catch her breath. Allegra was sitting on the side of the bed trying to get into her nightgown. Never, not even in the wagon, had she felt this close to Mama. She fanned the stove and ashes choked her, then the coals began to redden. A flame licked out. Heat crept from the stove in slow circles.

Allegra was huddled under the covers. "Get somebody, Lainey. Mary, or Sis Pritchard or anybody."

"Hamptons went over to Ruckers. Pritchards. Doggetts. Even Halfmoons. They're all gone." She finished under her breath, afraid to tell Mama the truth. They were alone in the norther. No one could come and they could not get out. The freezing wind held them like a steel trap.

"Get somebody," Allegra moaned again. "Saddle up Blackjack and ride."

This was a way out. She could get on Blackjack, turn him loose in the storm and escape from the terror in the house. No one could say she had done wrong because it was what Mama told her to do. Lainey jerked on her coat, tied the shawl over head. Her hand was on the latch, the wind screamed, mocking her. Surely there was somebody. Wellmans? No, they had taken Miss Swenson up to Guthrie for the weekend. Novaks? She wasn't sure just where their place was. East or west?

"Go on! Hurry."

This was her chance.

Slowly Lainey came back from the door. Slowly she took off the coat, folded the shawl in a neat square. As she put them down, a voice inside her said, "Fear not. Fear not." Slowly she walked over to the bed and touched Allegra's clenched hand.

"There isn't anybody but me. They're all gone. Hamptons. Wellmans. Doggetts. There's just me, but I'll do my best."

The blue eyes staring up at her looked black. The twisted mouth was open, panting. An agonized stranger lay upon the bed. Then Allegra's face came back into focus. She managed a weak smile.

"We'll get along fine, honey. After all, you're the Main Angel, you know."

Her eyelids drooped and she seemed to sleep. Her hand unclenched and reached for Lainey's. Fear not. Fear not. Lainey hardly dared to breathe. She was closer to Mama than she had ever been in her life.

"Put on some water to heat. Get the black-handled scissors and drop 'em in some water in the small stew-pan. Get out the leaf lard. Open up the trunk, there's an old sheet on top." Strange, conflicting things to do. There seemed no reason to them. "Build up the fire. Find the cotton-flannel squares."

As long as she could follow directions, as long as the calm voice came from the bed she was safe. Then came the moment when there was nothing for her hands to do, nothing to do but watch the beloved face strain and contort and the hands that were so firm and gentle on the organ keys turn into corded claws.

"Something to pull on," Allegra grunted. "Some rope, or tie some tea towels together. It's been so long, I can't remember. Ellen was there and Dr. Quimper and old Aunt Bitsy, and Bush standing outside the door."

Then later, far later, while the house shook in the grip of the wind. "Go get the axe."

"No!" What dreadful thing must she do now? "No. Please."

"Get the axe and put it under the bed. To cut the pain. Foolish, maybe, but Aunt Bitsy . . . Oh . . . Oh . . . Oh . . ."

Out in the blackness of the norther, finding the woodpile again. Sleet in her face and the ice-covered axe. Fear not. Fear not. Creeping back to the door, head down against the wind. Another trip for more wood. Bushrod Sheridan, my father. Bushrod Sheridan, my father. No. Bush did this to Mama. I hate him and I'll hate him every day of my life. No. No. Addie was wrong. There must be a mistake. Open the door and go back inside. Slide the icy axe under the bed. The clock struck eight slow strokes. Lainey had thought it was midnight.

"Bush ought to be home soon," Allegra whispered.

"He'll be here to'reckly." Uncle Hod, help me. Get somebody to come. Please. "Does it help? The axe?"

"I don't know. I don't . . . Lainey, if I die send me back to Riverview. I won't be buried out here. I won't."

"I promise. But you won't die."

'Died in childbirth.' Was that what this meant? Please, dear God, please.

More waiting, more straining and contorting. If only there were something . . . something . . . anything but this helpless waiting.

The clock struck nine.

"He ought to be here."

"He'll be here soon."

161

"Now. Now."

Finally Lainey gingerly picked up the tiny baby.

"Warm flannel. Put . . . here. . . on me . . ." Allegra panted. "Is it . . . all right?"

A thin, feeble cry. A little movement of hands.

"Yes. It's all right."

"The darling!"

How can she say that, after the pain? I would hate it. I would want to kill it. No. No. Her heart turned to water at the snuffling cry. No. I love it, too.

"Is it a girl?" Careful. Careful. Never ask for what you really want.

"I . . . No."

"A boy!"

"Allegra!" The door burst open and three men came in. They were so covered with ice and sleet you could not tell who they were. "Allegra!"

"Bush! It's a boy!"

Ice on his beard. Ice on his eyebrows. His coat stiff with sleet. Bushrod Sheridan knelt by the bed. "I left you alone. I left you alone."

"Shhhhh. It's all right. Lainey was here. It's a boy, Bush. Did you hear me?"

"I got scared when I got to town and went after Doc. We were four hours gettin' home."

"Get away, Bush," Dr. Harter peeled off his coat, hat, and gloves. "You'll give her pneumonia, you're that cold. Get some coffee started. Git!"

"Land o' Goshen! What a country," Pappy Vickers said. "Sweat one minute, freeze the next. Boy, you say it is? Good thing. He better be tough."

Lainey felt shoved aside. Forgotten. The long night when she and Mama had fought together was over. She could hand things over to somebody else now.

"Let's have a look." Dr. Harter found the wash bowl with

the ease of a man who has washed in many strange places. He dipped his hands in the soft soap.

Lainey measured coffee and water, her knees wobbling a little.

"Fine boy," the doctor said. "Run nine pounds or better. That head'll shape up in a few days. And how about you, ma'am?"

"I'm all right," Allegra said. "But I might not have been if it hadn't been for Lainey."

"Lainey," Bush said, coming over to the table. "Lainey."

But she had put her head down on the table and neither the wind, nor the sound of coffee boiling over, nor her father's voice reached her. Only in the deep recess of sleep she heard again a calling. Fear not. Fear not.

Chapter 15

January of 1893. A year to be remembered. It began well enough with Watch Night services and hopes and plans. It began the way other years did. Then something went wrong.

In the East money went out of sight. One minute it changed hands across the counter. The next it disappeared and the customer stood on one side, the merchant on the other with the counter a barrier between them. The Silver Crisis, men called it. The Republicans blamed Grover Cleveland; the Democrats anybody they could think of. Wheat fell to thirty-two cents a bushel. Stocks on the exchange dropped, down, down, down. Banks began to close. Things will right themselves economists said importantly, but there were long lines of men standing outside closed factories. And money stayed out of sight.

Down in Oklahoma Territory the early prospects for crops, stock, and the new businesses were good. The opening of the Cheyenne-Arapaho lands in 1892 had given an impetus to the growing population. Railroads were making big plans to crisscross the state. Randall had high hopes of getting one line or another to come its way. Tents had vanished from the town and houses of sawed lumber were appearing. A two-story house adorned the main street; board sidewalks lifted the citizens out of the dust and the mud. Randall was known around the new country as a good trading town and every Saturday the hitching racks were crowded. No reason to worry, in Randall, Oklahoma Territory, about what was going on in New York, or Chicago, or Washington. Or even in Kansas City.

Then empty buildings began to be seen in Guthrie where space had been at a premium six months before. Two banks in Oklahoma City closed. Tramps dropped off at the end of the railroad lines and roamed the country. Men would work for board and keep and tobacco, but no one could afford to hire them. Crops still looked good enough, but an atmosphere of caution settled in. Men shook their heads when their wives suggested a new buggy, a set of dishes, or a parlor organ. The school board of Jackrabbit School decided to let the old building do another year. Subscriptions to the *Randall Recorder* were paid in turnips, cordwood, eggs. Dr. Harter got chickens, sausage, now and then a ham, far oftener, nothing. Grocery stock stayed on the shelves. The settlers went back to parched kaffir, dried pumpkin strips, rabbit. "We did it once; we c'n do it again," they said, and pulled in their belts.

The loan sharks flourished. Those who had a little extra money were few enough, but some of them found that they could put it out on loan and the interest rates, unchecked by any ruling, rocketed as high as fifty percent. Many a man who had won his quarter by being fleet of foot or a better rider, lost it to a sharp pencil and a quick turn with figures. Covered wagons were once more a common sight on the roads, driven by men with bitterness etched on their faces. The old slogans were painted out and new ones read, "In God We Trusted, in the Territory We Busted." "Goin' Home to Live With My Wife's Folks." "Back to God's Country."

Then the weather, as if it had taken fright at the way men handled their affairs, turned against the Sac and Fox country. A drouth began. Day by blue day the sun rose in an unclouded sky. The earth that had been fertile, even lavish, in its first harvests, crumbled into dust. Every plow had red dust whirling behind it. Hot winds baked the crops and there was no rain to mellow the ground for re-planting. Lili Gervais' grape cutting drooped, withering to the ground. There was no rain at all. Men went out at the first light, scanned the sky, shook their heads and went about their chores. All day long, wherever you looked, you could see a man standing, idle, staring at the cloudless blue arch. Prayers for rain went up in the churches. White settlers asked their Indian neighbors what to expect and got a slow shrug, a turning outward of the hands, an answer in any language. Signs of rain that had been infallible in Missouri, Illinois, New York, or Nebraska, failed.

Rain crows called. Flies gathered by the door. Maple leaves turned silver side out. Still no rain.

No rain. No crops. No cash. No credit.

Bushrod Sheridan drummed on the oilcloth-covered table. "I don't get it. Henry Halfmoon's been here since '73. He says it always rains 'round the middle of August. Here it is September. Somethin's got to give!" He took up Lainey's pencil and started figuring on lined paper. "Somethin's got to give."

"Ellen wrote me they had an inch of rain back home last week." Allegra nuzzled the top of the baby's head. "Regular toad-strangler."

From across the table Lainey saw Bush grip the pencil and press down till the point broke. He took out his knife and sharpened it, making tiny curls of shavings on the table.

"I'd like to take Sunny back home for a visit," Allegra said. "Ellen says they had a good corn crop and she'll send me the money for my birthday."

"No." Bush said, and the pencil point snapped again. "No."

"But she wants to see Sunny. And I want him to see her. And Riverview. Some day he may . . . Oh, all right." She stopped, then started again with a quiver in her voice. "You know Dr. Harter said I had a hard time. He said I ought to be careful."

Bush winced, put the pencil in the pencil box. "We'll see." He held out his arms to the baby. "C'mon Sunny. C'mon."

Sunny Sheridan crowed in delight. He was blond, blue-eyed, chubby, and at nine months he owned his world. He had been named Saunders Sheridan by Bush while he was still in the throes of guilt for having left Allegra alone. But 'Saunders' was a solemn-sounding name and he usually went by 'Baby' until Pappy Vickers brought Henry Halfmoon over to see him.

"This good boy," he said to Bush. "All time I get girl. No boy. But I keep tryin'." His teeth were white in his copper-dark face as he grinned. Lainey was relieved that Allegra did not lift her eyebrows in distaste. Maybe she didn't even hear for she was watching Henry the way a mother cat watched when you picked up her kitten. But the flannel-swathed baby gurgled contentedly as Henry swung him slowly back and forth. Touching the fair hair

166

that curled back from the forehead, Henry said, "He hair like sun-shine. Call him Sun On Water." He repeated in the Sac tongue but it was too large a mouthful, and only "Sunny" stuck.

The name fitted the baby like the shirts Aunt Ellen knitted and sent him. He smiled most of the time, thrived on what was given him, and sat happily for hours in the horse-collar they put on the floor to keep him from rolling into the stove. Now he struggled from Bush's arms to go to Lainey. She put down her arithmetic.

"Did you bring in the baby's wash?" Allegra asked.

"No, ma'am."

"Well get it in right this minute. Night air's bad for clothes."

"Yes, ma'am."

Lainey unclasped the fat fingers one by one. Bush began to tickle Sunny with his beard. Allegra leaned toward them. "Hurry up," she said to Lainey. "Right now."

Lainey stopped at the door to put the crocheted shawl over her head. "I'll be fourteen next month," she said to nobody in particular.

"Gitchy-gitchy-goo," Bush said. Sunny tugged on his beard.

"The darling!"

Lainey walked out into the September night her cheeks hot. It had been a babyish thing to do. Practically ask for a birthday present. She had thought to be fourteen was special. But maybe it was sixteen. The things the neighbors had said when they came by to see Sunny had taken on a bitter meaning. "Nose outa joint?" "You're not the only one, now." "Kinda shoved you outa the nest, huh?" Sunny was a darling, like Mama was always saying, but . . . but . . .

The work he made! You wouldn't think, with him so little, it could be like that. The dresses, petticoats, bands, shirts, shawls, blankets, bootees, and the mounds of smelly diapers. She had washed and rubbed till her hands were sore. Good thing Bush had dug the deep well or, with the drouth, they'd never have made it. Mama wouldn't put him in dark dresses. Saunders babies always wore white for a year. On ironing day the starched dresses stood up alone, placed around the room. I ought to be ashamed, she told

167

herself, plucking clothes off the line. I love him. But . . . but . . .

The stars were bright in September. They glittered through tears on Lainey's eyelashes. She wiped her eyes on a diaper and shoved it under the others. Bush never talked to her any more. Everybody said a man wanted a boy, so it must be true. Even Mama, after they had been so close the night he was born and for weeks afterwards, even Mama never spoke to her except to tell her to do something for Sunny. "Be quiet and don't wake Sunny. Hurry and get that done up while Sunny's asleep. Don't ask me to make a new dress. Don't bring that noisy Doris home." Always the baby. Sometimes I wish he'd never been born!

Horrified at herself Lainey grabbed the last diaper off the line and ran toward the house. I'll wash everything he has. I'll stay home with him all the time. I'll never, never say such a thing again. Her rush brought her up to the back door Bush had cut after Sunny was born. She stopped to get her face arranged and looked up at the stars. The Big Dipper was still stubbornly holding the rain from the earth. "I didn't mean it," she whispered. "Honest, I didn't." But . . . but . . .

Allegra had taken Sunny to bed with her and pulled the curtain. Bush was still sitting at the table. The lined paper was covered with sums. Lainey went to work sprinkling and rolling down the clothes. She would get up before day and iron them before she went to school.

He watched her working. "You're mighty good to Sunny."

"I'm not either!"

Some vehemence in her answer made him look up, then the figures on the paper pulled his face down again. "Death and taxes. One's as hard to get ready for as the other."

It did seem foolish to iron diapers, as quick as Sunny got them wet, but Mama was firm. She pointed out the babies at church with flour-sack diapers as examples of what could happen if you 'let down,' but Lainey thought they looked like they were having a good time. Bush got up and went to the kitchen safe. He reached inside for the sugar bowl with the knobless lid where they kept the money now that they were in the house. There was a lonesome clink as he picked up a coin and let it slide back into the

168

bowl. He saw Lainey watching him and went over to her, his arm around her a support she had not known she'd missed.

"Don't be scared of money, Lainey. Having it or not having it." He was silent a minute then he yawned and stretched, up and up. A man so tall he could reach the roof of his own house. "If it'd just rain."

"It will," Lainey said with sudden confidence. "It always has."

There were more and more covered wagons on the road. Bush came home from Randall with mail, a few supplies, and the news. He sat down on the porch he had added to the front of the house by swapping work with the sawmill man for lumber and shingles.

"They're finally opening the Cherokee Strip." He picked a piece of foxtail grass and chewed the juicy end, staring out at the parched claim. "Finest cattle land in the world. I reckon."

"Your eyes look like holes burned in a blanket," Allegra said. "Can't you hire some help? There was a man asking just yesterday."

"No," Bush said. "Not enough to do to keep me busy."

"Did you get the coffee?"

"No!" he shouted. "Nor the sewin' thread, nor the paregoric, or any other folderols you wanted. I didn't have the money. And nobody would have the stuff I carried in to trade. It's out in the wagon right now. And nobody'll loan a dime on the best quarter in the whole Oklahoma Territory." His voice cracked and he put his face in his hands. Lainey saw the jerking of his throat muscles and her own throat swelled and ached. Allegra thrust Sunny into her arms and ran across the porch, little puffs of dust following her quick feet.

"Don't, Bush. You've worked so hard. Too hard. It'll be all right." One hand groped blindly toward her. "Allegra? Allegra?"

"I'm here. Right here."

"If it'd just rain."

At supper Sunny was the only one who had a mind to talk. He crowed, gurgled, and chattered in his own language. Lainey and Allegra cleared the table and washed dishes. Then there was nothing left to do and going to bed was admitting defeat.

169

"If you don't have any lessons," Allegra said, "we'll just turn out the lamp. The flame hurts my eyes." Nobody mentioned that the coal oil was low in the can.

Pappy Vickers wandered in. "Settin' in the dark? Puts me in mind o' ol' man Merk, back in Snyder County. Tightest man between Marney an' Jericho."

"I remember him," Allegra said dully. "He was in Papa's regiment."

"Th' same. Maje had to pret'neart courtmartial him to get him to fire good gunpowder at the damyankees. Well, after the war he got tightern' tighter. Brought his hogs to market so lean they had to stand twict to cast a shadder. Well, Emo Dodson stopped in there one time after supper . . . nobody stopped at Merks' mealtimes . . . an' the lamp was lit an' they sat, talkin'." Pappy Vickers took a sliver of wood from the woodbox and lighted it at the fire in the stove, then he put it to his pipe and Lainey watched his face as he drew in and the flame brightened. "Wellsir, ol' man Merk up an' says, 'Emo, you know what I look like an' I know what you look like so there's no sense wastin' coal oil for us to see each other.' An' with that he turned out the lamp. They kep' on talkin' an' ol' man Merk says, 'Emo,' he says, says he, 'Nobody here but me an' you an' we cain't see each other in the dark, so there's no sense in us wearin' out our pants settin' on 'em.' And he up an' took off his pants. Emo said that was when he left."

They laughed politely. It was a story polished by many a telling.

"I like the dark," Allegra said. "It's peaceful."

"So dang peaceful it makes me sleepy." Pappy stood up and yawned. "See ya in the mornin'." He called Bush to the door and they talked a minute, then he tramped away.

"The old rooster," Bush said, his voice shaky. "Offered me his rent money."

"Did you take it?"

"Who do you think I am? Old man Merk?"

Allegra went over to the organ. The music soothed the troubled room. Lainey curled around Sunny on his pallet on the floor, taking comfort from his warm, rounded little body. The music was like water to the thirsty. Uncle Hod's voice, calm and gentle, read aloud, "And the night shall be filled with music, And the cares that infest the day . . ."

"Hello the house!"

The music broke on a discord. Bush stepped to the door and Allegra quickly lighted the lamp. It was Bill Doggett, his face haggard, Bush's sledge hammer in his hand.

"Howdy, Bill. Come in and set a spell."

Bill Doggett slumped into a chair, nodding at Allegra and Lainey. He was a thin man with a surprisingly deep bass voice. His wife had been a schoolteacher before her marriage and she had often borrowed books from Uncle Hod's supply. That the Doggetts came from Illinois was about all anyone knew about them.

"Brought your hammer back. Sorry I kep' it so long."

"That's all right. Doubt if I need it unless I try to break a little ground." It was a poor joke and nobody laughed.

"Wanted to get it back to you. We're pullin' out." Bill stared at the floor.

"Goin' up to the Strip?"

"Hell no!" He glanced at Allegra. "Excuse me, ma'am. We're goin' back home. Illinois. Cain't make a living in the Territory. Our place is burnt up. Our money's gone. I figger we better get out while we got a team to haul us."

"What're you plannin' to do back home?"

"Work in a store, like I did. I was a fool to leave, but my wife . . . Why, I haven't had a pipeful of tobacco in a month!"

Bush pulled out his tobacco pouch and showed the lining. "I know what you mean."

"I tried smokin' that stuff some o' the Indians 'round here smoke, but I couldn't stomach it. I'm goin' back where I can anyway make tobacco money."

"Looks like Illinois's a long ways to go for a smoke."

Bill Doggett's thin face flushed, he looked up resentfully. "You know that's not all there is to it. Not by a long shot."

"How about your wife?"

"Funny thing, she wants to stay. But I won't see her and the kids go hungry."

"Has it come to that?"

171

"We-ell, not exactly. We got some grub. And there's rabbits. But I don't see a chance."

"If it'd just rain."

They sat without looking at each other. The lamp flickered. There was enough coal oil to fill it four more times Lainey reckoned. Bill Doggett rose to his feet.

"I'd better be gettin' along. Just wanted to bring this hammer back an' tell you folks goodbye. If you ever get up to southern Illinois, look us up."

"Wait a minute, Bill."

Bush walked over to the kitchen safe. Lainey heard the silver dollar slide up the side of the sugar bowl in Bush's fingers. She saw Allegra frown.

"I want you to take this."

"Looky here, Bush, I'm no beggar."

"Who said you were? We're neighbors. I'd give a lot more'n a dollar . . . if I had it . . . for a neighbor like you. Why, you helped put up this roof we're under. And Mrs. Doggett bringin' all that herb tea when Lainey got sick, and . . ."

"Oh, stuff like that. But this's money. I never took money from no man."

"It's not takin' money. It's like . . . like I'd bet you a dollar that it'll rain and we'll make a crop yet. I feel in my bones that it will an' I'm willing to bet on it." Lainey saw Bush lean forward, sweat on his forehead. "Take that dollar and go in to Randall and buy some tobacco. Then tough it out. You won't be sorry."

Bill Doggett fingered the dollar. "How'd you know I won't take this an' hike out for Illinois?"

"I know a man when I see one."

"Not much of a man, though, that'd run for home when things get rough."

"Shush, Bill, we all get in the dumps. This afternoon in Randall I'd have sold out for a plugged nickel, but nobody made me an offer."

Bill laughed, weakly, "Not you, Bush. You're the old man o' the mountain. Never saw you with your dauber down." He slid the dollar in his pocket. "Man feels different with a dollar in his jeans."

"That's right. Now go on home an' start unpacking."

"We never really got packed. The missus kep' holdin' off." At the door he turned back, his thin face beet red. "I sure thank you. This is one bet you won't lose by. I'll stick."

When he was gone and the sound of his horse's hoofs was a part of the night Bush looked at Allegra. "All right. Go on an' say it."

"I'm proud of you Bush. You did just the right thing."

"It *was* our last dollar. I wasn't playing games."

"I don't care. I'm proud of you." She laid her face against his arm. Lainey came to the other side and the three of them leaned against each other.

Bush winked at Sunny, sleeping on the pallet. "Glory be, boy! Don't ever think you know anything 'bout womenfolks. Here I figgered they'd have my scalp an' they're actin' like I was Big Casino."

A covered wagon creaked down the road. Something familiar in the weather-grayed cover. The patches. The legend, "Nebrasky or Bust . . ." The team drooped to a stop at the gate. Lainey and Allegra went out to answer the hail of the man.

"On our way up to th' Strip. Water barrel sprung a leak. Can we plug it up an' fill from your well?"

"The water's kind of low and muddy but you're welcome to what there is." As the man and his tow-haired boys went toward the well, Allegra frowned in recollection and spoke to the woman on the wagon seat with a baby on her knees. "Aren't you . . . didn't you . . ."

"I was jist about to say I'd seen *you* some place."

"The Run," Lainey said. "Deep Fork. You were next to us in the line-up."

"Well, who'd o' thought it!" She looked wistfully at the house. "You got a nice place."

"Get down and come in. Stay and eat with us." Lainey heard her mother with amazement. The open-handed hospitality of the frontier had not been part of Allegra's training.

"Thank you kindly, but we'd better be on our way. Quicker we git there, th' quicker we'll be there, as the feller says." The

173

baby began to whimper and she rocked it back and forth on her knees. "This place puts me in mind o' the one we had. We never got our house built, but we aimed to put it on a hill. But my man he didn't like the place to farm. Too patchy." She sighed. "We had real good neighbors an' the best garden I ever raised till it dried up."

"If it would just rain," Allegra said.

"That's right. I think we'd of made it this time, but no rain . . . Then the Strip openin' up an' all. My man got res'less."

"I know." Allegra put out her hand. "I wish you'd come in."

"Thank you kindly, but if I ever got set down in a rockin' cheer I'd never git up. Wish't you'd come with us. Just the sight o' somebody I've seen before perks me up."

The man and the boys came back from the well. "Shore. C'mon. Plenty o' room in th' Strip."

"No, we're here to stay, root hog or die," Allegra smiled. "But . . . good luck!"

"We'll make it this time, for sure," the woman said, "or I'll tell the old man whose hog et the cabbage!"

"Thanky for the water." The man clucked to the team.

"Goodbye . . . Take care . . . Goodbye . . ."

They watched the wagon down the road, waving to the towheads until the dog-leg in the road took them from sight.

"I think that's terrible," Lainey said. "That baby's younger than Sunny. If I was in her place I wouldn't pull up and go off someplace else. I wouldn't do it!"

"Hush!" Allegra said sharply. "You don't know anything about it. Not anything."

On the night of the 20th of September, Lainey, lying half out of the cover on her bed under the low roof heard the growl and mutter of thunder. She sat up, lay down quickly. Don't pay any attention. Pretend you don't notice. Another growl and a flicker of lightning. The wind had a smell to it that meant . . . No . . . no . . . Don't say the word. Don't even think it. She put her head under the pillow. The heat was oppressive. Through the embroidered pillow case, the ticking, the pad of goosefeathers from

174

Riverview, she heard the thud of the first drops. She threw off the pillow and jumped out of bed. Rain! In the purplish sheet lightning she saw the first big drops hit the ground and dust puff out around them. She leaned out from the window as far as she could. Rain pounded her head and she turned to let it hit her face. Her cambric nightgown was soaked. It was pouring. A gully washer. A toad-strangler. She said the words over and over like an incantation.

Then in the purplish lightning she saw a strange sight. It should have been funny but it wasn't. Sometime she might have laughed, but now, with the drouth broken, she looked without laughter at the sight of Bushrod Sheridan in his long white drawers on his knees in the burnt-up yard, his face upturned, and the rain streaming down his black beard.

Chapter 16

Mary Hampton picked up the mail in Randall and brought it out. She wouldn't come in and she wouldn't go home. Instead, she sat talking from the buggy while Allegra fidgeted with the stack of letters in her hand. She finally smiled apologetically at Mary.

"I wonder if you'd excuse me if I just glanced . . . My sister . . . Some of the Kentucky kin . . . Brother Hod . . . No, no, don't go. Just a glance . . ."

"My land, go right ahead. My folks aren't much to write and when I do hear it takes me all day to read with Ma's hand so shaky. Hamp never writes to *his* folks. Puts it all on me and all I ever get from them is complaints about why don't they hear more often. Get so I hate to open up the letters, but . . ."

"Why here's one from Oklahoma City! Who in the world could that be?" Allegra held up a square envelope addressed in a curly backhand.

"That's the way I always do and Hamp gets outdone with me. He says, 'Open it up and find out.' But I tell him life's too short to cheat myself out of the pleasure of wondering. Like that debate at the literary, 'Resolved that Anticipation is More to be Desired than Realization.' I thought they did real good, though why a woman the size of Sis Pritchard wears that red dress . . . but, my land, maybe it's all she's got."

"Why this is from Bertha Mebane!"

"Kinfolks of yours?" Mary craned sociably out of the buggy.

"No, we roomed together at the seminary. Her folks lived in St. Louis and she used to go home with me for weekends. Her husband's in a bank in Oklahoma City."

"My land!"

"Oh Bertha's not like that at all. Not at all. You'd like her." Allegra read down the page. "Good gracious! She wants me to visit them for

176

a few days and go to a reception they're having. She says the governor'll be there . . . he used to be a banker and her husband knew him in a business way . . . and a lot of other people. And she's asked Lainey, too. They have two girls about Lainey's age." She folded the letter and put it back in the envelope. "But it's out of the question."

"I don't see why it is," Mary said excitedly.

"Oh, there's Sunny . . . Bertha doesn't even know about him . . . and Lainey's in school. And my clothes. I haven't had a new thing since I came here. I couldn't possibly go."

"Allegra Sheridan! You're going!"

". . . and besides, there's Bush to think about."

"Bush can eat at our place, and it's not going to hurt Lainey to miss a little school. Teacher said she was ahead of her class, anyway. And I'll keep Sunny. It'd be a real treat for me to have him."

"But my clothes . . ."

"We'll fix your clothes. You've got a trunkful and a sewing machine. Besides, Allegra, I think you owe it to Lainey to take her."

"Well . . . I hadn't thought of it that way. Maybe . . ."

Mary's brown eyes sparkled. "Just think, a reception and the governor! It'll be almost like I'd been there myself!"

"I'm having such a good time I'm ashamed of myself," Allegra admitted to Lainey as the stage left the Half-way House. "I shouldn't have let Bush sell those calves to send us, but he did insist so. If only Sunny stays well."

"Bush said for you not to worry." Lainey wondered if the Mebane girls would know her dress was made from an old coat-suit of Mama's.

"He'll be perfectly all right with Mary, but the first time you leave a baby . . ."

A sallow woman with dark-circled eyes nodded mournful agreement. "I know what you mean. Our children are in Missouri with my folks."

"Missouri? What part?" Allegra brightened up.

"Tobe County. My husband's attached to the Indian Agency," she said, gesturing toward the man in the wrinkled brown suit

177

seated across from Lainey. "I couldn't drag my children around to all the places he's sent."

"Why Tobe County's right next to Snyder County. Do you know . . ."

The game of matching friends and kin was opened. Lainey held back a yawn. She had been up before daylight helping with the packing, getting Sunny over to Hamptons', skimping through her chores, riding the ten miles to Randall. She dozed, then jerked up.

"Nice nap?" The man in the brown suit was watching her.

"I was just resting my eyes."

"I used to say that after church when my wife caught me asleep."

It was one of Uncle Hod's tricks. To have it turn up here made them seem acquainted.

"Mind if I smoke?"

"No, sir. I like the smell of a good cigar." It was what Mama always said but the man laughed when Lainey said it.

"You do? Down in Old Mexico the ladies' smoke 'em. Maybe you'd like to try one?"

She knew he must be teasing but she shook her head anyway. Smoke curled from his mouth. His wife coughed and flapped her knitted lace gloves.

"Really, Mr. Garton, not in here."

"I asked the young lady's permission, Maida. She likes the smell of a good cigar."

"Oh. Well, as I was saying," she turned back to Allegra, "*her* mother was a Clay . . ."

"Do you live at the agency?" Lainey asked.

"Part of the time. I travel around a bit."

"I know a girl who goes to school there. Her name's Annie Half-moon."

"Sac? One of Henry's girls?" He blew a smoke ring. "Do you know her mother?"

"A little. They live next quarter to ours. I don't think she wants Annie to go to the school." As soon as it was out Lainey wished she had not said it. A man who was "attached to the Indian Agency" might be angry to hear such a thing.

"Not many of 'em do," Mr. Garton did not seem upset. "They

178

have all kinds of dodges to keep 'em out of school. Then when the children do come, they run away. June or July, around Buffalo Dance time, a lot of them skip out."

"Annie ran off once."

"I know. I went after her. Her mother's a remarkable woman; I've known her for years. She's one of those who went back to the blanket."

The words had an odd sound to them. Was this one of those grown-up things that must not be asked about?

"Twenty years I've worked around Indians," Mr. Garton said, "and I still don't know all the answers."

"Mr. Garton, don't go filling that child full of your wild ideas!"

"You stick to your kinfolks, Maida, and I'll stick to my Indians. At least they don't scalp without a warwhoop."

"Mr. Garton is such a talker," his wife smiled but her eyes were wary. "He doesn't mean half he says, not half."

Mr. Garton blew another smoke ring and winked at Lainey.

The Mebanes met them at the station in Oklahoma City. Lainey was drooping with weariness but Allegra, under a blue velvet hat with the white birds perched on it, looked as trim as when she had started.

Guy Mebane was a small dry-looking man with a sandy moustache and a forehead that reached to the middle of his head. He had freckles on his hands, Lainey noticed as he picked up their suitcases, and matching freckles on as much of his neck as showed above his high starched collar. Mrs. Mebane engulfed Allegra in a wave of hugs, kisses, welcomes, reproaches, and plans. The girls were heart-broken, she said, not to meet the train but they were at a birthday party and would be right home.

Lainey hung back while Mr. Mebane arranged their baggage in the shiny black two-seater drawn by a pair of matched bays.

This was a far cry from their first arrival in Oklahoma City, and Lainey felt a flicker of homesickness for the covered wagon, the crowded wagon yard, Bud, and the Run. But as the elegant upholstery caressed her bare hand she could not help murmuring, "I like this, too; I like it all."

179

"Just like old times," Bertha Mebane squeezed Allegra's hand. "Only then I was always going to your house. Now, I want to hear everything, all the news. Tomorrow our ladies' club meets. Current events, you know. I cut a couple of items out of the paper for you just to have on hand."

Does she think we don't know anything because we live on a claim?

"Our house is on 10th Street. It's pretty far out but we like it that way. Friday there's a whist drive. I didn't know if you played so I said I'd let them know."

Mama plays a better game of whist than you do. She won the prize twice at Marney.

"Friday night our church's having an oyster supper to raise money for a new building. Every church in town is building, it looks like! And Saturday is the reception. The governor . . . a friend of Guy's . . ."

We've had governors at Riverview. They're nothing to get so set up about! Jeb Saunders could have been governor if he'd wanted to. Who cares? Who cares? Who cares?

"And a baby boy? I can't get over it. With Lainey almost grown! Well, we never know. How in the world did you get along, out there in the country?"

"Lainey stayed with me," Allegra said. "She did it all. Everything."

Lainey was torn between pride in the way Mama spoke and humiliation at the way Mrs. Mebane looked at her, as if she had done something improper. Unladylike.

Guy Mebane took the bays around a brewer's wagon.

"Drive down Main Street, Guy. Past the bank," Mrs. Mebane said.

"Nothin' to see. Way to look at a bank's to look at the statement."

"There on Grand is the Overholser Opera House," Mrs. Mebane came as near pointing as a lady could. "You'll meet them at the reception. Lovely people."

Main Street was crowded with stores, elbowing each other at the line of wooden sidewalks. In the windows Lainey glimpsed saddles, racks of china, furniture, shiny new pianos. Grocery stores had bushel baskets of produce outside. A meat market was distinguished by its screened sides and the bunches of rabbits dangling in front. But here and there were empty store buildings, too.

"Did the panic hurt the town much?" Allegra asked.

"Some," Guy Mebane said. "Things are better now. There was a time . . . Two banks closed, you know. Cleveland. Democrat."

"Now, Guy, Allegra comes from Snyder County."

"No offense meant, but the Democrats just aren't sound money men. There's the bank."

It was a solid, ugly building. Its very homeliness added, somehow, to a feeling of confidence. Gold letters gleamed on the front.

"Ought to go in," he fretted. "Got some letters . . ."

"Now, I simply won't have it. Allegra's here for a visit and the girls will be wild to see Lainey."

"Well," he drove on down Main Street. "Had a little trouble ourselves in the panic. Nothing serious. Bank's as sound as a nut. Sound as a nut." He rolled the phrase as if he enjoyed saying it. "After the others closed the rumor got around we were closing, too. Nothing to it. Sound as a nut. But those things get started. Well, sir, folks began comin' in for their money. Line of 'em from the cashier's window clear to . . . there." He pointed with his whip. "Run like that can break any bank . . ."

In his dry precise voice he recited the story. The leaders of the city agreed that the run must be stopped. If a third bank closed the town was done for. One of them agreed to appeal to the territorial treasurer to deposit territorial funds in the bank. It was a chancy thing, but time was running out. He took the night train to Guthrie, and in the morning when the line of frantic depositors stood at the bank door up came a mule-drawn wagon carrying money sacks. Armed guards walked down the line into the bank and flung the sacks in front of the cashier. He poured the silver dollars from the first sack onto a table, paying off a half dozen depositors.

"You could feel things loosen up. In no time at all the line was gone."

181

"What a splendid thing to do," Allegra said, "save the bank that way."

"Sure was," Guy Mebane gave a dry chuckle. " 'Specially as that first sack was the only one that had money in it. The rest had iron railroad washers." Lainey looked at him, pop-eyed. "It was all the money the treasurer could scare up that time o' night. But the iron washers did just as well."

"But . . . but . . ." Lainey stumbled, "but . . ."

"Folks in that line just needed to *see* money. Bank was sound as a nut."

Don't be afraid of money; having it or not having it, Bush said. Suddenly she liked the slight man with the freckles and the eyes that twinkled. "I wish you knew Bush. Bushrod Sheridan, my father," Lainey corrected herself as Allegra's eyebrows rose.

"I do too, Lainey. Bank needs a good man from that section."

The Mebane girls, Phyllis and Judith, were copies of their mother. Curls, fancy dresses, pink cheeks, giggles and squeals. They were ten and twelve and Lainey was fourteen. "About your age," indeed! They kept telling her about the birthday party, each interrupting the other to say, "But she doesn't know about that!"

During supper Lainey made up her mind to even the score. As she ate her way through the meal served up by Tenny, the Negro cook brought from St. Louis, Lainey selected details for her stories. Coyotes turned into wolves, Indian neighbors to marauding tribes, blacksnakes to rattlers and the deadly blue racer that could outrun a horse. She tossed in a few outlaws . . . well, didn't Mrs. Shipp keep a poker red-hot in the stove in case an outlaw showed up? . . . and lay in wait for the girls. They listened, wide-eyed. Lainey heard them whispering in terror in the room next to the one where she slept with Mama. Stiles Park and band concerts! Pooh! She punched down the big pillow. Why, I got an autograph album last Christmas from a boy! I wish I'd brought it along.

But the next day things were better. It was fun to be a visitor and not to have to do chores and worry with Sunny. While the girls were in school Lainey went shopping with Mrs. Mebane and Mama and in the afternoon she was supposed to rest while the

182

ladies dressed for the club meeting. She did lie down on the bed but she kept her ears wide open as Mama and Mrs. Mebane hooked each other up and admired each other's clothes. Mama was wearing the braid-trimmed drab to the club meeting.

"I ought to tell you one thing," Mrs. Mebane inserted a rat behind her pompadour. "Just don't be surprised if you see the same silver and china at different houses."

"You mean the same patterns?"

"No, the same articles. We do a lot of borrowing from each other. Things get passed around. I brought a dozen ice-cream forks when I came and I hardly saw them at all the first year. Susy Tower's after-dinner coffees were the same way. It's not like it was at first, but I've still got chairs promised from four houses for the reception."

Sharing wasn't just for the claim, then!

"The first meeting of our church society was at our house. I just didn't know what I was going to do for chairs. Fortunately, the husband of one of the members was in the grocery business. He sent up twelve wooden boxes." Mrs. Mebane peered at her coiffure. "Back home in St. Louis I wouldn't have thought of such a thing. But there, I promised Guy I'd stop saying 'back home.' He thinks the Territory is perfect."

"So does Bush," Allegra began coiling her golden hair.

"I'm having roses for the reception. There's a florist here now, but right at first we used wild flowers." She giggled. "All the color schemes were yellow, then. Sunflowers, golden rod, black-eyed Susans . . . But it was fun. Such fun."

"Do you ever think about going back home?"

Lainey stopped tracing the design woven in the counterpane.

"Only when I get at outs with Guy. Then I take the train every ten minutes. But I wouldn't really go. I love it here."

In a minute Mama would say, 'So do I.' Lainey waited, finger in the center of a Grecian key. Mrs. Mebane waited, too, but Allegra had her mouth full of hairpins. Before she took them out the doorbell jangled.

"Oh, good heavens! I'm not half dressed."

The night of the reception arrived. The day had been devoted to moving all the furniture out of the two front rooms, stacking it in the back yard, looking at the sky and declaring, firmly, that it would not rain. With Phyllis and Judith Lainey ran through the house, tasted small iced cakes, tried the punch, skated on the waxed floors and helped carry in the borrowed chairs.

Up in the guest room Allegra looked uncertainly at the dress over which she and Mary had labored.

"It looked all right on the claim, but I don't know . . . one of the ladies at the club who is coming is wearing a Worth model." The cream silk faille had been ripped, turned, the sleeves reduced to the vanishing point and the neck cut daringly low. Blue velvet bows looped the skirt and a dust ruffle of blue satin . . . once a coat lining . . . peeked from the edge. "If it only had a train! But you can do just so much."

Lainey suffered the same qualms over a plum-colored taffeta cut down for her from one of Aunt Ellen's dresses. The dark color seemed to go badly with her complexion and her hair appeared possessed to stick out the wrong way. Why had she ever let Mary Hampton wet it with water that had stood on quince seeds?

Bertha Mebane in brocaded black satin trimmed with cut-steel beads came into the guest-room door. "Will you hook me up? Guy's gone to get the musicians settled and the girls always get one hook off." As Allegra drew the black satin together, soft flesh bulged over the edges. "Oh dear, and I had this made for tonight. Now it's too tight already."

She surveyed the cream faille laid out on the bed. "Just perfect. You must have a wonderful dressmaker. But if you'll just let me . . ." She hurried away and came back with a pair of sixteen button blue gloves. "Your hands were always smaller than mine, but if you'll tuck in the fingers. And this feather boa matches."

For an instant Lainey saw a hint of Aunt Ellen's jaw line. Then Allegra laughed. "Well, Bertha, if you can borrow chairs . . . And my hands do look terrible. That boa will fill in the neck, too. Mary's scissors slipped and we had to cut it too low."

"Not with your shoulders!" Mrs. Mebane looked enviously at the white arms and throat and the swelling bosom held up by a high-busted corset. "I don't see how you do it." It was a question but Allegra only answered with a smile. Lainey felt the old ache to be as pretty as Mama spreading from her wishbone.

With a final desperate smoothing of her hair Lainey went out to join Judith and Phyllis in the hall. They were not to come to the reception but would be allowed to sit on the stairs and watch until eleven o'clock and then have refreshments. "And not one minute later. And if I catch you trying on coats the way you did last time . . ."

The girls were dressed in white embroidered organdy with blue sashes, their curls polished cylinders of brown hair. Lainey felt big and awkward beside them. The smell of cigar smoke preceded Guy Mebane up the stairs.

"Well, girls?"

Phyllis and Judith squealed and threw themselves on him. "Papa! Papa!" Lainey felt like an outsider caught peeping in a window.

"Mighty pretty dress, Miss Sheridan." She looked at him doubtfully. Nobody had ever called her 'Miss Sheridan.' He must be making fun.

"It's made out of an old one of Aunt Ellen's," she said, daring him to laugh.

"That's what I call smart. Girls, take notice." He tugged at their curls. "Now I had a little something for each of you. Don't know . . . may have lost 'em." He pretended to hunt through the pockets of his black evening clothes. Lainey stood very still. It was babyish to want presents. An outsider would not be treated like daughters. And pretty ones at that. "Here we are." From an inside pocket he produced white jeweller's boxes. There were three. In Phyllis' and Judith's boxes heart-shaped gold pins rested on white cotton. In Lainey's a four-leaf clover done in exquisite enamel. "To remember the occasion," he smiled.

"Is this for me?" Lainey wondered.

"For you. It's the color of your eyes."

He had noticed the color of her eyes! She threw her arms around his neck and kissed him. His sandy moustache tickled her. "Oh, thank you, Mr. Mebane! Thank you."

"Kiss a feller and call him 'Mister'?" he twinkled. "Uncle Guy."

185

"Thank you Uncle Guy!"

"Papa, I want one like Lainey's. I'm tired of having things like Phyl's," Judith complained. "I want one just like hers."

"Wait till you've fought panthers and Indians and outlaws." He left them.

Had they tattled or had he listened. It didn't matter. Uncle Guy knew what to believe and what not to. She touched the green enamel. Are my eyes really like that?

"Here comes the first hack," Phyllis reported. "It's from Duff's livery."

The arrival of guests at all social affairs was governed by the number of hacks that could be hired. Since there were not many in town it took a good many trips back and forth to assemble all the company. The dresses made Lainey stare. Tomorrow's evening paper would describe them: "Mrs. Clinton, gray taffeta, tinsel braid, gray gloves, diamonds. Mrs. Merton, blue taffeta, gold braid and buttons, white gloves, pearls. Miss Drayton, white Swiss, pink sash, rosebuds *en corsage*, white lace mitts. Mrs. Bratton, black silk, pointed basque, black gloves, jet ornaments. Miss Gurney, white corded silk, draped, lace bertha, violets. Mrs. Sterne, green plush, black gloves, diamonds . . ."

The cream silk faille looked perfectly at home. The blue gloves and the blue feather boa added an elegant touch. Uncle Guy had sent Mama . . . and I guess it's 'Aunt Bertha,' now . . . and Aunt Bertha pink rosebuds. The three-piece orchestra was placed on the canvas-enclosed porch to give more room for dancing. The receiving line dissolved and the gentlemen offered the ladies their arms. To the girls on the stairs it was like a kaleidoscope of silk, satin, velvet, lace, plumes, and jewels, moving to music. Lainey watched Mama dancing the German with a short dark man. She danced with the grace of a true musician and looked as if she had never seen a covered wagon, milked a cow, rubbed goose grease on a congested chest, or cleaned chickens.

People are . . . are different . . . to different people, Lainey thought, hanging over the stair rail. Mama is one person to me, and somebody else to Bush and somebody else to Aunt Ellen and somebody else to that funny little man she's dancing with.

186

But if that's so, then how can anybody ever *know* anybody? It was like the mirrors in the millinery store that show you looking into a mirror into a mirror into a mirror . . . down an endless corridor.

"See that lady in the yellow brocade?" Phyllis hissed. "She came here to get a divorce."

"Divorce? Oh." Lainey did not know what the word meant, but she would not ask.

"Came clear from Boston. You can get a divorce in the Territory real quick. Papa said it was a boon, but Mama said it was a shame. Mama didn't want to have her to the party but Papa put his foot down. He said he wasn't going to set himself up to be bigger than the Territory laws."

"I should say not." Lainey felt safe in that. Nobody was bigger than the law.

"There's the governor!"

The Mebane girls pointed excitedly at a quiet-looking man with curling moustaches and a half-bald head. He had arrived with a group of other men and Lainey couldn't see how he was different from the rest of them. She watched him, hoping for some special sign, something to report on the playground at school. A good governor, Bush said, a lot better than some of those fancy-pants boys who thought they were going to be struck by lightning. The governor shook hands with Uncle Guy, bowed to Aunt Bertha, and sat down on one of the spindly borrowed chairs. But he did nothing more exciting than to hitch his coattails out from beneath him. Lainey gave up and began to follow the figure of the lady in yellow brocade instead.

Suddenly the front doorway was filled by a big dark man in full evening dress. His black beard was closely trimmed and glistening, a cape lined in white satin lay casually across his broad shoulders. "Who's that?" Phyllis demanded. "I never saw *him* before."

This was the way a governor should look. Or a president. Or a king. The music had come to an end and the polite spatter of kid-gloved hands seemed to be for this stranger. He stood there, easy, smiling, and the light from the chandelier caught a glitter on his shirt front. Guy Mebane hurried to greet his guest and then a path

187

divided for them through the dancers. The lady in yellow brocade dropped her black lace fan. The big man picked it up, bowed as he handed it to her. She smiled.

"Who is it?" Judith asked. "Who do you s'pose?"

Lainey stood up on the stairs. She felt light as if she might float right down to the dance floor. There was no way to conceal the pride she felt so she didn't try but let her voice ring out above the genteel chatter below.

"That's Bushrod Sheridan, my father!"

In the guest room Lainey found she had been demoted from the big double bed to a small cot at one side. Tenny was making it up with grunts and groans.

"Just like Mist' Guy. Whole house full. Big party. Brings somebody new. 'Tenny, make another bed,' he says. How I gonna make 'nother bed?"

"It's her papa," Phyllis put the blame on Lainey.

"She calls him by his first name," Judith said with awe. "I'm goin' to call Papa 'Guy.' I want to be like Lainey."

Tenny rolled her eyes. "Nobody but trash do that. Nobody a-tall."

"Shhhhh, Tenny, she's comp'ny."

"Don' you let me hear you talk that way! Git for bed. 'Way past 'leven."

The music from below drifted into Lainey's sleep. Then she heard the door open and whispers and quickly muffled laughter. She sat up on the lumpy cot.

"Bush? Mama?"

"Lainey? What're you doing awake?" From the tone of Bush's voice she wished she had played 'possum, but it was too late. He groped his way to her cot. When he kissed her he smelled like the barber shop in Randall.

"Where'd you come from?" she asked him.

"The claim. Mebane sent word he wanted to see me so I came up."

Little noise of steel hooks and a long sigh meant that Mama

was coming out of the cream silk faille, the high-busted corset.

"I never saw you dressed up like that before."

"Oh? The monkey suit? Well, it's quite a tale. I dropped in to see Kate Tillery when I got off the train. Bud Menifee was there and he has a friend who's a dealer for a gambling house. This feller's about my size so they rigged me up."

"You'll have the whole house knowing," Allegra hissed.

"Oh, I told Guy. He thought it was a good joke. Wanted me to tell the governor."

"I don't see how you had time, the way that woman in the yellow brocade kept falling over you."

"Say, she's quite a looker! From the East and she wanted to hear about the Territory."

"She's here to get a divorce," Allegra whispered in scandalized tones. "Bertha didn't want to ask her but she has friends in St. Louis that know Guy. Ninety days for a divorce! I think it's awful."

"If you're going to get one, I don't see that it matters how quick."

"That's right. Take up for her."

"How's Sunny?" Lainey asked.

"Fine, fine." The cot creaked as he put his arm out into the darkness and pulled Allegra nearer. "You were the best-looking one there."

"In this old dress? Made over?" Allegra said.

"Dresses don't matter. Not a woman there could hold a candle to you."

"And when you came in the door you made all the men there look . . . piddlin'."

"Allegra . . ."

"Bush . . ."

They had left her. She heard them walking toward the bed, heard Bush swear as he kicked a chair, heard the low whispering go on, but it was all from some place far away where she had never been, could never go. She rolled onto her stomach and pulled a pillow over her head.

Chapter 17

The room was full of light when Lainey awoke. In the big bed Allegra slept with her golden hair tumbled on the pillow and one arm outstretched. Bush was nowhere in sight. His coming might have been all a dream, if she hadn't seen the satin-lined cape on a chair and the dent in the pillow by Mama's arm. Lainey crept out of the tangle of covers and put on her clothes. Then she tiptoed out into the hall. Downstairs last night's crowded rooms stood empty and forlorn. The borrowed chairs were stacked to be returned. Punch cups, washed and polished, were grouped together on the sideboard. In the middle of the floor Lainey tried a few waltz steps. It was like flying, easy to do in a dream but impossible when you were hampered by arms and legs. A whiff of coffee led her toward the kitchen. Tenny must be up. Then she heard the rumble of men's voices through the swinging door.

"A mighty generous offer. 'Specially, seeing's how you hardly know me."

"Knowing men's my business. The bank needs somebody who can judge land values. Nobody knows anything for sure in the Territory; it's all so new. Now, with the Strip lands . . . it's hard to make valuations."

"I've never done anything but farm. Worked in a general store when I was a boy."

"That's all to the good. We can hire plenty of clerks who know banking. What we need is a man who can look at land and tell us what it's worth."

"I'd have to think it over."

"Sure. Talk to your wife about it. And don't forget that girl of yours. Smart as a whip, and pretty, too. A year in the city . . . schools . . . advantages . . ." The clink of cups, the gurgle of coffee, and in Lainey's ears the pounding of her heart.

"How do you stand on statehood, Guy? Single or double?"

This had become a division point. Indian Territory, deeply conservative, openly opposed statehood, or reluctantly agreed to its possibility for the remaining Indian lands, alone. Oklahoma Territory at first strong for making the whole area a single state had now got its dander up and there was rising sentiment for going into the Union on its own. Statehood conventions held in every sizable town in both territories debated every shade of the question, occasionally ending in violence. It was an issue nobody could keep quiet on. And nobody did.

"I'm for statehood right now for Oklahoma Territory," Guy Mebane said stoutly. "We've got the money . . . the business . . . the potential . . . Indian Territory can come along or go hang! More coffee?"

"It's sure good coffee. I'm dead against you on statehood. I want to see both territories go in at the same time as one state. Why for one thing it'd give us more population than any other state's brought to the Union. But that's not really it. I just feel like this is Indian country and we all belong together . . . in or out."

"But doggone, Bush, they're stubborn. Kind of clam up and dig in . . ."

"Yeah, I know. But I reckon they've got plenty of reasons, the way things were in the past. I'd just like to see one place where . . ."

"Cigar?"

"Lord, Guy, it's been a long time since I smoked anything like this." There was a pause and Lainey could almost see him holding up a long brown cylinder in admiration. "When I smelled coffee this morning I knew you were my kind of man. Coffee 'fore sunup's the best cup of the day."

"I was raised to get up early. My folks back in Illinois were farm folks. Bertha clacks about it but I tell her the early bird gets the worm and it takes plenty of worms to run things the way she likes 'em."

"I never had any money," Bush said. "Still and yet, I get a lot of fun out of things."

"Take this place with us and you'll have both."

"It's just that . . . well, it sounds kind of womanish . . . but I'd hate to leave my claim."

The outside door creaked. "Good morning, Tenny."

"Lawd, Mist' Guy, comp'ny in the kitchen?"

"Best place in the house, the way you keep it. But we're finished now." Chairs scraped back. Lainey tiptoed through the quiet rooms. The sun was driving the smoky haze out of the sky. A hard maple sapling across the street burned like a flame. Sycamore trees dropped curls of bark and brown balls. Lainey sat down on the porch steps. Life in the city was fine . . . so far. And it had whatever Uncle Guy meant when he said, 'Advantages.' If he thought she was pretty, maybe other people in Oklahoma City . . . But the claim! And Jackrabbit School. And Arch. I'm fourteen and that's almost grown-up and I thought grown-ups knew what to do right away . . . but I don't. The claim? The city? The claim?

The men came out on the porch, their cigars rich smelling in the fall air.

"Now you folks ought to come see us," Bush was staying, "We'll do some huntin', Guy. Henry Halfmoon . . . he's the Sac Indian on the next place to ours . . . can find us a deer if there's any left. And there's still wild turkey. Quail. Lots o' rabbits."

"That sure sounds good, but I keep pretty close to the bank. Maybe, sometime. It's been years since I held a gun." He aimed an imaginary gun across the street.

Lainey saw Bush watching him, the shadow of a frown between his heavy eyebrows.

Bush and Guy went to town to return the borrowed suit of evening clothes and Lainey begged to go along to see Kate Tillery. Clucking to the bays Guy said, "Mrs. Tillery's one of our big depositors. A shrewd woman."

Kate was the same as ever, her welcome hearty, her clothes rough. Bud lounged by the round stove, whittling, and when Bush thanked him he grinned. "That feller owes me somethin'. Been cleaning me out every Sat'day night fer years."

Talk about business, crops, statehood began . . . man talk. Lainey wandered out into the wagon yard. Families who had spent the night there for the charge of fifty cents were getting

192

ready to pull out. She listened to them, remembering the Run.

"We came from Indianny. Figgered on the Strip, but we didn't make it."

"Got some kinfolks down in the Cheyenne-Arapaho. They spotted a place we can get relinquishments on. Left Tennessee a month back. Lord, it's a long ways."

"I was down here at Oklahoma Station before they opened the land first time. Now we're back to stay. They'll never miss us in Iowa."

"Back in '89 I sold a lot on Main Street for ten dollars and a busted gun!"

"We made the Run to the Pott country, but we didn't like it. But I spotted a piece in the Kickapoo . . ."

She tried to tell somebody that the Sheridans had come from Missouri to the Sac and Fox lands, but they weren't interested. Their eyes were big with their own dreams. Only a homesick woman from St. Joe took time to listen.

"Marney? I knew folks there. Lived down by the river."

Lainey edged away from her.

Kate was in the doorway saying goodbye. "Better take Guy up, Bush. Git tired of workin' for him you c'n always git a job with me."

"Well, maybe so. We'll see. Thanks again for the suit, folks. It cut a wide swathe."

They were back in the carriage going toward Tenth Street to pick up Mama. They drove up Robinson Avenue where the people, dressed in their Sunday best, were arriving at the churches. Guy's hat was off his head more than it was on as he bowed to those they passed.

"Good town," he said, switching his cigar from one side of his mouth to the other. "Be the capital of the state someday. Mark my words."

At Guthrie they changed from the train to the stage. As they settled down against the dusty cushions Bush fingered the fringe on Allegra's cape.

"Guy wants me to . . ."

193

"I know, Bertha told me."

Lainey, sitting across from her mother and father sharpened her ears. The claim? The city? I don't want to go! I don't want to leave the claim!

"What do you think?"

"It's hard to know what to do."

They sat in silence. The stage jolted ahead.

"A lot to be said for it," Bush tugged on the fringe. "Guy's a man that's going to get ahead. Even a country jake can see that. And I'd be working with land. And there's Lainey and Sunny to think about. Then I'd like to see you up there with the others. Last night sort of opened my eyes."

"I'm fine right where I am." She took the fringe out of his fingers and straightened it. "I just want you to be happy."

Lainey stared at the floor, not wanting to see in Bush and Mama's eyes what she feared she might. I don't want to go! I don't.

"The bank owns some lots in Maywood . . . that's a new addition. We could have them cheap."

"Bertha wants me in the ladies' club. And Lainey could go to that school her girls go to. There's talk of a ladies' music club later on." Allegra pressed her gloved fingers into her eyelids. "Let's not talk about it any more. Tomorrow."

Bush nodded. Lainey's fingernails were digging into the palms of her hands. I don't want to go! She practiced saying it to Bush. Mama. Uncle Guy. Aunt Bertha. The governor.

Only one more time on the long ride to Randall was anything mentioned about the change. As the stage scattered a covey of quail, Bush spoke up.

"I'm not what you'd call set on going huntin' all the time but it would seem kind of . . . of odd not to go if you wanted to."

"What are you talking about?" Allegra asked.

"Well, I asked Guy down for some deer huntin'. He said he'd like to, but he couldn't get away." He frowned, thinking. "Maybe that was just a polite way of saying, 'No thanks.'" He took hold of the strap and hoisted himself to another position. "Well, I reckon a man either has time or money. Hardly ever both."

The Hamptons met them at the drug store in Randall. Sunny bounced and crowed, his round nose rosy in the nippy air.

"Best baby I ever saw," Mary declared. "And he took his first step for his Aunt Mary."

"He didn't!" Allegra hugged the baby till he squawked.

"He did for a fact," Hamp said. "Your easy time's over. That boy kin walk!"

"Now tell about the party," Mary said. "And how did your dress look?"

"My dress was fine, thanks to you," Allegra took a page from her pocketbook. "This is what Bertha said would be in the paper. I made a copy."

Mary squinted in the fading light. " 'Cream of local society . . . Gentlemen in full evening dress . . . Ladies a blaze of jewels . . . Orchestra . . . Ices . . . Punch bowl . . . Roses . . .' Oh, here it is . . . 'Mrs. Bushrod Sheridan of near Randall, O.T., house guest of the Mebanes, wore cream faille trimmed with blue velvet.' " She sighed. "To think I put the bastings in that dress."

" 'Ices and punch' don't sound like much of a spread," Arch said to Lainey where they were sitting at the tailgate of the wagon.

"It wasn't," Lainey said, thinking of the table in the dog-run at Pritchards'. "Dab of ice cream. Little bitty cake. Tenny sneaked us some more."

"Who's Tenny? I thought they just had girls."

She knew with a pleasant quiver that Arch was jealous and delayed answering till the wagon rattled down a draw and up the other side. To leave the claim meant to leave Arch, too. I won't go. I just won't.

Bush helped Allegra and Sunny down while Arch and Hamp carried in the suitcases. Mary stayed in the wagon shouting remembered bits of news. Hamp hitched up his pants and said goodbye at the door, then, hesitating a little added, "Glad you're home. Neighborhood ain't the same when you folks ain't here."

Allegra ran her gloved hand down the door frame. Lainey saw it pause at the nick where the axe had slipped and cut Bush's finger and she had bound it up with lamp soot.

195

"I'm glad to be home, Hamp. I don't want to leave for a long, long time."

"You don't, huh? I thought all that fancy business might unsettle you. We talked about it, the wife an' me. We thought maybe you might want to leave the claim."

Allegra stamped her foot. "Is that all you think of me? That a party and a few silk dresses would make me give up . . . all this? I came to the Territory to make a home for Bush right here on our own land."

"Glory be!" Bush came out of the house where he had lighted the lamp. The soft yellow glow shone through the window. Lainey felt a need to sit down, her knees wabbling. "That's all I want to know."

"Don't stand there gabbin'," Mary called. "Allegra's tired out."

"I'm not tired," Allegra called back. "Not one bit. And I want you and Doggetts and Pritchards and Wellmans and everybody else that wants to to come over Sunday afternoon and we'll have a singing."

Lainey felt the chilly air grow warm and welcoming. She put her hand on the ground and patted the red dirt. Glory be! I don't have to leave. Glory be!

The night had gone far toward dawn when Lainey stirred in her bed under the roof and heard, or thought she heard, the sound of crying. Muffled, as if someone wept into a pillow. But it was hardly to be heard under the wind that sang around the hand-rived shingles. In the morning she had forgotten that she ever awakened.

Sunday afternoon at the Sheridan place became a custom. After preaching at Jackrabbit Schoolhouse . . . Brother Gordon came out from Randall . . . the neighbors drove on over to Sheridans'. Even some, like Jurd Morehouse, who never went to church found their way there, drawn by the music.

Allegra made them all welcome, and in turn she bloomed in her own hospitality. The wind, the sun, the hard water, and the endless work had roughened her white hands, stolen her pink and

white complexion, and darkened the shining crown of her hair.
Yet, as she sat down to play the organ, Lainey thought, Mama's
prettier than ever. I wish Aunt Ellen could see her now, the way
she talked about the Territory! The neighbors, too, found themselves liking Mrs. Sheridan who had been under suspicion of being
stuck up because of her fancy clothes.

"Common as an old shoe," they agreed with each other in high
tribute.

The first few singings were made up only of hymns. Several
families had copies of the *Old Sacred Harp Songbook* with its
shaped notes. Whatever song they began with, they always closed
with "The Parting Hand." When Allegra struck the opening chord
the young bachelors would sidle up to their chosen girls as they
sang.

> *"My Christian friends in bonds of love*
> *Whose hearts in sweetest union prove.*
> *Your friendship's like a drawing band,*
> *Yet we must take the Parting Hand."*

Then the families and the couples drove off across the country
on the long straight roads, or the little branching wagon tracks,
calling back to each other, "Goodbye . . . Take care . . . Come
see us . . . Take care . . . Goodbye . . ." They carried the
music with them all week long, mothers singing to their children,
men whistling as they struggled with the red dirt, boys and girls
straggling across the prairie on their way home from school. Until
the next Sunday.

One Sunday Sis Pritchard suggested that they sing, " 'Way
Down Upon the Swanee River." It wasn't a church song she admitted, but still . . . They sang the plaintive song better than
they had sung anything else for there wasn't a soul in the room,
except Sunny and the other babies, who didn't have a "far, far
away," to remember. The room was too quiet as Allegra's hands
slipped from the organ keys. Then she looked up at Bill Doggett
with a bright stiff smile. Did he know, "The Cat Came Back?"
Bill whose voice could call hogs from a mile away cleared his

197

throat and gave the rollicking song all he had. In no time everybody had joined in. After that it was easy to sing "Old Grimes" and "O Susanna!" Sis Pritchard sighed gustily.

"I declare, that makes me want to pat juba."

But nobody took up her hint and some of the more devout church members frowned. Dancing was the pastime of sinners and rich folks. Play parties might be all right . . . though there were those who called them Presbyterian waltzing . . . but not dancing!

In the fall of '94 Jurd Morehouse's uncle came to stay with him. A stringy old man from the Ozark hills, he brought his "dulcimore" to the Sheridan place one Sunday. Holding the slender, thin-bodied fiddle against his thigh, he swept its strings with a piece of leather. Allegra chorded as he played "song ballets" that had come across the country with the earliest settlers. Lainey loved best the mournful "Bar'bry Ellen" as he sang it, his Adam's apple bobbing over the collar of his hickory shirt. But Sunny had his favorite song, too. He begged for it each time.

> "Mama, Mama, have you heard,
> Papa's gonna buy me a mockin' bird.
> If the mockin' bird won't sing,
> Papa's gonna buy me a diamon' ring.
> If the diamon' ring is brass,
> Papa's gonna buy me a lookin' glass.
> If the lookin' glass don't shine,
> Papa's gonna shoot that beau of mine."

The little ones took over the singing at that and Lainey went outside to the porch where Arch and Jeff Doggett were deep in a game of stick-knife. She could see Arch was letting Jeff win because he was just a kid and pretty soon the little boy lost interest and went over to watch Pappy Vickers whittling a fork out of red cedar.

"I'll be glad when school starts." She watched Arch's knife bite a pattern into the dirt. "Miss Swenson's comin' next week. Cotton's all in."

"Yeah," Arch balanced the knife on the back of his wrist. "I'm

198

not going." He struck his wrist and the knife flipped and stuck upright in the earth. "Somebody's got to dig in and get us over the hump. Might as well be me."

Lainey sat very still, recalling bits she had heard from Bush and Allegra. A claim contest where Hamp had bought off the claim jumper instead of going to court. A note he had signed to oblige a no-good who had skipped the country. A debt back in Kansas. And now Arch who was at the top of his class had to quit and go to work. It wasn't fair! Miss Swenson said Arch ought to go to the University Preparatory School over at Norman. She thought resentfully of big, paunchy Hamp, always so willing to work for other folks. But if Arch felt resentment no one would ever know. He threw the knife at a cedar chunk and she noticed how the handle quivered as he threw harder and harder.

"I'll miss you. School won't seem the same."

"Listen at that ol' coot!" He jerked his head toward the house. Old man Morehouse's dulcimore whanged. The crowd sang with him.

> *"Took my gal to the party,*
> *Whaddya think she done?*
> *Sat right down in the middle of the floor,*
> *An' chewed her chewin' gum."*

"There's a party over at Wellmans' Saturday. Candy pull. Dad said I could have the buggy. Want me to stop for you?"

It was his way of telling her he didn't want to talk about not going to school. Usually they walked to parties, bunches of boys and bunches of girls. On the way home they might split up into couples. To go in a buggy with a boy was special.

"It would be nice to ride," she said.

"'Bout seven." He got up quickly and went inside and joined the singers.

> *"I wisht I was an apple,*
> *A-hangin' on a tree,*
> *An' every time my true love passed,*
> *He'd take a bite of me."*

Is Arch my true love? How do you know? Folks are beginning to say 'Arch 'n' Lainey' like 'meat 'n' potatoes,' 'bread 'n' butter.' Is that the way it begins? If he were a stranger it would be easy to know. Suppose a stranger came to Wellmans' party while they were playing post office and called for me. 'Special Delivery for Lainey Sheridan.' She shivered. Then I'd know. Right away, I'd know with a stranger.

Old man Morehouse came out on the porch flexing his fingers. "Little somethin' to wet my whistle an' I'd have 'em cuttin' up in there. Sunday or no Sunday."

Pappy Vickers laid down his whittling. "It might be managed." He glanced over his shoulder. "Didn't I hear tell you was with Johnston at Shiloh?"

"I sho' was." The bristly chin jutted. "Wanta make somethin' out of it?"

"Nothin' you couldn't swallow from a tin cup. Le's go."

The two old men jogged down the road. Allegra began to play "Juanita" and some of the singers hummed, dragging a little at the melody. Lainey leaned back against the house and let herself drift with the music. A stranger. Someone you'd never, never seen before.

"Far o'er th' mountain . . . breaks th' day . . . too soon . . ."

The party at Wellmans' was cut to a pattern. Every girl who came brought a pound of white sugar and Mrs. Wellman set it to boiling with water and a little vinegar. The girls, with fancy beribboned aprons over their dresses, pretended to watch the bubbling syrup when they were really watching the boys who hung around the door, shoving each other in and out.

Mrs. Wellman tested the candy with an iron spoon till it spun a hair, then poured the first batch onto greased pans and platters. Nobody ever waited until it was properly cooled, but began picking up the skim as it formed on top, screaming over burned fingers, and starting to pull much too soon. The boys crowded into the room and submitted to having their hands greased. Mrs. Wellman gave everybody blistering wads of candy to pull. Recognized

200

couples put theirs together, pulling from one hand to the other with much squealing from the girls and an occasional spill to the floor. A few earnest, unsought girls, like Doris Shipp, pulled their taffy to shining loops that Mrs. Wellman snipped into eating-sized pieces. Most of the others ended with a grayish mess on their hands, mouths, shoes, and clothes, that had to be eaten, scraped, or washed off.

After everything was cleaned up Mr. Wellman brought out a jug from which he got a tune by blowing. They played, "Old Dan Tucker," "Weevilly Wheat," and "Green Gravel," their sticky hands clinging together as they met, circled, bowed, and backed.

The tinny whir of the clock striking ten broke up the party and the stiffness of the early evening came back. The boys herded together again and the girls, saying, "Goodnight, I hadda nice time," to Mrs. Wellman, watched them out of the corners of their eyes. A few were confident they would be met outside and took their time arranging curls under fascinators. Others, resigned, pretended disdain.

Lainey, in the unaccustomed luxury of the Hamptons' buggy, watched the little groups of lanterns bobbing off across the prairie. It was silly, but she wished she could be with the girls, walking home, giggling over what the boys had said. All at once Arch seemed someone strange and she had nothing, nothing at all to talk to him about. He, too, sat in silence, but at least he had the horse to drive, the lines to hold. They were nearing home when he cleared his throat so loud she jumped.

"You cold?"

"Why no, I'm not. Not a bit." No sooner was it out than she regretted it. Dotty Sullavan would have said, 'Sure, hon',' and slid across the buggy seat. "I guess I am cold, a little," Lainey retracted feebly.

"I've got the buggy robe. Ma made me bring it." He flung its dusty length over her.

"Thanks," she sat muffled, stifling.

Silence for half a mile.

"That Bert George is sure a pistol!" Arch said.

"He sure is." She had known Bert for two years but she couldn't

201

think of a thing to say about him. She couldn't even remember what he looked like or where his folks lived.

The clip-clop of the horse's feet, the creaking of the buggy, the riffle of the wind.

"Well, here we are." Arch turned in at the Sheridan place and twisted the lines around the whip. Lainey wriggled out from under the buggy robe then waited as he came around and helped her down. A lamp burned in the house. Bush always waited up for her. Arch would say goodnight and she would go in the house and Bush would ask her about the party and that would be all.

"Thank you for taking me," she said politely. "I hadda nice time."

"Lainey!" His voice was deep, then it cracked and went high. "Lainey!" He caught hold of her and kissed her, full on the mouth. Not a post office kiss, not a forfeit-in-a-game kiss.

She stepped backwards out of his arms, her hand pressed against her mouth.

"Lainey," he said again, but she turned and ran, hurrying in the windy night up to the porch and the square of yellow lamplight. Once there she wanted to run back, but Arch had jumped in the buggy, jerked the lines free, and hit the startled horse a lick. "Goodnight," she heard him call.

Her hand was still against her mouth. She took it down and the wind made a cool print of Arch's kiss on her lips. Inside the house Bush was sitting in the rocker with his shoeless feet propped on the woodbox, his mouth open in sleep. She ought to go in and wake him so that he could go to bed and get his rest. But if she did he might look at her face and know. She climbed the ladder to her room, standing a long time on the top rung to stare out into the starry night where Arch had gone.

"Goodnight," she whispered to the wind, "Goodnight."

Chapter 18

"C'mon out, I've got somethin' to show you."

It was Arch calling, but whether to go or not, Lainey was not sure. It had been a week since the candy pull and he hadn't been around once. For three days she had kept the kiss a secret treasure to dream over, but when Wednesday passed and she hadn't heard from Arch she had told Doris Shipp. Just treat him cool, Doris counselled. That'll bring him to time. Boys don't respect a girl who's too easy.

Had she been too easy? The kiss became something to worry over. And now here was Arch, large as life and twice as natural, acting as if nothing had happened at all.

"Hey, Lainey!" At least he could come in the house. Out there bawling like a bull calf! "Laineeeee!"

"For goodness sakes be quiet," she stalked out. "Sunny's asleep. Mama and Bush went over to Pritchards' and I'm keeping Sunny and he's taking a nap."

"All right, but I've got somethin' to show you."

She tossed her head and started back inside. Then curiosity stopped her. "What is it?"

"That's for me to know and you to find out." She tossed her head again. He looked at her critically. "Say, have you got a crick in your neck?"

"There is *nothing* the matter with my neck." Be cool, Doris said, real cool.

"Well, you don't have to get so huffy about it. C'mon," he coaxed her. How blue his eyes were! If he'd only make his hair stay down. "Just down to Pappy Vickers' place. Sunny won't miss you if he's asleep."

"Well," she looked in the door at Sunny asleep on the big bed, his favorite rag doll beside him. "Just for a minute, then."

Arch led her down the road, refusing to answer a single question. Then he made her promise to stand with her eyes shut and for one delicious frightened instant Lainey thought that he was going to kiss her. But instead she heard him tramping away.

Quiet. The thin warmth of the sun on her back. The wind on her face with a smell of smoke from a far-off grass fire. Then the crackling of leaves and grass and the clean, sharp smell of a horse.

"Arch!" her eyelids flew open. "Where did you get her?"

He sat the palomino without a saddle. A long lean blond boy on a golden mare. Her creamy mane and tail were hardly lighter than his own hair as they tossed and tangled in the wind. In the lift of the mare's head was a pride that was echoed in the boy's blazing eyes. This is something perfect I'm seeing, Lainey heard a whisper say. Then the mare nickered and Arch's face turned red under its tan as if he had given away a secret without meaning to.

"Aw, I traded for her."

"Not Dumps?"

"Don't be a ninny! Of course not. Traded work and a little money, those two shoats that were the runts of the litter, the bead belt I got off Joe Wingbone, Dad's old grasshopper plow. Some other stuff."

"Look at the star on her head," Lainey crooned, "and her two white stockings."

"Fellow I got her from, over past Griffensteins', he got her off a Kickapoo that brought her up from Mexico. This man, he showed me how her hide matched a ten-dollar gold piece." He slid off the mare and put the reins in Lainey's hand. "She's lady-broke."

"I'd love to try 'er, but I'm afraid Sunny . . ."

"Just a canter. Her name's Beauty." The mare pricked her ears.

It was more temptation than Lainey could stand. She put her foot in Arch's cupped hand and mounted. Riding astride was not lady-like, but her skirt was long and full and there was no one to see. Even Pappy Vickers had gone hunting.

She rode to the dog-leg in the road, took a little turn in the track that ran up to Halfmoons' and came back at a rocking-chair canter. Then she put her heels to Beauty who went into a gallop. Lainey laughed in sheer delight at the mare and the fun of the surprise and the thought of Arch waiting for her. Horseless carriages indeed! She pulled up by Arch, breathless.

"Don't get off," he said, "she'll carry double."

He was up behind her, an arm around her waist, his other hand reaching for the reins. Lainey stiffened, remembering what Doris had said. Be cool; that'll bring him to time. She felt his breath on the back of her neck. What did Doris know? She'd never had a fellow. Arch nudged Beauty and she carried them to the house. He slid off and caught Lainey, lowering her slowly to the ground as if she were a delicate piece of china. She could not look up at him.

"Well, I better be goin'."

"Well, I better go see about Sunny."

Their words collided and they laughed foolishly.

"Wait just a minute," Lainey said and ran toward the house. Hunting for a reason to keep him she found none, but the words were hanging in the air. She'd bring out something for them to eat. Bread and pumpkin butter, if nothing else.

She was reaching for the bread when she stopped in her tracks. The house was empty! She knew it with such certainty that she did not even need to turn her head toward the big bed.

"Sunny, Sunny," Lainey whispered. Then, "Sunny! Sunny!" A scream brought Arch, running.

"He's gone," she said hoarsely, pointing to the little hollowed-out place in the middle of the bed. The pillow had slid to the floor.

"Maybe he's just hiding."

Lainey grasped at this straw of comfort and they ransacked the house. When there was no place else to look they looked again. And again. Arch stepped outside, came back, his face bleak.

"Foot tracks outside the back door. They look pretty fresh."

In the soft dust where the hens wallowed were the clear prints of small boots. The copper-toed boots Bush had brought Sunny from Guthrie. He loved them so much he would never allow them to be taken off for naps. A blurred print beside them was probably the dragging rag doll.

"He can't be far. I wasn't gone but a little while." Lainey's heart

205

squeezed. It must have been a half-hour at least. The rattle of the buckboard warned them that the Sheridans were coming home. Bush waved to them. Lainey hid her face.

"I can't tell them. I can't."

"I'll tell 'em. It was my fault. I tolled you off."

"They'll hate me. They love him best anyway."

"Hush that." Arch walked toward the buckboard, his shoulders leaning forward as if he were struggling against a strong wind. Bush and Allegra were admiring Beauty.

"I can't stand it!" Lainey cried and ran past Arch. "Bush! Mama!"

The story tumbled out, then Lainey repeated it, needing pain. She had left Sunny alone and he was gone.

"Now, honey, maybe he's just hiding. He did that one time." From the shelter of Bush's arms Lainey watched Allegra's face go white, then gray.

"When was it? How long?"

"An hour now, maybe longer," Arch said.

"Bush! Those Indians we passed!"

"Aw, they wouldn't do that. Likely he's in the barn, or down field."

"What Indians?" Lainey said.

"I don't know," Bush muttered, "Strangers to me. All gaumed up with paint."

"They do steal white children. That Quanah Parker's mother . . ."

"That was years ago. And they were Comanches; none of them around here. Arch, let's take a turn around."

It seemed hours until they came back. Bush put on a smile.

"Little scaper's gone further'n I thought. Found this by the cornfield." He held out the dusty rag doll.

"Dear God!" Allegra whispered. "Dear God!"

"Now, Mama." Bush touched her hand. Lainey had never heard him call Allegra that before. "You go on in the house and start supper . . ."

"Do you think I can cook a meal while my baby . . . while Sunny . . . I'm going to look."

"You'll just get yourself all worn out and worked up." But she

206

was halfway to the cornfield. Bush sighed. "I'll get Blackjack, Arch. You take your horse and round up a few of the neighbors."

"Yessir." Arch started for Beauty, then came back. "Don't be too hard on Lainey. It was my fault. I made her go. She didn't want to."

"I don't need you to tell me how to treat my girl," Bush snapped.

"I didn't mean that. I just meant . . ."

"I know. Go on an' get the neighbors. And for gosh sake, hurry!" The break in his voice sent a chill through Lainey's heart.

"Bush, you don't think those Indians . . ."

"I don't know what to think." He was looking toward the cornfield where Allegra's blue calico fluttered, her calling voice high and eerie, like a bird call in the night.

"Do you hate me, Bush?"

"No. You're my girl and you always will be. No matter what." He smoothed her hair. "But we don't want to lose any daylight. Get a bed-sheet and put it on a pole out the window."

It was a sign of distress. Nobody in the Territory ever passed by a house where such a sign was hanging.

Mary and Hamp were the first to come.

"He'll turn up," Mary said cheerfully. "Just strayed off. That's all. Now I'll hustle up some supper. Ought to light the lamps, too." Mary had an instinct for knowing where other people's things were kept.

Men and horses trampled the fields. Torches flared as night came on. "Eat a little soup," Sis Pritchard urged. "Miz Wellman brought it."

Lainey could not seem to swallow. A woman she had never seen sat down beside her and patted her hand, over and over.

"I gave my oldest boy the wrong medicine," she said. "Night-time, an' I got the wrong bottle. He never saw the light of day. That was ten years ago."

"No," Lainey whimpered. "No. No."

Mrs. Doggett pushed the woman away. "Don't give up, honey. He'll be all right. Bush and your mama have done too much good. God can't treat people that way!"

"Miz Doggett!" Mary cried, "don't say a thing like that!"

207

"I don't care! I mean it!" Mrs. Doggett squared her jaw. "If it hadn't been for Bush we'd be back home, stuck in that awful store, in debt, no chance to get ahead. He gave us his last dollar, an' I don't care who knows it. And the way she plays the organ Sundays . . ."

The woman plucked Lainey's shoulder. "He'd been sick a long time an' I was worn out nursin' him. He was frail from the first. They said it was for the best, but it wasn't. It wasn't. Ten years, come January."

A man walked in and led the woman away. "I'm sorry. It all comes back to her this way, times like this. We shouldn'ta come in, but we saw the bed-sheet."

"Poor soul," Mary Hampton said, "I guess it eases her to talk."

"I can't stand it," Lainey said, not caring that she spoke out loud.

"Yes you can," Sis Pritchard said, and the iron in her voice came strangely from her fat, cheerful face. Lainey remembered hearing that she had lost three babies from the flux, buried back home. "You can stand what you have to stand."

"We've been over every inch o' ground," Bill Doggett despaired.

"Don't you say that!" His wife flew at him. "There's some little place . . ."

"Those Indians . . ." Allegra spoke from the bed where Mary had forced her to lie down.

"Jim Renick's gone over to the agency," Bush gulped scalding coffee. "They'd know if any strange ones were around. But it don't stand to reason . . ."

"I wisht Henry Halfmoon was home," Pappy Vickers said. "He's a tracker from Trackersville. Or if I just had my eyesight back. One time on the trail . . ." His voice died off.

"Hot cawfee?" Sis Pritchard carried the pot around.

"I brought some gingercake, just in case," Mary Hampton said.

The coffee cooled in the cups. The gingercake sat, brown and solid, on the table. The night paled. Men mumbled to each other, 'Got to get home to the stock. Be back soon's I feed an' milk.' Curly Pritchard and his friends talked of raiding the Indian village. It had been hours since Lainey had seen Arch. She put on her coat and went out into the cold pre-dawn light. He was standing by Beauty, his head pressed against the golden neck. Lainey cleared her throat.

"Arch?"

"Yeah?"

Silently they stood together.

"If I'd just left you alone," Arch said. "Or brought Beauty to your place. But I had to act like a gawk."

"No, I was the one. I did it."

"I tolled you off. I had to show you how smart I was." His voice cracked and he leaned against the mare. "I can't stand it!"

"Yes you can. You can stand what you have to." The words made her feel stronger.

In the east the sky was white. The stars had disappeared. The rooster in the chickenyard beat his wings and crowed. Frost on the roof sparkled in the first rays of the sun. Mrs. Wellman came out to the cowshed and presently Lainey heard the milk talking to the bucket. Blue smoke puffed from the chimney. Sunny was lost, but the sun rose bright and tranquil above the blackjacks.

Mary Hampton called from the door. "Lainey, your mother wants to see you."

"Yes, ma'am."

I'd rather be killed. I'd rather be dragged by wild horses.

Lainey walked stolidly into the house, the neighbors separating to let her pass. Bush was at the table, head in hands, a cup of cold coffee with a sickly skim of cream by his elbow. Mrs. Doggett was on her knees at the organ stool, her back stubborn and unrelenting. The path to the bed where Allegra huddled under the silk crazy quilt was wide and long.

"Poor Lainey! Poor child!" Her mother's words fluttered past like brown leaves in the wind. "You must get some rest. I need you."

Unspoken words struck Lainey like a blow. I need you; you're all I have left. As she tried to back away Allegra pulled her down to the bed. Lainey wanted to say, 'Look what I've done to you.' Instead she laid her head on Allegra's breast and listened to the beating of her heart. Thud-thud-thud. They had been close the night Sunny was born. Now they were close again, the night Sunny . . . No, no. Don't think it. Don't give up. Thud-thud-thud, Thud-thud-thud. Then suddenly the thudding was no longer Mama's heart but the quick sound of hoofbeats coming up the road. Lainey lifted her head to see Mrs. Doggett come up from her knees, Bush shove back from the table.

Hamp yelled in at the door, "Horse comin'. Looks like . . ."

Bush knocked down the chair. Lainey thrust Sis Pritchard out of her way. But Allegra was quicker. They never knew how she got untangled from the quilt and out of the door before anybody else, but there she was running down the road toward the paint pony carrying Lydia Halfmoon on his back. With every stride the pony took, the blond curls of Sunny Sheridan bounced on the red blanket wrapped around him.

The paint slid to a stop. Allegra grabbed for Sunny who squealed in protest and hung onto the bright bib of beads around the Sac woman's neck. His face was dirty, his hair was matted, but hearing his voice Lainey knew with almost unbearable relief that he was sound and well. Reassuring the child in her own tongue, Lydia Halfmoon untangled Sunny's fingers from the beads and handed him down to Allegra. Bush caught both of them in his arms and Lainey let herself be pushed back by the crowd that swarmed around, talking ninety to nothin'.

"Little booger! Don't seem a bit scared."

"She found him in the strawstack? Likely that kep' him warm."

"Dogs led her to him, she says, I wonder they didn't harm him."

"She an' Henry been up to the stomp dance at the Iowa village. We shoulda known that."

"Bet he went down that dry gulch. I thought I saw a little old print there."

"Suppah!" Sunny called. "Suppah!"

They laughed, elbowing each other.

"Well, I don't want to hurry, but I got to get back to my place."

"Me too. Got work waitin'."

Mrs. Doggett, her pale face bright with triumph, called out, "It's the Lord's work, bringing him home safe. I knew He wouldn't do otherwise. I knew it!"

"Praise God from Whom all blessings flow! Praise Him all creatures here below." Bill Doggett started it and they all joined in.

Praise Him! Oh yes, now and forever! The terrible burden of fear Lainey had known was too much to be cast off in an instant but it was going. Going. Praise Him, and praise Mrs. Halfmoon who had brought Sunny home safe. And praise the neighbors who had held off the terror in the long night.

"Well," they said to each other, "well . . ." Work nagged them. They began to leave, pushing aside Bush's and Allegra's thanks.

"You'd do the same for any o' us," Sis Pritchard spoke for all of them. "I don't grudge a mite o' sleep. Only, you'd better put up a c'ral for that young'un."

"I mean!" Pappy Vickers said. "Hawg tight, hoss high, an' bull strong!"

Bush turned to Arch and took his hand. "All's well that ends well, boy. Go home and get some rest, then bring that mare back. I want to really look her over." Lainey watched Arch ride away. Some of the lift had come back to his head.

When all the others had gone Mrs. Halfmoon still stood watching Sunny, a smile deep in her dark eyes, as the little boy smeared gingercake on his face.

"I feel as if I'm going to drop," Allegra said. "Won't you come in and have some coffee with us? There's plenty on the stove."

Mrs. Halfmoon smiled shyly and ducked her head. They walked into the house, a tight little group held together by the terror of the night and not quite able to believe the fearful thing was over. Once inside Allegra busied herself at the stove and Lainey got down the Haviland cups. Bush sat, unmoving, with Sunny in his arms. No one noticed Mrs. Halfmoon until a sound came from the organ as she pressed one of the keys.

"Mu-sic box," Bush said, forming the syllables with great distinctness.

The woman nodded, smiled, looked back at the organ and forgot him. Forgot all of them. She twirled the stool and sat down, her long calico skirt sweeping the floor. The music book was open to Brahm's "Lullaby." Leaning forward she studied the music, pushing in one stop and pulling out another. Her feet moved on

211

the pedals, her fingers pressed the keys. She faltered, then began again. Allegra, open-mouthed, looked at Bush and Lainey. This time the music swelled softly, sweetly, filling the house with peace, banishing the lingering terror of the night. Sunny stirred, murmured, went to sleep. The pages of the music book flicked. Lydia Halfmoon was playing Chopin's "Valse No. 2," her earrings swinging to the lilting music.

"My Lord!" Bush whispered, "and I said 'mu-sic box.'"

Another page flicked. "The *legato* is hard here."

"I have trouble with it, too," Allegra said. "Where did you learn to play?"

"I went to college in Kansas. Before they moved us down here." The words came slowly and the shining black head did not turn.

Mrs. Halfmoon finished the Chopin, stumbling a few times at the end but going back until each note was perfect. They heard her indrawn sigh of happiness as she turned the page. Lainey half-rose in her chair to see the title. Beethoven's "Moonlight Sonata." She played it, then sat with her head bowed, the straight part in her hair reflected in the mirror above the music rack.

"My graduation piece," she repeated a chord absently. "I wore yellow satin."

"On Sunday afternoons," Allegra said, "the neighbors have been coming over to sing and I play for them. Would you come and play? Not a program, just a get-together."

For a long time the Indian woman sat, motionless. Then Lainey saw the long earrings begin to swing as she shook her head, 'No.' She stood up and pulled the top down over the organ keys.

"Please don't go," Allegra begged. "I didn't mean to stop you. You have no idea what it means to me to hear you play. The way you play . . . I . . ."

"I . . . I go home now." Lydia Halfmoon was out of the room and gone before anyone could say a word.

The wind scattered the dust the paint pony had raised and snatched a golden handful of leaves from the tree with the catface brand. Hens clucked in the chickenyard. Blackjack and Stretcher stood, hipshot, in the barn lot. The forgotten cow and the calf looked over the bars toward the pasture where they should have been grazing and blew discontentedly in the dust. Smoke from a grass fire this side of Taney drifted in faint blue layers. Peace lay over the Sheridan place. Sunny was safe.

Two weeks later, on a Saturday, Bush, having business at the Sac and Fox Agency took the family with him for the trip. The day was overcast and cold and at noon they made a fire and cooked bacon and coffee.

"It's like when we camped out on Deep Fork, after the Run," Lainey said.

"Only we have Sunny now." Allegra hauled him away from the fire. "If we'd had him then I'd never have made it."

"I wish he could have seen the Run, though. Or Randall when it was new."

"Randall's plenty new enough for me," Allegra said. "Main street's hub deep in sand."

"Oh, there've been a lot of changes," Bush said. "New barber shop. Striped pole and everything. And the Methodists finished their church."

"I hope Hamptons don't change off and go there," Lainey said.

"You'd miss having Arch walk you home from preaching."

It was fun being teased about Arch, but Lainey went on recounting changes in Randall. The post office was in a store now, instead of a shack. There was a hitching rack in front of the drug store for the stage to stop at.

"And don't forget the hotel," Bush put in. "The new brick one."

"You two!" Allegra laughed. "You ought to get together with Guy Mebane and talk about the Territory. I never heard such goings on!"

But there was no edgy bitterness in her voice as there might have been when they first came. Sunny had done what neither Bush nor the new country could. He had crowded Riverview, Snyder County, and even the Saunders family to the back of Allegra's mind. Wrapping the left-over food in a tea towel for a snack on the return trip, Lainey reflected it had been a long time, a really long time, since she had heard Mama say, "back home."

They forded Deep Fork and drove on to the agency, a group

213

of red-brick buildings with an air of authority about them. Once Bush had brought Lainey here on Allotment Day, the day when the quarterly payment was made to every man, woman, and child on the tribal rolls. What a sight to see! Reed-mat houses, cooking fires, the camp a riot of color. Indians dressed in their best, buckskins, broadcloth, red, purple, and blue calico. Beads and silver ornaments flashing in the sun. And more than anything else Lainey remembered the noise. The laughter, the shouting, the chanting of the women, the rattles of the dancers, the shouts of the *ko-nun-chuk* players . . . Never would she hear the book-term, "silent savage," without remembering the joyous uproar of that camp. But today the place was quiet. A few families camped back of the dormitories, but that was all.

Bush went into the low frame building where the firm of licensed traders operated. Allegra and Sunny followed but Lainey trailed behind, hoping to catch a glimpse of Annie in the dozens of pupils who marched back and forth from the school rooms to the dormitories, to the dining hall, to the model farm laid out to teach the white men's methods. A piano tinkled and through the window Lainey saw the agent's pretty daughter keeping time with her forefinger as she gave a music lesson to an Indian girl. It might be Annie; then again, it might not.

In the traders' building Allegra and Sunny were watching while a tall powerful Indian touched the tip of the pen with one finger as the clerk wrote his name. A skinny white man at the door was haranguing a Fox tribesman, holding to his blanket. "Creditors," the clerk behind the counter said. "Sell 'em anything on time, then hang on like leeches."

Across the room stood cases of bright beads. Ribbons and shawls crowded the shelves. Bolts of navy-blue broadcloth lay about in piles. Broad-brimmed hats with the Stetson label were stacked high. In another room Lainey could see layer on layer of tanned hides. The rank smell of them reached through the door.

Lainey nudged her mother as the front door opened. "It's Mr. Garton!"

"Good afternoon," Allegra said cordially.

"Why, good afternoon, ma'am. And it's the young lady who likes cigars." The same twinkle in the tired eyes. "My wife was saying only yesterday she would love to see you again.'

"I came in hopes of seeing her, but I wanted to see you, too."

"I'm delighted, though I'm not up on Snyder County, like Maida." He held the door open and they walked out, Sunny stepping on Lainey's heels.

"It's not about Snyder County," Allegra said. "It's about Mrs. Halfmoon, our neighbor." She told the story of Sunny's loss and how Lydia Halfmoon had brought him back and how she had come in and played the organ, then hurried away. "Why, it's almost as if she were frightened at the idea of the neighbors hearing her. And she's a wonderful musician. I can't understand it."

Mr. Garton patiently disentangled Sunny from his legs. "There might be those, Mrs. Sheridan, who would wonder to find *you* here. It isn't exactly the place . . ."

Allegra's eyebrows rose haughtily. "That's quite another thing. My husband . . ."

"I don't mean to be offensive, ma'am, but Lydia Halfmoon has a husband, too. It might be that she left your house so quickly because she didn't want to risk setting up a barrier between them. One she had once scaled."

"I'm afraid I don't understand. Henry Halfmoon's been at our house. He seems like a reasonable man. Surely, music wouldn't . . ."

"It isn't music. It's everything that goes with it. White people's clothes, houses, talk, thinking . . . that's it, mostly. The thinking." He frowned. "I don't often talk this way, but I think you'd really like to understand."

"Oh yes, I would. The way she plays . . . to be buried in the backwoods . . ."

"Well, I'm not sure that I understand it all myself, but it goes a long ways back. Lydia was her father's favorite. The old man got converted when the tribe was still in Kansas. He sent her to live with the missionaries because he wanted the very best for her."

Lainey pushed Sunny toward a rope swing, hoping to keep him quiet.

"They taught her to speak and dress and live as they did. And

215

they gave her music lessons. Presently they sent her to college. They tell me she was an apt pupil."

"I wish you could hear her play!"

"She was kind of a show-piece, I gather. Trotted out when visitors from the East came. I'm not criticizing anybody. A pupil like that is something to be proud of. But then the old man got sick. The rest of the family had died in one of the small-pox epidemics and he was feeble and he took consumption. Lydia came back to the reservation to take care of him. Life was pretty primitive there and you can see how hard it would be for her. She struggled along trying to live both ways. But even her language was different. The way she cooked. The way she nursed the old man. And as he got worse he turned more and more to the old ways."

"But what did she do?"

"She went back to the blanket, and being something of an artist she went all the way back. She put on Indian dress and she never wore the clothes she had at college."

The yellow satin dress! Lainey thought.

"When her father died she blackened her face with charcoal to mourn him. That was the first time I saw her. The people who had taught her felt she had let them down badly, but I don't know. She did what she thought was right. Then when Henry came along . . . he belonged to another band that wintered on Green River . . . they were married and they've had a good life together. I think Lydia is trying to keep it so.'

"But how about her children?"

"Oh, they go to school. But if they run off we have to come after them."

"But Mr. Garton," Allegra spoke slowly, "do you think this is all wrong?" She gestured at the school behind them, the model farm, the infirmary.

"No. It isn't wrong, but some of it may be mistaken. If we could just find a way. Half ours and half theirs." He took a cigar from his pocket, cut off the end, struck a match and let it burn out in his fingers. "Our hope lies in the children. Every generation we learn a little. But it's slow. Slow."

216

"Will she ever come back to our house? Mrs. Halfmoon? I want to be friends."

I don't believe it, Lainey thought. I didn't hear it right. But she looked at Allegra's face and knew that she had.

"I don't know," Mr. Garton said, "The thing to do is wait. If she comes it will be worth waiting for. The friends I've had . . . Chasing Hawk. Hole-in-the-Sky. Spring Frog." His whole face lighted up and he looked years younger. "I guess that's why I keep at it," he said. "I guess that's reason enough."

On the way home from the agency a buck deer flashed across the road. Lainey held Sunny up to see.

"Some venison would taste good," Bush said. "I'll get Henry and go huntin' next week." Then, "That reminds me, Guy Mebane sent word by the banker at Randall to ask if I'd changed my mind."

"Have you?" Allegra asked.

"Not as long as you're with me. And Lainey. And Sunny."

"I don't want to be anywhere else but with you," she said, and moved closer to him on the wagon seat. Lainey held Sunny tight, kissing him on his soft little-boy neck. She wanted to say how glad she was that they were on the claim to stay but the words stuck. Presently when Bush began to hum she joined in loudly.

> " 'Way down south on Beaver Creek,
> Sing-song-kitty-cantchee-ki-me-O . . ."

Chapter 19

Fall was over. Not a single dagger-pointed red leaf remained on the sumac. The golden hearts of the cottonwood had shivered and whirled to the four winds. Winter was short, but cold and blustery. Clothes froze on the line. Bush cracked ice in the pitcher on the washstand every morning. Thin patches of snow sometimes made a new pattern on the woolen log-cabin quilt on Lainey's bed. Allegra complained that Sunny was driving her wild, cooped up in the house, but if she let him go outdoors he was back in five minutes with his hands and feet aching.

This year Lainey was ready for Christmas. There would be no shilly-shallying about whether to give Arch a present. He would have one and it would be store-boughten.

Last spring she had planted castor beans and by summer they had grown to a towering crop. Since Bush had hired a Negro family from Sweet Home to help with the cotton, Lainey had more time to hoe and cultivate her patch and the harvest of reddish-brown burrs was bigger than she dreamed it would be. She put them in a popping pit, her stomach queasy at the smell, and took the oily brown beans to Randall. The money she received for them had been in her keepsake box since fall, but it had been so hard to earn that she could not bear to spend it quickly.

Now, with only two weeks till Christmas, Lainey went to Randall with Bush. She knew by heart the entire drug store stock, but she examined it again before buying Arch a razor with a white celluloid handle in a splendid imitation leather, green velvet-lined case. The rest of her presents could wait until the next trip.

"Do you think he'll like it?" She unwrapped the razor on the way home.

"Sure he will," Bush laid his thumb on the blade. "I'll put an edge on it with my hone."

218

"The man said it came from Germany."

He handed it back to her. "Arch shavin' pretty reg'lar now?"

"I . . . I . . . don't know. The man said it was just the thing for a young fellow. I think Arch's going to give me a comb and brush set. I told the man which one I liked, in case."

When they got to the house they were half frozen. The smell of sassafras tea and newly baked teacakes reached out and welcomed them. Allegra was beaming.

"Right after you left," she said, " I stepped out back to pour some hot water in the chicken's trough and when I came back there sat Lydia Halfmoon! I didn't hear her knock or call, and I really don't believe she did. We visited a little and pretty soon then she went over to the organ and played awhile. Then I baked some teacakes and made some tea and we ate and she left."

"I've heard that's the way they do," Bush said. "Come and go."

"I wouldn't like it," Lainey said. "I hate somebody coming up on me."

"Well, it's sort of surprising," Allegra said, "but with a friend . . ."

"That's right," Bush said, "with a friend it's different."

As the months went on Lydia Halfmoon came more and more often to the Sheridan place. Appearing without a sign, she would go over to the organ, play a little, talk a little, and disappear as quietly as she had come. Bush and Lainey never saw her, but they could tell when she had come by Allegra's delight.

"She's so . . . restful," Allegra told Mary Hampton as they sat patching shirts one afternoon in late June. "When I hear her play I feel better, even if I'm half-dead from ironing. And Sunny's just crazy about her. She's taught him to count."

"*Nicote, neese, nessay, ne-a, ne-o-len,*" Sunny rattled off.

"My land, and him only just past three," Mary marvelled, setting tiny stitches in a three-corned patch. "You folks going to the Fourth at Randall?"

"Bush wants us to. I'd as soon stay home, but you know him."

For weeks the *Randall Recorder* had been publishing accounts of the plans for the Fourth of July. Parade. Basket dinner. Program. Patriotic speaking. "Buffalo chase" by the Indians of the Sac and

219

Fox Agency with wild Texas cattle. Horse race sponsored by the fair association. And at night a platform dance.

"I wouldn't miss it for anything," Mary examined the patch. "All but the dance. We don't hold with dancing. We're certainly not going to let Arch go."

Across the room, Lainey, reading the last book sent by Uncle Hod, clamped her jaws tight so as not to laugh. For the youngest Pritchard boy had been over this very morning with a note from Arch asking her to go to the dance with him.

"Oh, I don't know," Allegra said. "Dancing's not bad in itself."

"Maybe not, but the things it leads to . . ." Mary hinted darkly. "Anyway, Hamp's put his foot down."

Lainey buried her face in her book. Hamp was too easy-going to put his foot down on anything. She had a new white mull with a pink sash and she was going to take it to the picnic in a box and ask Mama if she could go to Eastmans' and dress for the dance. Merry Eastman was sure to be going and reasonably sure to ask Lainey to spend the night with her.

Eastmans came from Snyder County, too, though quite a ways east of Marney. Aunt Ellen had written Mama about them and they had struck up a friendship with the Sheridans. Trips to Randall were more fun, now that they could go to Eastmans' house. Merry had lots of clothes, a piano, a pony and trap, and a bedroom with bird's-eye-maple furniture. She belonged to the Jolly Mandolin Club, besides.

"Lainey, pay attention. Mrs. Hampton spoke to you."

"Oh don't bother her when she's reading," Mary said from the door. "I was just going to ask her to see to it that Arch starts home earlier. He was out till nearly eleven Friday and got up before day to work for Jim Renick. I thought if Lainey . . ."

"I'll tell him," Lainey said demurely. Eleven! Arch must have shoved the hands of the clock back the way he'd told her he'd done before. It was twelve when he brought her home from the home-talent play at Taney schoolhouse.

"See you at the picnic," Mary called back. "Goodbye and take care."

The Fourth of July was hot, bright, and clear. Allegra shuttled from the house to the wagon, checking off things on her fingers.

"Fried chicken. Bread. Butter. Potato salad. Green beans . . . leave those on the stove till last. Tomatoes. Don't forget the salt and peppers."

"Pappy Vickers won't eat tomatoes." Lainey slipped the hand-painted salt and pepper shakers into the tub. They were so much more elegant than the old tin ones in case Merry Eastman brought some of the Jolly Mandolin Club around. "He says he won't eat anything a hog won't eat."

"Apple sauce. Peach pickle. Chocolate cake . . . I hope that icing will stand this heat. I made that peach pickle from the first clingstone peaches Gervais' raised."

Gervais? Lainey had to stop to remember. The Run was a vivid picture in her mind, but the people who made it up were getting fuzzy when she thought about them. All but Arch. She knew exactly how he looked when she ran into him.

"Stop mooning and put that smear-case in the bowl. You've salted it twice already."

"I sure hope Doris goes to the celebration at Shawneetown."

"Hand me the bread-knife. I thought you and Doris were such big friends."

"We are, but she gets mad if I talk to Merry and Merry thinks Doris is funny. And they both get put out at me if I . . ."

"Did you pack the cracked plates?"

"I put some plates in."

Allegra dug into the tub. "Well! If you think for one minute I'm going to have those Haviland plates broken just because you want to show off . . ."

"I hate those old cracked plates!"

"That Haviland could never be replaced. I want you to have it in your home, some day."

A blush warmed Lainey's face. She lifted out the Haviland and replaced it with the old cracked brown-stained plates. Then she took out the hand-painted salt and pepper shakers. My home. My own home.

221

"Laice Saunders brought those dishes from Kentucky," Allegra ran her finger around the edge of a plate. "I brought them out here. I wonder where *you'll* take them?"

My own home. Lifting the plates back to the top shelf of the safe Lainey thought of the stranger she had dreamed of as Allegra played "Juanita." When he came she would know him for her love and go with him forever.

Outside Pappy Vickers broke into a song, a relic of his days on the trail.

> *"O, it's mornin' noon an' night boys,*
> *There's somethin' you must do.*
> *It's jack the wagon up to grease,*
> *Or a limpin' steer to shoe.*
> *Or else some other blasted thing,*
> *Until you want to die.*
> *It's whack the bulls along, boys,*
> *Root hawg or die!"*

"Root hawg or die!" Sunny echoed.

"Do you hear that?" Allegra asked, as Bush sloshed his face at the washbowl. "He copies everything Cap'n Vickers says."

"Why, the boy's the apple o' the old man's eye."

"But his language. And that awful white mule he drinks!"

"Don't worry about it now." Bush mauled his face with the roller towel. "I want to get to Randall before the sun gets to bearin' down. Find a shady place to hitch. Buy my gal some red lemonade." He kissed Allegra on the back of her neck.

"Bushrod Sheridan! What will Lainey think?"

"I dunno." He kissed her again. "I'll ask her next time she spends an hour tellin' Arch goodnight."

He looked expectantly at Lainey but she was covering the mounded washtub with a white tablecloth, smoothing the folds as she sang under her breath, *"Soft o'er th' fountain . . . ling'ring falls th' southern moon . . . Far o'er th' mountain . . . breaks th' day . . . too soon . . ."*

The road to Randall was well-marked now. Grass no longer brushed the bellies of the team. Boulders where wagons had once

222

faltered had been dug out or by-passed. Wild game rarely broke cover now at the sound of wheels. Plank bridges had been thrown across the little creeks or the dry washes that were growing imperceptibly deeper, year by year. Every mile or so you could see a house. Lainey, on a kitchen chair behind the wagon seat, was proud that she could name the family in every one. As they drove to town her thoughts sped backward . . .

In the fall it would be five years since the Run. There had been three land openings since then and each group of settlers felt a distinct superiority to the latest set of newcomers. Lainey had ridden her new mare, Nellie, over to Deep Fork with Bush in May of 1895 to watch the opening of the Kickapoo lands. And she had felt like an old timer as she surveyed the covered wagons, the mounted men, the scattered women and children and the blue-coated soldiers. Her new side saddle, a present from Riverview, had creaked as she leaned toward Bush.

"I wouldn't trade our place for anything in the Kickapoo, would you?"

"Huh?" he had fidgeted with the reins. "Oh, no, no. I reckon not. Steady, boy, steady." Blackjack was moving nervously, arching his neck. "Still . . . there's somethin' about new country . . ."

The hands of Bush's watch were nearly together now. The line of mounted men was tense and quiet. The Kickapoo opening would start any minute.

The gun had sounded and suddenly Bush dug his heels into Blackjack and took out as if the Devil himself were after him. Splashing through Deep Fork, urging Blackjack up the other side, jockeying through the slower wagons and buggies, he had made his way to the front of the line. Watching the tall man on the black and white horse, Lainey did not realize she was pounding her knee with her fist, or that tears splashed down on her new jacket. Bush rode a half-mile into the Kickapoo country before he had wheeled and come cantering, shame-facedly back.

"Just wanted to see. Just wondered if I could."

"You were 'way out in front. You could have had any claim in there."

He looked as if he wanted to believe her but he wouldn't let himself. "Nope. We wouldn't have lasted." He shoved back his hat and for the first time Lainey noticed a finger-wide streak of gray cutting through his black hair. "Or, maybe there's just one Run in every man and horse."

In the barn as they had hung up the saddles she saw him slip Blackjack an extra measure of feed. "Long as I live, old boy, you've got a place in clover."

The Sheridans heard Randall long before they saw it. The town boomed, crackled, hissed, and thudded with gunpowder. A half dozen young men raced out on horseback yelling and firing pistols. They divided and tore around the Sheridan wagon. Dust like a red blanket rose and settled.

"My hat! The lunch!" Allegra wailed.

"Young whippersnappers," Pappy Vickers grumbled.

"Boys will be boys," Bush pounded dust from his coat. "Hope they were firin' blanks."

"I'm sure I forgot the pickled beets," Allegra fretted.

"Are you sure you brought enough chicken?" Bush asked. "I'd hate to come up short if anybody stopped by."

"Nobody ever went hungry at my table. I wasn't brought up to skimp comp'ny!"

"All right, all right. I was just askin'. I didn't mean any harm at all."

A terrific boom came from the north end of town. The team tossed their heads.

"I bet that's the anvil at the blacksmith shop. Arch said they were going to fire it."

"Sounds more like somebody dynamited the jail."

"I hope they got plenty of ice water," Pappy Vickers said piously. "I got a thirst, I could drink the creek dry."

Back down the road Lainey was sure she saw Beauty's golden hide. Arch had bargained with Hamp to do the early chores if he could stay late for the dance. Hamp had agreed if Arch just wouldn't let Mary know he had given in. Lainey stood up to wave, spilling Sunny and his precious package of firecrackers out of

224

her lap. A red-wheeled buggy cut around them. Miss Swenson waved from beside Curly Pritchard.

"Wellmans asked her down for the Fourth," Lainey supplied. "Miss Swenson wants me to go to the college at Edmond and learn to be a schoolteacher."

"There's plenty for you to learn at home," Allegra said. "The way your room looks . . . a regular hurrah's nest. I'm half sorry Bush put in those inside steps."

"You went off to school. You went to the seminary."

"That's different. A girl's school. If we could send you back there . . ."

"I don't want to go back there. I want to go where Merry and Anna May and . . ."

"Now don't start that up again," Bush said. "We're here to enjoy ourselves."

Lainey subsided. Allegra shaded her eyes with her hand. "I declare that gray horse coming up looks like Eastmans' new horse. But why would they be leaving town?"

The dappled gray came smartly up to the wagon, flinging his head so that foam flew from the bit. Merry was calling excitedly before her father said "Whoa!"

"Lainey! The most wonderful thing! Evvy Thomas has come down with the mumps!"

"That's not a very nice thing to say," Joe Eastman grinned.

"But it's true, Papa. Hardly anybody has mumps in the summer and here she is, all swelled up like a poisoned pup, and that leaves us one short for the girls in the States-of-the-Union float. Papa's on the committee and I got him to say we'd get you, Lainey. It's to ride in the parade and be up on the platform at the program. If I have to sit by Gwenny Bean I'll die! Please Mrs. Sheridan, please let Lainey. Pretty please."

"But I was counting on Lainey to help with Sunny. And what about a costume?"

"Just a white dress, and she can wear one of mine. We have red, white, and blue sashes that go across the shoulder and have the name of the state in gold letters. And we'll both help with Sunny after it's over. Please!"

225

"I brought my white mull," Lainey said excitedly, "in case I got to go to the dance. You said there was no harm in dancing and Arch asked me. So I have my dress!"

"Well," Allegra frowned, and then laughed. "It looks as if I'm out-numbered. Go on, but behave yourself. Joe, tell Eleanor I'm looking for you folks to eat with us. Don't bring a thing. I've got worlds of everything."

"That's mighty fine. We'll sure be there, and I've got a freezer of cream packed down for this afternoon. C'mon, girls," Joe Eastman looked at his watch. "Parade starts in one hour, sharp."

They were almost in town before Lainey remembered she had promised Arch she would watch the parade with him from the bank corner. Well, he'd just have to like it or lump it. She wasn't going to turn down a chance like this.

There was only one flaw. It came to light as Merry and Mrs. Eastman hurried Lainey into the white mull. "Which state will I . . . was Evvy . . . going to be?"

"Rhode Island, dear," Mrs. Eastman said. "Turn around and I'll hook you up. The sashes are all just alike. Couldn't be told on a galloping horse."

Rhode Island? The smallest of the forty-five states. A pink dot on the map.

"Which is Merry going to be?"

"Texas," Merry said promptly, "but Rhode Island has a lot more letters and I'd rather be you because, think of the gold."

The States-of-the-Union float was on Hawkins' dray, smothered in red, white, and blue bunting. Mr. Hawkins' big Percherons, Doll and Babe, had streamers on their harness and every bit of brass was polished to a high gleam. The states sat on planks balanced on nail kegs. Right back of Mr. Hawkins stood Genevieve MacDouglas, robed in yellow taffeta with a sash twice as wide as the others, emblazoned, OKLAHOMA TERRITORY.

"Pull," Merry whispered to Lainey. "Her father gave the sashes."

In front of the float was the Randall band. They had no uniforms, but each man wore a rosette of red, white, and blue in his coat lapel and the wind tossed the ribbons gaily as they marched.

Prrrrrum-tum-tum. Prrrrrrrum-tum-tum.

226

Drums rolled, horns blared, a triangle clanged. The band leader started off at a fast walk, looking anxiously over his shoulder. Doll and Babe leaned into their collars and as Mr. Hawkins chirruped to them the float began to roll. The states grabbed for each other, got their balance, straightened up, each one extending her decorated bosom in a ladylike sitting-down-strut. Rhode Island might be little but she was going to be seen. Lainey edged up on the plank, smiling sweetly at the crowd.

The main street of Randall was lined with people. They cheered the band, cheered the floats, cheered a boy with tight-checkered pants who threw a firecracker at the bass drum. Down with the British! Up with liberty! Hurrah for the Boston Tea Party, the bridge at Concord! Hurrah for George Washington and Thomas Jefferson! Hurrah for freedom and independence! And hurrah for Oklahoma Territory! Hurrah! Hurrah!

Lainey searched the crowd for Arch. She shoved her hip out against Merry who was taking up more than her share of the plank. No one was going to push Rhode Island around! Where could Arch be?

The band began playing "John Brown's Body," and Lainey hoped Pappy Vickers was out of earshot. Four boys on bicycles rode around the float, toiling in the sandy street. "Scorchers!" Mr. Hawkins growled. On a second float, prepared by the Women's Relief Corps, Liberty stood on a pedestal with Justice, Peace, and Mercy crowded around her feet. A drum and bugle corps from Taney came next. Behind them Al Colwater . . . sheriff of the county now . . . rode his black stallion, his chill gray eyes searching the crowd. Then came the Ship-of-State float and then came the old soldiers.

They marched together not as men who have practiced but as men who have fought. Only a few of them had uniforms. A campaign hat, a strip of tarnished gold braid, a pair of patched calvary boots, here and there. The years had taken their toll of the trappings of war, but the old soldiers were still unmistakable. They had fought; they had seen men die and that was uniform enough. Antietam. Chickamauga. Bull Run. The Wilderness. They had carried the flag before them, and now, years later in Oklahoma

Territory, as the western wind whipped out that flag against an incredibly blue sky they remembered the battles they had fought and the crowd along the hot dusty street remembered, and there was glory in remembering.

"*John* Brown's body lies a'*mould*'ring in th' *grave*." The band blared and the old soldiers stepped out heavily on the downbeat. "*John* Brown's body lies a'*mould*'ring in th' *grave*." New country. New battle. Sod, soil, and drouth instead of men this time, but a fight all the same. And the same flag. "*John* Brown's body lies a'*mould*'ring in th' *grave*, but his *soul* goes marching *on*."

Pappy Vickers and old man Morehouse stood at attention as the flag passed. Our flag, too, boys. We fought on the other side, but somehow we loved it too. We fought for what we thought was right and the old flag's always stood for that. You were good boys and good fighters. Just a leetle too much for us, that was all. No reason not to pull together out here in the new country. ". . . but his *soul* goes marching *on*." Hate those words, but, man, who cares. It's a good tune. Not's good as "Dixie" but there ain't none as good as that. Le's go have a drink to a new star in the old flag. Gonna be one, sure's you're born!

"Stop shoving," Merry said out of the corner of her mouth. "I'm nearly off the plank."

Lainey leaned the other way momentarily, then slipped back. There's Pritchards. And Bluebell Shimer with Pug Barton! There's Doris and she won't even wave! But where is Arch? We're nearly to the bank corner now.

The bank corner was behind them. In front of the drug store a man lazing against the door frame caught Lainey's gaze and held it. His tall, motionless figure stood out in sharp contrast to the pushing, shoving crowd. Mr. Hawkins pulled up Doll and Babe to keep from overriding the band.

The *Randall Recorder* said people were coming to the celebration from everywhere so there was no telling who he was but Lainey was sure she had never seen him before. She would not have forgotten that hair that gleamed like a crow's wing, and the dark, dark eyes that held secret laughter. A wide-brimmed tan hat swung idly from one hand and Lainey sensed without actually seeing that he was wearing cowboy boots. Look someplace else, she ordered herself. Don't go on staring.

"Who's that?" Merry nudged her.

"Who? Where?" she lied.

"Over by the drug store, you goose. Looking right at you."

Lainey deliberately looked at the hardware store that had been freighted down from Kansas. "Do you mean Arden Lawrence?"

"Not him! The one right over there!" But Merry had jumped like a grasshopper. "Do you know what Arden had the nerve to write in my autograph book? 'The ocean's wide and you can't step it. I love you an' you can't help it.' I told him I'd tear it out, but I didn't. Oh, there's my folks." They both waved.

"Grab aholt, girls," Mr. Hawkins touched Doll with his tasselled whip. Oklahoma Territory wobbled, found support on Massachusetts' shoulder. Texas and Rhode Island helped Ohio back in her place. When Lainey looked back the man was gone.

Chapter 20

The picnic was held in the same grove in which the first church services had taken place. Acres of tablecloths and sheets were joined together making room for everybody. Every woman brought her best cooking and looked with apprehension at the dishes next to hers.

Mrs. Otto Hiersch's yellow crock of celery-seeded kraut sat beside the mould of sweet cream butter Lili Gervais had wrapped in grape leaves. State-of-Maine apple turnovers made room for sliced ham cured by an Old Dominion recipe. Green beans cooked down with salt meat filled a black kettle that had swung under a wagon on the road from Arkansas. A hickory-nut cake that was the pride of Oak Valley, Iowa, towered over a pan of ginger cookies famed in Dutchess County, New York. "Shorrrrtbread," a woman from Scotland announced as she put down a blue willow plate of crusty squares next to a platter of Tennessee summer sausage. Smear-case, potato salad, boiled eggs . . . some of them colored in beet juice . . . every kind of pickles; tomatoes that ranged from great scarlet globes big enough to fill a pint measure to little cherry tomatoes, the size of a man's thumb; cucumbers, Spanish onions sliced in vinegar, corn relish. And fried chicken. Crisp, crusty brown heaps that were offered to everyone in sight. "Have a piece of ours. Just a wishbone. Turn that back over; there's a liver hid there."

As this was election year, candidates for office travelled up and down the tablecloth taking a bite here, a piece there, a slice somewhere else. The Republicans were strong around Randall, but the Democrats had made a fusion ticket with the Populists that gave them double strength. William Jennings Bryan, coming out of Nebraska with his flaming oratory, had captured the imaginations of the homesteaders. No matter what their politics, they loved the way his ringing phrases clothed the cause of the common man in glory.

The men gathered around the stock tanks where cakes of greenish ice floated in the drinking water. Dust soon covered it with a reddish film, but it was easy to grab one of the dippers tied to the tanks, push back the dust and gulp a drink. Children ran everywhere, a drumstick in one hand and a hunk of homemade bread and butter in the other. Young men and girls in separate groups strolled endlessly through the grounds, plotting elaborate schemes to meet by accident. They would split up into couples after dinner; in the meantime they eyed each other and drank red lemonade.

Allegra caught Merry and Lainey walking past, arms around each other, giggling. "Now you two sit down and eat. I won't have you filling up on trash."

They filled their plates and ate, stopping to smother laughter, watching always for Arch and Tubby Merton. If Lainey looked for someone else, besides, no one ever knew. Allegra ate with one hand, waving a tea towel with the other.

"I can't stand those flies!"

"Have to eat a peck o' dirt before we die." Bush reached past her. "Those tomato preserves are mighty good, Edras. Wish my wife had the receipt." Mrs. Wellman blushed.

"You won't eat 'em at home," Allegra said. "And a peck of dirt doesn't mean *flies*."

Down the table a dozen places a young woman chewed up food for one baby while she nursed another and buttered bread for an older child. "I don't get much chance to enjoy myself at a picnic," she said to a neighbor, "but I do get off the place."

"I mean!" A woman with a stairstep of dark-haired children chimed in. "My youngest's been ailin' for a week but I brought 'im anyway. Go crazy stayin' home all the time." She brushed the flies from the face of the placid baby "Love his heart! And he's so good with it all."

"Allegra, these beet pickles are delicious," Mrs. Eastman said.

"The Quaker lady from the mission's here," Mary Hampton

said. "She brought some little Indian girls. They bowed for grace before they ate. Made me ashamed."

"She's a pure wonder," a man with a Texas drawl spoke up. "Comin' down the road the other night I heard a team rattlin' along. There she was settin' bolt upright on the driver's seat, sound asleep. Trained those little old mouse-colored mules to take her home, an', by gum, they were doin' it."

"Mama, Merry wants me to spend the night and go to the dance with her. Can I? May I?" Lainey had picked her moment to ask. For Allegra had her hands full fanning flies, sampling Lili Gervais' spiced gherkins which had wandered down the tablecloth, and trying to keep an eye on Sunny who had darted off after a stray dog.

"What? Oh, chase those flies off that cake! Why, I guess so. Go after Sunny."

"I knew she would let me if I caught her right," Lainey said. Then she and Merry found Sunny at the water tank where he was trying to "give the poor doggie a d'ink."

"I went down to the city to hear Bryan," Joe Eastman forked over the platter looking for white meat. "Finest speech I ever heard. Three hours long."

"This free silver," Bush said. "I'm not sure I get just what they mean."

"It's like this," Joe tucked a bite in his mouth. "Say I've got a million dollars stashed away. The gov'ment ups an' changes the ratio of coinage to sixteen to one . . . the way Bryan wants 'em to . . . why then I got just a half a million, but my debts an' mortgages'll be cut in half, too. See?"

"If you got a million dollars, Joe, or even a half-million, you got no business with debts an' mortgages."

"That was just a manner o' speakin'. If the gov'ment . . ."

"I don't figger it's up to the gov'ment to get me out of debt. If I got in, I'll get out. I'm from Misouri, you got to show me."

"Missouri or not, you're for that Free Homes Bill, tail an' hide."

"Why they'll get that back in taxes. I've improved my quarter, haven't I?"

"Now you look ahere, Bush . . ."

232

"Look here, yourself . . ."

"Joe!" Mrs. Eastman shook his arm. "Remember what I told you."

"Bush! You promised!" Allegra said. "Politics on a day like this."

"Don't know a better day for politics than the Fourth of July," Bush grumbled.

"We were just talkin'," Joe reached for the chocolate cake. "Women ain't got a bit o' sense about politics and here they want the vote."

"Mama, I'm going with Merry. The states have to get lined up for the program."

"All right. Hold up your shoulders. Don't stay too late at the dance. Do whatever Mrs. Eastman says. And be sure to get back here to help me pack up."

"Yes, ma'am." Lainey dropped a kiss on Allegra's cheek and ran after Merry. Near the water tank she saw a tall man in a tan hat reach for a dipper. She stopped to re-tie the bow of her ox-blood slippers. When he turned around the sight of his grizzled yellow hair and the whitish film over one eye struck her like a blow.

The states sat in rows behind the speaker's stand on the bunting draped platform. In front of them the Boy Orator of Deep Fork in knee pants, a dazzling white shirt, and a flowing tie recited the Declaration of Independence.

"When in the course of human events . . ." his clear young voice rang out. Young words, spoken long ago by young men who dared to make a new country. The listening people felt a sense of kinship with history. ". . . And for the support of this Declaration . . . we mutually pledge to each other our lives, our fortunes, and our sacred honor."

A roar of applause. The chairman lifted his arms. "Th' Star Spangled Banner!"

The crowd came up like the opening of a giant, rainbow-colored umbrella. They sang the first verse, mumbled the others, and came in strong on the chorus. A young lady elocutionist wept over "The Dying Drummer Boy." Ten little girls in starched white dresses moved cautiously through a drill carrying hoops wrapped

233

in red, white, and blue. The dappled shade over the platform disappeared. The sun blazed down. Jewels of resin oozed out of the planks. Lainey moved experimentally and felt her dress stick to the seat. She could see Arch and Tubby off at one side. She had made it up with Arch while they rode on the merry-go-round about not meeting him at the parade. The speaker, imported from Guthrie, acknowledged a flowery introduction and started in to fight the Revolution from Concord to Yorktown.

Lainey pleated her program into a fan and shaded her eyes. She had looked at every man in the crowd and not a one had the dark hair and the secret smile of the man she had seen in front of the drug store. Not that it mattered, but it seemed as though a stranger who had come to town for the Fourth of July would surely come to the picnic and the speaking. She counted the white spots on her nails. If they came out even, she would see the stranger as soon as she looked up. If they came out odd . . .

". . . from the rockbound coast of New England," the speaker shouted.

I could count the cracks in the platform. Even or odd, Lainey thought. Or monkey them out. Monkey, monkey bottle of beer . . . then however I come out, when I look up he'll be looking right at me.

". . . men like Ulysses S. Grant!" The old soldiers cheered. "Robert E. Lee!" Pappy Vickers gave a Rebel yell. "Andrew Jackson and Thomas Jefferson!" The whole assembly applauded. "And George Washington, father of his country!"

One, two, three, out goes *he,* Lainey counted. But I'm not going to look up right now. I'm going to do it over, then I'll be sure. Monkey, monkey . . .

". . . and the flower of this great country, united and indivisible. The latest, greatest commonwealth, the soon-to-be state, the Territory of Oklahoma!" The shouting and applause seemed to shake the red hilltop. Lainey found herself clapping till her palms stung.

"That girl you told me about, that Dotty Sullavan's over there making sheep's eyes at Arch," Merry whispered under the cover of the applause. "Don't look now!"

The moon dimmed the lanterns around the dance platform. The fiddlers made Randall ring with music. The high-pitched voice of the caller swung the dancers through the figures. Lainey's white mull dress fluttered as Arch whirled her and his arm lingered around her waist.

"Behave," she whispered, "or I'll go dance with Arden Lawrence."

"Do and I'll beat his brains out. If he's got any!"

He thinks he owns me, Lainey seethed. Just because he lives on the next claim. And why can't he make his hair stay down?

At the edge of the lantern light a tall man with a tan hat looked down at a girl with red curls. Dotty Sullavan! Lainey craned her neck, stumbled.

"Get yo' pardners for the next dance!" the caller shouted.

"How about it?" Arch asked Lainey. She saw with quick distaste the streaks of sweat on his face. Dancing was hard work for Arch.

"I'm tired," she said, and it was true. She had looked forward too long to the day and the night. Now that it was here nothing was as good as she had thought it would be.

As they left the platform Dotty Sullavan was coming up. From a fat silver heart that dangled almost to her knees on a silver chain came waves of perfume. Over her head Lainey looked into smiling secret dark eyes.

"Don't block the landing," Dotty sniffed. "Other folks want to dance if you don't."

Lainey ran down the remaining steps, through the circle of lantern light, past the flaring torches into the black and silver shadows. Arch was following, his boots clumping on the kicked-up ground.

"What's the matter?" he panted.

She did not answer for there was no answer. Only a need to get away. But Arch would not let her go. He ran along at her side. She slowed to a walk, hating the questions he was sure to ask.

Instead he said, "Thanks for getting us away. Too hot to dance anyway, and that crowd's going to get rough."

235

He guided her listless steps up the empty, echoing board sidewalks to a side street that wandered off through the trees. The houses scattered along the way were dark. The fiddle music and the calls of the dance came to them as if from another world.

"Black as the inside of a cow," Arch said, dodging a low branch. "Want to go on over to Eastmans'?"

"No, it's too early. Merry'll be mad if I get home first and wake up her folks." She matched her steps to his. They walked, swinging hands, as they had walked coming home from school. The Fourth of July was like a fever that had come and gone, leaving Lainey peaceful and weary. "Let's go over to the point."

The point was an outcropping of rock from the shallow soil of the hill, a favorite place for town couples to walk on Sunday afternoons. It was deserted now, shut off by the scrub oaks from the town. Arch and Lainey stood, leaning against each other, looking out into the night. In the valley a creek curled through the bottom land.

"Remember how it was, right at first?" Arch said. "The Run and all?"

They shared this thing between them. The Run. Hundreds of others shared it, too, but tonight it seemed as if the memory was theirs, alone. She was conscious of Arch's arm around her as they perched on a rock, but she did not make even a token objection. The wind was sweet and cool. Why had she acted so crazy? Running off at the dance?

"Wheat's going high this year," Arch said. "Might carry cotton up with it. Corn's doing pretty good, too."

Lainey waited, half afraid of what he might say next. Then, when he said nothing at all, she wanted to urge him to go on. A mocking bird on a treetop down the hill filled the night with almost unbearable sweetness.

"I've rented a forty from Jim Renick," Arch said finally. "With luck I'll make it through to grass. Next year . . ."

She knew what he was saying. That by next year Hamp's debts would be paid. By next year he would be his own man. Next year on the Fourth of July she would be seventeen, going on eighteen. That was grown-up. Next year was a long time. The days stretched ahead endlessly. Now, something in her whispered, *now, now.* But Arch said nothing.

At last Lainey sat up straight and tucked back in her pompadour the strands of hair that had been loosened by the wind. She picked up a chip of sandstone and tossed it down the hill. Before it fell some imp made her ask, "Who was that with Dotty?"

"Huh?" Arch came back from a dream. "I don't know. Some swamp angel."

"Let's go," Lainey said crossly, "There's no sense sitting around here all night."

They found the path and walked over to Eastmans with its width between them. Merry and Tubby were waiting.

"Where've you been?" Merry hissed. "We looked all over for you. Mama's dropped her slipper three times and you know what that means."

"G'night, Arch."

"G'night, Lainey."

"Thank you for a nice time. The merry-go-round. The lemonade. The dance."

"Oh sure . . . Uh . . . Lainey?"

"Hmmmm?"

"Oh, nothing. G'night."

Lainey was glad when the boys were gone. Glad Merry was so excited over Tubby's kiss that she wanted to talk about nothing else. Glad, so glad, that the Fourth of July was over.

It was a long time before she went to sleep. A rooster in the lot behind the house crowed twice. Lainey slipped from her bed to stand at the window. The moon was gone; the stars were faint. A lone man on horseback trotted by. A pistol shot or a left-over firecracker exploded in the distance. An intolerable longing swept over her, but for what she did not know. Climbing back into bed beside the sleeping Merry she pulled the sheet tight over her shoulders.

Chapter 21

Lainey was cleaning her room. She had dragged everything out from under the bed, dumped the dresser drawers, unloaded the nails behind the curtain, and now she was looking at her belongings with disgust. Indians are smarter, she thought; they have a giveaway every now and then. She picked up the smocked challis Aunt Ellen had made the year they came to Oklahoma Territory. She had kept it, meaning to "do something with" the smocking. Had she ever been small enough to wear it? Holding it up against herself Lainey looked in the mirror. The stubby braids had disappeared into a hair-do that was brushed up and pinned with a pink bow. She was a foot taller, and though it wasn't a thing to think about, she didn't need the "fluffy-ruffles" some of the girls wore to pad themselves out. Only her eyes were the same. Peering into the mirror she wished they were either green or brown.

The sound of buggy wheels coming up the road drew Lainey to the window. It was Miss Swenson! Giving the room a final desparing look Lainey kicked part of her clothes under the bed, jammed the drawers back in the dresser and went downstairs.

She met Miss Swenson at the gate, noticing how she hesitated, the dark circles under her clear gray eyes, and the little extra accent in her voice that always came when she was upset.

"You mother? Iss she home?"

"She's out in back hanging up wash. Sunny's had running off of the bowels and we've washed every day this week." She blushed, aware of the indelicacy of her talk. Miss Swenson seemed hardly to hear her. "Come in the house, please. I'll get Mama."

Allegra came in, blinking from the brilliant July sun. "You can say this for the Territory; it's no trouble to dry clothes!" She hung her apron on a nail. "I haven't seen you since the picnic, Miss Swenson. Did you enjoy it?"

238

"The picnic? Oh yess, yess. Just fine."

"I thought the parade was nice. The program was a little . . . well, you know."

"Yess, yess. It was all good."

Sunny came in and crawled up in Allegra's lap.

"He hasn't been himself for days." She smoothed the sweaty curls back from his forehead. "Not since the picnic, really."

"D'ink," Sunny burrowed in Allegra's lap. "I wanna d'ink."

"Say 'drink,' Sunny. Say 'drink' for Miss Swenson."

"D'ink," Sunny said, his lower lip out.

"Draw some fresh water, Lainey. A cool drink would be nice for all of us."

Lainey passed around the best glasses filled with water from the well outside the back door. Sunny grabbed at Allegra's, spilling half the contents.

"Never mind, it'll dry out in a minute."

Miss Swenson set her glass on the table. "Mrs. Sheridan, I came to ask you . . ."

"Lainey, take Sunny outside to play."

It was the same as saying out loud, 'You're too young!'

"No," Miss Swenson said, "don't send her away. Lainey iss my friend. She won't tattle."

Her pride restored Lainey dampened a washcloth and busily sponged Sunny's hands.

"If it's anything about the school, I can call Bush."

"Oh, no, please." The fingers of Miss Swenson's hands laced and unlaced.

The clock ticked. "Is it about Curly Pritchard, then?"

"Yess!" A sigh of relief. "But how did you know?"

Allegra smiled. "The whole school district knows."

"Oh!" Miss Swenson's hands flew to her face but between the fingers Lainey glimpsed the painful red of her cheeks. "All right, it's true. I love Curly. He loves me. He wants us to get married. But back home, before I came to the Territory, there was Ole. We grew up together. My family . . . his family . . . the same town, even, back in Sveden . . . same church . . . same school." She paused, then went on. "Before I came I gave him my promise and

239

he gave me his mother's ring." She fished a chain out of her pocket and from it dangled a gold ring with a claw-set pearl. "Then . . . I met Curly."

"Have you told Ole?"

"No. That iss what makes it such a . . . sin. Gus, my brother in Guthrie, he will not let me. Ole keeps writing. By now he has the money for our marriage. Gus says I must go back and marry him. Gus says if I marry Curly our family can never hold up its head again. He says I promised and that I am . . . bad."

Allegra's nodding frown of recognition brought echoing back to Lainey the thing Bush had said. 'Your Mama had a fellow too, Tom Bridges.'

"He says . . . Gus says . . . Curly is a no-good nester."

. . . 'A hired man,' Cousin Martha May had said. 'A hired man!'

"Our mother iss old and feeble. Gus says it will kill her if I marry Curly. But I love Curly. I l-l-love him." Miss Swenson put her head down on the table and burst into tears. Allegra stroked her clenched hands.

"You poor girl! You have been having a bad time. I didn't think anybody else . . . but there, I guess we never do. Go on and cry; it'll do you good. When you get finished we can plan the wedding."

"Wedding?" Christina's eyes, set in tear-wet lashes, were like gray stars.

"You must have a wedding and if your brother's set against it you can have it here. A blue dress, I think. White's not very practical with all this red dirt."

"Then . . . you think it's all right? For me to marry Curly?"

"There's only one reason to marry a man . . . that you love him. If you're sure . . ."

"Oh, I am sure! But my family? And Ole?"

"Your family will get over it and so will he. But if you married Ole not loving him, or worse, loving Curly, he'd never get over it and neither would you."

"You make it sound . . . so simple."

"It's not simple. Loving a man is the most mixed-up thing there is. But if you love him, go with him. No matter what." Lainey

240

watched Allegra staring through the door at the heat waves shimmering over the field. A dust devil whirled past the door and spun up to the sky.

Four days later a red-faced, bull-necked man jerked his team to a halt at the Sheridan place. Miss Swenson was sitting beside him. Climbing down from the driver's seat he heaved a humpbacked trunk over the tail-gate of the wagon into the road. Then with a jerk of his head he told Miss Swenson to get out.

As Bush came from the barn calling a greeting the man roared, "Your vife, she done this. Christy vas a good girl. Now . . ." he spat a word at his sister that needed no translation and stumped back to his seat.

"Shut up," Bush said. "You can't talk like that to anybody on my place."

"I talk to my sister like I please. She's crazy. She act like a loose voman. She marry that nester, I cut her off. Like that . . ." he dusted his palms.

"Please, Gus, please!"

"I give her home, get her yob, now she act like this!" He glared at his sister. "One more chance I give you. You go back home an' marry Ole like a good girl?"

"I can't," Miss Swenson whimpered, "I love Curly."

Swedish and English exploded in the glaring noon sunlight. "You keep Christy, then," he yelled at Bush. "Your vife, she done this!"

"She can stay here as long as she wants," Bush said, "but I'll take no lip outa you about my wife. Get off my place before I beat the livin' tar outa you!"

Bush's voice had risen to a bellow. Lainey and Allegra clutched each other in the door. Miss Swenson screamed, hiding her face in her hands. Gus grabbed the heavy wagon whip, lashing at Bush, then at the team. The horses leaped forward. A cloud of dust racketed down the road.

Bush ran for the house, his face deadly white except for the red welt that cut across his cheekbone and disappeared into his beard. As he grabbed for the Winchester Allegra caught him by one arm, Miss Swenson by the other.

241

"Get outa my way! I'll kill the son of a gun! Hit me with a whip, will he? I'll kill him!" He shook off Miss Swenson but Allegra clung on. "Let me get Blackjack! Let . . . me . . . go . . ."

Lainey dashed out the back door to where Blackjack stood saddled. Jerking off the bridle she loosened the cinchstraps and pulled the heavy saddle to the ground. "Git!" She slapped the horse on the haunch, heading him to the open gate. "Git, boy, git," she pleaded. He rolled his glass eye at her, trotted down the road, then halted. She picked up a clod and threw, "Git!"

The uproar in the house had quieted but Bush still held the gun. The welt on his face had raised and darkened.

"Don't do it, Bush," Allegra begged. "Christina'd never get over it!"

"Nobody horsewhips me!"

"It was all my fault," Miss Swenson cried, "I'll go back and marry Ole. I'll do anything, only, please, Mr. Sheridan . . ."

"You'll do what?" Bush said, startled. "You'll marry Curly Pritchard if I have to hogtie and hobble you!"

"There," Allegra loosed her hold on his arm. "Get some sweet cream, Lainey. I'll make a poultice."

"His blood would be on my head," Miss Swenson's lips trembled. "When we were little he vas so good to me. I have a doll he carved. And when the snow vas deep he carried me to school on his back. It's just this makes him so . . . so . . ."

"Put the gun back," Allegra directed Lainey. "I don't want to spill cream on it."

Bush was reluctant to let the Winchester go. "I don't want all that goo on me. It wasn't much of a lick. Just the tail-end caught me."

"Now for goodness' sake, don't anybody tell Curly about this," Allegra said. "We don't want the wedding spoiled by a shooting."

"I swear," Bush tipped his face back to keep the sweet cream out of his beard, "I don't understand women a-tall."

Lainey went back outdoors to whistle Blackjack home. The little humpbacked trunk sat in the road like an abandoned child. Lainey had tugged it over to the fence and was perched on top of it when Curly Pritchard came up on his strawberry roan. His yellow moustache was thick, now, curling at the ends in a way that put a perpetual smile on his face. He was bigger, heavier than before. He had quit the wild bunch he used to run with and worked his land harder than Ab did. At the sight of the trunk his face beamed.

"I got word *she* might be along," he said, as if there were only one girl in the Sac and Fox country, in the Territory, in the world.

"Miss Swenson's in the house with Mama," Lainey said primly.

Bushrod Sheridan came out the door, walking toward them with his easy, loping stride.

"Hi, there, Curly-boy. Just in time to give me a hand with the baggage."

"Moses in the mawnin'! What hit you?" Curly's eyes squinted. "You have any trouble with that big hunk o' . . ."

"Got in a hassle with that durn cow o' mine," Bush passed his fingers tenderly along his cheekbone. "She shoulda been soupmeat long ago. Hop off the trunk, Lainey."

"Yessir," she watched the men carry the trunk to the door. How good Bush was! No wonder Mama loved him. No wonder the neighbors came to him in trouble. Bush was . . . well . . . he was just Bush, that's all.

The sewing machine whirred. Allegra mumbled around a mouthfull of pins. Mary Hampton whipped on lace. Lainey was in charge of bastings.

"I declare, I think it ought to be at the schoolhouse," Mary said. "I know a dozen that would bake cakes. And there's lots of flowers right now. I could bring my begonia and put it right up by your desk and . . ."

"We just want a few people. You folks and Ab and Sis, and Wellmans. That's plenty," Miss Swenson murmured. "It seems more . . . homey."

"Oh, well, they'll all be at the shivaree, anyway." Mary threaded her needle.

"I think those things are dreadful," Allegra measured boned belting.

Lainey wound a basting thread around her tongue, then into a

243

ball. Shivarees were fun but Mama wouldn't like it if she said so. If I get married and nobody shivarees me . . . us, I mean . . . I'll die. Just die.

Mrs. Hampton reached for the scissors. "How many of your folks will be here, Christina?"

"Isn't it a shame," Allegra said quickly. "Her brother's family's all down with chills and fever. A lot of it up by Guthrie because of Cottonwood Creek, you know." She measured the belting again, turning Miss Swenson around until she faced away from Mary. "But you ought to see the present they sent."

Lainey opened her mouth, closed it again, as Allegra gestured toward the sheeted golden oak rocker with carved lion's heads on the arms. Bush had bought it in Randall for two dollars. There had been a discussion of the price but Allegra had insisted that they get something nice.

Mary twitched the sheet aside and ran her hand over the carving. "That's elegant!" She looked at the clock. "My land, I've got to get home; I'm gettin' as bad as Hamp. This is Thursday and I've still got those plague-taked tomatoes to can up in the morning, but I'll be over tomorrow afternoon to help get things finished up. And the wedding's Saturday noon! I just can't wait, Christina," she added as she bustled out the door.

"Lainey, go wake Sunny," Allegra said, "I don't like for him to sleep so late in the afternoon."

Sunny lay on his side, curled in a tight curve, his hands tucked between his knees. "Wake up," Lainey shook him gently. "Wake up, boy." The heat of his body struck through his thin shirt.

"Mama, he's awful hot."

"Lainey, do watch your English." Allegra stood up, holding a lapful of scissors, spools, scraps, and a tape measure. She put the back of her hand on Sunny's forehead. Frowning, she reached under the curve of his chin.

"He does seem hot, but it's hot weather. I'm hot myself." She tested her hand against her face, then put it back on Sunny's forehead. "I do believe he's got a little fever, but with all that running off it wouldn't be surprising. I think I'll let him sleep till suppertime."

At suppertime Sunny was still asleep. When Lainey waked him he cried, burrowed into the bed, then asked for a "d'ink" and promptly vomited.

"He'll feel better," Allegra said, "now he's rid of what was bothering him."

Lainey washed the dishes and Miss Swenson dried while Allegra basted up the long seams of the blue silk wedding dress. Around eight o'clock Curly rode by to say he had seen Brother Gordon and the preacher had promised to come Saturday morning. The two sat, politely talking, until Bush shooed them out on the porch.

Lainey started up to bed, careful not to glance at the porch where two shadows had become one. Allegra was still sewing. Sunny twisted and muttered in his sleep. "Do you think he's better?" Lainey asked.

"I don't know" Allegra snapped. "This seam won't go right and my head's splitting."

Bush looked up over the glasses he had bought from a pack peddler. "Stop fretting. He'll be fine in the morning. Just something he ate."

During the night she wakened to hear Sunny retching, Allegra running for the slop jar, and Bush's comforting rumble, "There, little fellow, there, there."

"Do you think you'd better go for Dr. Harter?" she heard Allegra ask.

"Ummmm. Let's wait till morning. Then we'll see how the gander hops."

"If it should be . . . anything . . ."

"I've been thinkin', could he have got into some of those green sand plums?"

"That might be it. Oh my goodness, there he goes again."

In the morning Sunny was propped up in the big bed, his face as white as the pillow sham. Lainey did not have to ask about his fever, it showed from his eyes. A scatter of unwashed dishes lay on the table and the smell of burned bacon hung around the stove. Allegra was stitching on the wedding dress, her face almost as white as Sunny's.

245

"Can I fix him some breakfast?" Lainey jerked her head toward the bed.

"All he wants is water and he throws that up as soon as you give it to him." Allegra bent to the sewing machine. The pedal began to race.

Miss Swenson was coming down the steps, full of apologies for having slept past sunrise. She looked at Sunny and her hand flew to her mouth.

"Bush's gone for Dr. Harter."

"Won't you let me do that sewing?"

"No," Allegra stabbed the needle into the blue silk, "I'll finish it. Then Mary's coming over and we'll make the cake. I have Ellen's receipt for white icing."

"But Mrs. Sheridan . . ."

"Sunny will be all right," Allegra said and Lainey saw her jaw muscle twitch. "He'll be perfectly all right in time for the wedding."

Washing up the breakfast dishes Lainey had the feeling that she had never seen them before. She examined a chipped plate and ran her finger down the brown line of a crack on the small platter. Looking at Sunny became a thing she rationed out to herself. She went down to the garden for some tomatoes and found herself standing in the middle of the path, her pan half-filled, staring at the scurrying ants that ran up a sunflower stalk. Back in the house the child on the bed looked like a stranger. His chubby round face had taken on harsh, sharp angles. His head turned from side to side on the pillow. When Lainey put the gourd rattle Lydia Halfmoon had given him into his fingers he dropped it as if it were too heavy to hold. And still Allegra stitched. She sat by Sunny's bed, her needle flashing as if it were a sword by which she held some enemy at bay.

It's eleven o'clock, now, Lainey thought. Bush can make it to Randall on Blackjack in better'n an hour and a half. Say Dr. Harter's on a call. An hour and a half back. But the doctor will be slower in his buggy. Say two hours. She gave it up.

"Try this on, Christina," Allegra said hoarsely.

"Mrs. Sheridan, I really think . . ."

"The waist may have to come out a little."

246

Wordlessly, Christina Swenson put on the blue dress. It fell around her in flowing lines. A perfect fit.

"D'ink," Sunny mumbled.

"Don't give it to him. He can't keep it down."

"D'ink."

"Oh, well, just a little."

Lainey held the silver cup that had come from Kentucky to Sunny's lips while Allegra supported his neck. He gulped at the water but it was barely down before it came back, a greenish stain in the washbowl. His flesh burned with fever and he seemed to be having trouble with his tongue.

"A sponge bath?" Miss Swenson suggested. "Once my sister's oldest girl . . ."

"Maybe it would help." Allegra sponged Sunny but the water almost dried ahead of the washrag. "I wonder if we put some wet towels around him . . ."

Once Sunny opened his eyes and smiled and Lainey ran outdoors and put her face against the sun-hot wall of the cottonwood siding.

It was past twelve when they heard the sound of horses on the road. Bush had Blackjack at a high lope and the doctor's buggy was close behind him.

"Had to go clear to the mission to find him," Bush said. "One of Jane Baker's class is down." He pulled the saddle off Blackjack and rubbed him down quickly with a gunny sack. "Good boy, good boy."

"Well, here we are," Dr. Harter swung out of the buggy. "Sure different weather from the last time I came. Good stand of cotton, Bush. Corn looks good, too."

They all followed him to the house, hanging on his words. If the doctor could talk about weather and crops, then surely things could not be too bad.

He thumped down his bag, washed his hands. "Now let's take a look."

They stood in a tight knot at the foot of the bed hanging on Dr. Harter's every move. They collided with each other, rushing to get things that he asked for. They hardly breathed while he put the slender glass column under Sunny's armpit, felt for the pulse, and stared at his heavy gold watch. When he clicked the watch cover shut the sound was loud as a shot. They strained to see the thermometer that he held up, squinting.

"Hmmmm. How long has this been going on?"

Everyone tried to answer at once, each giving a treasured piece of information held back for this minute. The doctor listened patiently, nodding his head.

"I guess we should have sent for you last night," Allegra finished.

"Why, no, ma'am. These things have their course. You say it was after the Fourth?"

"A day or two. He started having the back-door trots." She told the story over again, each of the others adding his part.

"I see." He pulled down the sheet and lifted the nightgown. It was shocking to see how Sunny's ribs stood out from his body. "I wish I had a little ice."

"I'll get some, Doc." Bush started for the door.

"Hold on a minute," Dr. Harter sat studying the child. Then, frowning, he looked at the bottles of pills and liquids in his bag. Finally he selected a bottle, decanted some reddish stuff into it, sifted in powder from a twist of paper and shook up the mixture. "If he could keep this down . . . or if we could break the fever . . ."

"We gave him sponge baths," Allegra said.

"Best thing to do. Hang some wet sheets around his bed. This heat . . ."

Lainey and Miss Swenson met at the well.

"Your dress," Lainey said, "you'll get it wet."

"Oh, I forgot." The sun made the blue silk gleam. "I'll change in a minute."

They wrung out the sheets together; their hands touching at the center and clinging an instant for company.

"No more water," Dr. Harter was saying to Allegra. "A little ice on the tongue. Try the medicine. Keep up the baths. And I'll be back."

"Stay and eat with us, Doc," Bush said automatically.

"I'd stay if I could, but there's a lot of sickness. Broken leg at Millers'."

248

Bush followed him out to the buggy and Lainey was close on his heels.

"Corn ought to bring a good price this year," the doctor said. "Wheat's sure up."

Bush said, "Doc, is it . . . the flux?"

Dr. Harter put his bag in the buggy. "Looks like it." The ground rocked under Lainey's feet. "I wish I could tell you different, but you'd better know."

"Is he . . . bad?"

"Pretty bad. But I've seen 'em pull out of worse."

"If I just hadn't taken him to the picnic!"

"Don't blame yourself, man. It's like lightning; you never know where it'll strike. We always have a little with the children in the summer."

Bush covered his face with his hands. "But Sunny . . . Why?"

"God knows," the doctor said with sudden weariness in his voice, "God knows."

There was a meal of sorts on the table. They ate in silence, taking turns sitting by the bed. Miss Swenson had changed from her wedding dress but sewing still littered the house. The wet sheets and towels dried so fast in the thirsty heat that they were all kept mercifully busy changing them. Bill Doggett had seen the doctor's buggy up the road and had gone for the ice in Bush's place. They waited for the ice now with a faith that sought for something to cling to. In the middle of the afternoon Mary Hampton pulled up in her buggy.

"I thought I'd never get off," she said to Bush as he helped her down. "All those tomatoes and here comes Hamp with a bushel of beans somebody gave him. I brought my begonia and the Boston fern. And my pink beads, just in case. And a little present for the bride; not much, but something. And . . . What in the world's wrong?"

"Sunny's sick."

"Well, my land what're you lettin' me stand here and gab for?" Bush caught her arm.

"Mary, Doc Harter's been here. He says it's . . . the flux."

"Oh, the poor little fellow." She tried again to pass him.

"Don't you see? You might come down, too. I've seen it go through whole families. And Pa told me about wagon trains . . . forty graves on a ridge out near our place at home."

"Let go my arm, Bushrod Sheridan! Don't you think I know about flux? Two sisters died with it and I helped nurse them both. I'd never be able to live with myself if I didn't go help Allegra. Besides, I love the little fellow."

Bush looked down at her helplessly and stood aside.

Mary took Allegra in her arms. The golden head rested against the brown one for an instant. That was all. In no time Mary was tying on her apron, washing dishes, clearing up the sewing. All the long, hot afternoon the flow of her talk fought off the dreadful silence.

At sundown Hamp came over and did chores. Arch drew water to fill the tubs and the iron washpot. Mrs. Doggett brought supper; Mrs. Shipp, a remedy that had saved more than you could shake a stick at. Old man Morehouse brought a jug of whisky. Bush stopped trying to keep the neighbors out. You'd do the same for us, they said, and it was true. But no matter how many came, or what they offered to do, nothing could stop the turning of the little head on the pillow, or still the hoarse whisper from the cracked lips. "D'ink . . . d'ink . . ."

Dr. Harter came at nine. At ten he was still there. At eleven Lainey noticed he was nodding in his chair, lines of weariness plowing down from the corners of his mouth like furrows in new-cut sod. At eleven-thirty Bush sent Lainey up to bed. She started to protest, but he said, "Git!" and she dragged up the stairs, dreading to go, dreading more to stay.

"Crack a little of that ice," Dr. Harter said, "We'll drop some whisky on it. Brandy would be better, but . . ."

"I'll go," Bush said. "I'll get some, someplace."

"No. No, you'd better stay here."

Lainey heard the hammer crushing the ice. She heard the clink of the jug. She heard the weak retching, and she reached out and pulled a pillow over her head.

Sunny Sheridan died just before full daylight.

Chapter 22

Won't it ever be over, Lainey thought. Won't they ever stop whispering and talk out loud? Won't they ever go away and leave us alone?

The house was full of women who walked on tiptoe. The table was crowded with strange dishes, pots, and bowls. The yard was full of men who talked in hushed voices. They had been there when Brother Gordon rode up and shouted, "Fine day for a wedding! Where's the happy pair?"

They had reproached themselves that no one had told him, but they were relieved when he went in and sat beside the bed where Allegra, white-faced and stony, stared at the ceiling.

"If she'd just cry," Mrs. Shipp worried. "Not a tear. Not a single one." Tears brimmed out of her own eyes and ran, unchecked, down her face. "I buried three and I can't pass the cemetery without cryin'."

"We're all different," Mrs. Doggett said, "I don't think we should judge."

"Bush says to have the funeral this afternoon," Mary Hampton reported. "Brother Gordon can stay and all the folks are here and it won't be any easier to wait till later."

"Don't hardly seem right," Mrs. Shipp said, "not to set up."

She and Mary had washed and dressed the wasted little body. Death had returned some of the beauty to Sunny's face. The sharpened features and the drawn-down angle of the mouth had gone. Hamp and Joe Wellman dug the grave in the sheltered valley where the Sheridans had camped when they first came on the claim. There was a cemetery in Randall, but it was a lonesome place on a bare hill and the graves were few and scattered. Jurd Morehouse came, hesitating, to Bush, some planed polished boards under his arm.

251

"I brought 'em from back home," he said, "Walnut. Off our old place. I had it in mind to make my own coffin and have it ready, but I'd ruther he had 'em."

"It's kind of you," Bush said.

"You folks've been good to me. Most of 'em 'round here, they think I'm a hard lot. I don't go for their psalm-singin', pulpit-poundin'. No, and I don't go for that feller Bryan, neither. But Mrs. Sheridan . . . she asked me to come to the singin'. She made me welcome."

"I'd take it as a favor if you'd let us have 'em," Bush said. "It's good, hard wood."

"Yep," Jurd Morehouse ran his finger along the edge of the boards. "I'll go home and put it t'gether. Don't want her to have to hear it. Lonesomest sound I ever heard, the hammers knockin' on my wife's coffin. She died on the trip to the Territory."

"I didn't know."

"Never told nobody. Let 'em think I'm mean and ornery." He stumped away.

In the corner by the back door Lainey heard Mrs. Shipp and Sis Pritchard whispering.

"I'd love to see one," Sis said. "I'd sure love to."

"Well, it's a sure sign the one that's died has gone straight to glory. When my pa died there it was, right in the pillow. He was a hard man, drinker an' all, but there it was. It gave my ma a lot of comfort."

"Wonder if she'd mind if we looked?" Sis Pritchard glanced at the curtained-off bed where Allegra lay. "She comes from big rich folks."

"Rich or poor, we're all the same in the sight of the Lord," Mrs. Shipp sighed.

"I don't see as it'd do any harm. The pillow's out on the wash line."

As they tiptoed out Lainey waited a minute, then followed. She saw the two women lift the pillow from the line and walk to the barn with the air of conspirators. She didn't know what they were going to do, but Mama wouldn't like it. Lainey knew she wouldn't.

In the dusky, dry-smelling barn they were leaning over the pillow, Mrs. Shipp ripping the threads at one end with a small clasp-knife.

"There. I knew it!" she exclaimed. "That child was an angel if I ever saw one!" Mrs. Shipp took her hand out of the mass of white goosedown and on it was a delicate circle of interlaced feathers, fragile as a snowflake. It moved at a breath.

"A feather crown!" Sis put one finger on it, then drew back. "Oh . . . Lainey."

Mrs. Shipp turned to her, beaming. "Look, Lainey, a feather crown! It means the one that died on that pillow went straight to heaven!"

The pillow! Sunny's golden head moving back and forth, back and forth. Lainey could not speak, nor could she look away. Goosedown drifted through the bars of sunlight.

"Straight to heaven!" Mrs. Shipp crooned. "Don't you want to hold it, dearie?"

"No!" Lainey choked. "No! I want him back! I want him back!"

She turned and ran. The men in the front yard looked at her disapprovingly. She ran on, through the cornfield, the green blades slashing at her, down the hill, to the safety of the dry gulch. There she flung herself on the hot sand.

After a long time she sat up, pushed back her tumbled hair, and ground her knuckles into her eyes.

"Annie!" she whispered.

Near her a slender, copper-skinned girl fingered a round red rock. She looked up, then back at the rock.

"I thought maybeso you come."

"But you were at school," Lainey said stupidly.

"I come home 'while. They want me go 'nother school. Long way."

"Do you want to go?"

"I don't know. Maybeso." Annie tossed the rock from one hand to another. "You know Tom Ackley?"

"Sure. He goes to church at Jackrabbit. Red hair, freckles, real nice." She saw that Annie was blushing along her high cheekbones. "But I thought Joe Wingbone . . ."

253

Annie giggled very softly. "Maybeso Joe think so too."

The burden Lainey had borne, it seemed forever, slid from her shoulders and rested in the sand of the dry gulch. She and Annie swapped news, talked trifles.

"Say, I met a Mr. Garton from the agency. He's nice but I don't like *her* much."

Annie widened her nostrils, lifted her eyebrows, and began to talk nonsense in a high, affected voice. Lainey laughed. The sound of her laughter, loud in the narrow walls of the gulch, brought her back to the pain and sorrow that was yet ahead.

"Annie, did you know? About . . ."

Annie nodded.

"That feather crown," Lainey blurted. "It was awful! And they said it was a sign he went straight to heaven."

Sand sifted through Annie's fingers. "Heaven long way off." She made the sign of a journey in the language of the plains . . . a man on a horse and the sun crossing the sky.

They climbed out of the gulch and walked up the hill through the cornfield. At the road Annie turned back.

"I come tomorrow," she said.

Mary Hampton met Lainey at the door, her face worn and anxious. "We've looked every place for you. Bush wants to go ahead. I guess everybody's here. Those French folks came. I don't know how they heard. And Eastmans drove out from Randall. Allegra won't talk to any of 'em, but I think it's some comfort to her that they came. I hate to keep on asking Bush every little thing . . . poor fellow, he's takin' it so hard . . . but I never once thought about the music. Allegra's the only one that can play the organ and of course she can't be expected to. I declare, I don't know what to do!" her lips quivered.

"Did Halfmoons come?" Lainey asked.

"Why of course! I never once thought . . . But do you suppose she'll play? I don't hardly know her to ask a favor of her."

"I'll ask her."

"You will? Well, I hate for you to have to do it, but we ought to have some music. Brother Gordon thinks it'll help your mama.

254

Now just say . . ." Mary, talking, in a sharp whisper followed Lainey through the crowded room.

Miss Swenson was there, and Curly. Their wedding day! And there were Eastmans, looking troubled and a little out of place among the neighbors. Lili Gervais, fingering a Rosary, and Violette as pert as ever in spite of the black dress she wore. Although the room was filled with people, the space at the end that held the coffin seemed enormous. Fruit jars of cosmos, zinnias, prince's-feather, and petunias, were on the floor. Mary's begonia and her Boston fern were at either end. Somebody had worked a wreath that was drooping a little on the dark, polished wood. It was made, Lainey realized, of carrot tops, and the tiny white flowers of radishes going to seed, and adorned with a white satin bow. The golden oak rocker had been unsheeted and left for Brother Gordon to sit in. Three other chairs faced the coffin.

In the far corner of the room, by the cold kitchen stove, stood Lydia Halfmoon. Henry was over with the men, his wrapped braids making a little spot of color in their sober garb, his face full of sorrow. Lydia, with her eyes downcast was expressionless, the bib of bright beads she always wore missing.

What would she say Lainey wondered, and then she just blurted, "Will you play the organ?"

Lydia stared at the floor. "Did your mama say to ask?" she whispered.

"No, but there's nobody else. And you're her friend."

The woman looked across the room at her husband. It was plain that she was not asking permission, but help. It was plain, too, that the help came to her. Still she struggled with her own decision.

"If you only would," Mary was saying, "we'd be ever so much obliged. Allegra's that bad off I don't know what we're going to do to help her through. I know how much she thinks of your music, and if you'd just this once . . ."

Lydia Halfmoon had turned away and was walking across the room. There was a craning of necks from the neighbors as she sat down at the organ. Bush and Allegra and Brother Gordon

255

moved out of the alcove and took their places. Lainey seated herself beside her mother. Allegra's face was gray and immovable as granite.

Lainey looked down at her hands as if they belonged to a stranger. Head line. Heart line. Life line. A long line . . . a long life. And Sunny only three years. It isn't fair! It isn't fair! The lump in her throat began to swell. Bushrod Sheridan, my father. Bushrod Sheridan, my father. But Bush's shoulders were sagging. He could not help her.

" 'Suffer the little children to come unto me and forbid them not, for of such is the kingdom of Heaven . . .' "

Sunny didn't need a feather crown. 'Straight to heaven,' they said. But heaven is a long way off.

" 'In my Father's house are many mansions . . .' "

Riverview was a mansion. People always said, 'What a mansion, and out in the country.' Sunny at Riverview, running down the hall, sliding down the bannisters, climbing up, up, the ladder to the tower.

She stole a look at Brother Gordon. He believes every word he's saying, she said to herself. If he believes it, maybe I can. Sunny at Riverview. Not in heaven. Not in that dark polished thing over there. She drew a long breath and tried to believe, but from deep within her a thin, insistent cry whimpered, "I want him back, I want him back."

Brother Gordon closed his Bible and nodded at Lydia Halfmoon. Her hands touched the keys, her feet moved on the pedals. The gentle melody of Brahm's "Lullaby" stole through the room like a cooling wind.

"Lullaby, and good night, with roses bedight . . ." The organ was singing and Sunny was sleeping. Lainey heard the long breath Allegra drew in, like the wind that comes before rain, and her arms went around her mother as she put her face on Lainey's shoulder and began to cry.

"C'mon in," Pappy Vickers called to Lainey and Bush as they passed his place. "Time we had a pow-wow."

The half-dug-out was so small it could barely hold three of them at once and the August heat was sweltering. Lainey perched on the bunk. How could Pappy stand even the sight of that old buffalo robe in weather like this? Bush tossed his hat on the floor and wiped his forehead. The white streak in his hair had not so much widened as scattered.

"Somethin's got to be done about Allegra," Pappy said abruptly. "An' right off."

A cold catch of fear made Lainey shiver. Allegra had not been herself since the funeral. She drove herself at the housework and when it was done went out in the garden and worked as though possessed. She rarely spoke and what she said was sharp and bitter. If anybody came to the place she disappeared. Even Mary Hampton had stopped visiting after she had caught sight of Allegra's skirt whipping across the garden as she came in at the front door.

"I'm not one to get my feelings hurt," she said to Bush, "but I think I better stay away for a spell. I want you to know why."

"But Mary, after all you did for us," Bush choked.

"That's just it; she can't stand the sight of anybody that was here then. It brings it all back. Now don't go thinkin' I'm mad. I'm not. But I'll just pass the word around to stay 'way for a while." There were tears in her bright-brown eyes.

So nobody came, now, except sometimes, Arch. He was working too hard on the extra land to do much more than report the news of the neighborhood. From him they heard how Curly and Miss Swenson had outwitted the crowd that came to shivaree them. After their marriage at Brother Gordon's place in Randall the young couple had gone to Curly's homestead in the Kickapoo country. There the crowd had gathered with cowbells, shotguns, rocks in tin buckets and all kinds of noisemakers. They had circled the cabin for nearly an hour while two figures sat unnoticing at the table inside. Finally, tired of their own racket and ready for the "treat" the crowd had jerked open the door. There sat two dummies, carefully stuffed with straw. On the table were bowls of hard candy, doughnuts, and even a box of cigars, with a lettered notice, "Help yourselves. Gone to Guthrie!"

When she heard this story Allegra had smiled for the first and

257

last time since Sunny died. Yes, Pappy was right. Something had to be done.

"But what can we do?" Bush worried. "Day in, day out, she won't say a word more than she has to. And night . . . well . . ."

"She won't eat," Lainey added. "Half the time I take her plate off without a thing touched."

Pappy Vickers combed his beard with clawed finger. "It's like she was trying to kill herself without usin' a gun, or anything quick an' easy."

"Allegra can't do things quick and easy. She wasn't raised to it."

"You can't tell me a thing about the Saunderses, boy. I went to war with Maje . . . her pa . . . I've knowed Ellen since she was knee-high to a duck. My pap knew old Jeb, the he-coon o' the lot. They're stubbon as mules and techy as blooded horses. They can't be drove, but they *can* be got around. If she'd go back home for a while . . ."

"I offered to send her and she almost took my head off."

Lainey closed her eyes remembering how Allegra had blazed out that if Bush had sent her back when she wanted to take Sunny . . . or if they had never come to this dreadful country . . . but go back alone . . . Never. That was the night Bush had come home so late and Lainey had heard him stumble on the threshold and speak in a strange thick voice.

"We-ell, then, it looks like I'm elected," Pappy Vickers put on a smile but his eyes were bleak. "Th' way I see it she's got to get away and Riverview's the place for her an' she's got to have an all-fired good reason to go."

"I don't know what . . ." Lainey began.

"No need for you to know," the old man said. "Just rally 'round the flag, boys, when I start in. Now git for home, the both of you."

"Look here, Pappy," Bush said.

"Shet up, boy, and mind your manners. I'm your elder by a good deal. Git!"

"I'm not goin' to have you . . ."

He shooed them out the door. "She'll be missin' you up to the house. Git!"

"What's he going to do?" Lainey asked as they walked up the road.

"God knows. I just hope Pappy does, too. And I hope it works."

Pappy Vickers dropped in that night for supper. Allegra heaped his plate with stewed chicken and dumplings, and fished the "little eggs" that she always cooked for him out of the broth. Pappy picked at his plate, pushed it back, and shoved his chair away from the table. Bush and Lainey ate stolidly, trying not to notice.

Pappy took out a stick and began to whittle aimlessly. At last Allegra frowned and brushed some slivers of wood off the table.

"Don't you like your chicken, Cap'n Vickers?"

"It's well enough. It'll do. It'll do." He sighted the stick by his eye.

"I could fix you something else."

"No, no. Don't fancy my vittles the way I used to." He slashed at the stick. "Had a dream last night. Dreamed I was eatin' one o' Bill Smithwick's hams. B'iled in cider."

"Ellen's tried for years to get him to tell her what they do that's different. But he won't." It was the first time Allegra had volunteered a remark in weeks.

"Them Smithwicks are all mean. But they c'n cure ham." He whittled a little while as Allegra dished up canned blackberries, then folded the blade of his clasp knife and put it in his pocket. "I come to tell you folks g'bye."

"Goodbye?" they chorused.

"Yep. I got a notion to go back home an' see my folks."

The clock ticked noisily. Lainey thought of skinflint George and whiny Minnie. They were his only folks left. She'd heard him say so a hundred times.

"But Cap'n Vickers we thought you were happy with us. We want you to stay."

"Oh, it's well enough here. But a man my age . . ." He let his voice trail off, then blurted out, "I'll take my foot in my hand an' go."

"How'd you aim to get there?" Bush asked.

"Walkin's not all took up yit. Leg over leg, the dog went to Dover, as the feller says."

"But you can't. It's too far. Something might happen." Allegra said.

"Don't fret yourself. I been makin' my way in the world a right smart time." He stood up and stretched. "Be leavin' in the mornin'. If I could trouble you for a snack."

"No!" Allegra seemed shaken out of the dark dream that had held her. "I won't have it. Not if I have to go and take you myself!"

"Looky here, gal . . ."

"I won't have people saying that I let a Snyder County man . . . and one that fought with my own father . . . I won't do it . . . if you're bound to go home, you'll go on the train with me. I've got money for the tickets. Ellen's sent it to me twice." She looked at Bush as if she dared him to refuse her. "And we won't go in the morning. Next week is plenty soon enough."

"I wouldn't want to be beholdin' . . ."

"You're like my own folks," Allegra said and Lainey had forgotten how sweet her smile could be. "You can't be beholdin' to your own."

"Well, if you put it that way . . ."

"I hate to think about you going back there," Bush hoisted Pappy's pack into the wagon. "That George . . ."

"Oh, it'll be some fun to disappoint George. He thought he was rid o' me." The old man set his Confederate hat at a cocky angle and climbed in the wagon. "Don't shut the door, Bush. Leave 'er open this trip. Looks more friendly-like."

"Any time you want to come back . . ."

"Well, we'll take that up when we come to it."

"I sure thank you for what you did."

"If there's any thanking to be done, I'll do it. With me it was allus new country. I grew up when Missoury was plum' wild. Then when it started settlin' down I went on the trail. Now you folks gimme another chance. Consarn you, Bush, load that stuff. You'll have me blubberin'."

260

They stopped by the old campsite where Allegra had gone to put flowers on Sunny's grave. She was standing by the red sandstone slab on which Bush had cut, "Sunny Saunders Sheridan, Born and Died on this Claim, 1892–1896." There were tears on her cheeks under the spotted veil, but she did not wipe them off, nor did she shed any more, or even look back as the wagon rattled down the road to Randall.

Chapter 23

With Mama and Pappy Vickers gone . . . and Sunny, too . . .
life in the house on the hill was painfully empty. The neighbors
had lost the habit of coming to the Sheridan place so Bush and
Lainey spent most of their time alone and gradually they redis-
covered their old comradeship. As they picked the early cotton,
working in parallel rows, Bush talked about his dream of single
statehood for Indian and Oklahoma Territories, of what it meant
to him that these two great stretches of land, from the western
plains to the eastern hills, should stand together. If only the
leaders . . . but surely they would come to it.

In spite of Bush's confidence the matter seemed further than
ever from settlement. The leaders in Oklahoma Territory smote
the rostrums in fervid oratory; the leaders in Indian Territory
folded their arms in stubborn resistance. Both sides sent delegation after delegation to Washington, and the halls of Congress
echoed to "the Oklahoma question." As late as last January Bush
had gone down to Oklahoma City when a call for "single staters"
was issued, but the "double staters" came, too, and the newspapers
reported that the racket resembled a lunatic asylum. The chairman had had to turn out the lights in the hall to adjourn
the meeting. Still, Bush hoped.

Lainey's hopes were different. She did not talk to Bush about
the ones that concerned Arch. Since their talk the Fourth of July
night on the point she had seen little of him. It was almost as if he
were sorry he had spoken at all. He had planted more cotton than
any one man could take care of, Bush said, and he stayed in the
field from the time the sun first licked the dew off the bolls till
the light was too far gone to work by. Lainey felt she knew why
he was working so hard, he had as good as told her but 'as good

as' wasn't quite enough. If he'd just come around once in a while, or even let her come over and help him in the field.

But she knew Arch too well to dare suggest it. He had his back bowed and he must go it alone. When she saw him at church the deep tan of his face made his blue eyes startling. The reedy boyish thinness had given way to the tall, heavily muscled frame of a young man. Hard work had made Arch Hampton grow up before his time. Only his blond cowlicks were unchanged.

There were other hopes Lainey could talk to Bush about as they went about the work of the claim. She wanted to be a teacher. At Christina Pritchard's urging she had gone to the county seat, taken the examinations and passed. True, she had faltered a little in higher arithmetic, but Arch's coaching his last year in school had pulled her through and on her dresser there was a teacher's certificate, her name on it in fine, curly script. When Mama came back she would try for a school.

When Mama comes back . . . When Allegra comes back . . . Their talk began that way, over and over. The words hung on the air until one of them . . . it must have been Bush . . . suddenly stopped saying them. Lainey followed suit.

Letters came from Allegra. Pages of closely written news. Bush read them aloud after dinner. " 'Joe's going to put corn in that creek strip.' " He looked up over his spectacles, "Never do a bit of good there. Drown'd out before it sprouts. 'Ellen and I made apple butter from the first Wealthies. Mattie's getting pretty feeble but she won't let on. Red clover hay brought a good price this year. Jimdandy's getting Clytie's last colt ready for the horse show. Ellen and I went to St. Joe last week and I bought something nice for Lainey's birthday. I'll mail it tomorrow when we go to Marney.' "

Lainey let the cloud of steam from the dishes she was scalding rise between her and Bush. She had heard his voice falter as he read. Her birthday wasn't until the first of October. It was Mama's way of saying that she wouldn't be back then. How much longer?

" 'Mot Bucklin bought the old Menton place for his second boy. Addie runs the house, now that her mother's gone. Dropsy. Mot brought over a bushel of late crabapples and Ellen made them up

263

in pickles. I took Addie a jar.' Times have changed for sure," Bush said, "Ellen neighboring with the Bucklins! But Mot's all right, no matter what they say about his pa." He took up the letter again. " 'Pappy Vickers comes over every time George will drive him by, which isn't often. He sends love. And so do I.' "

He folded the letter carefully in its original creases and put it back in the envelope.

"How old will you be, honey?"

"Seventeen."

"It don't seem possible!" She had known he would say that. Grown-ups always did.

"Look here," Bush said, "how about you driving in to Randall with me tomorrow? We'll have a kind of celebration."

They were on the road by nine thirty. The day was fine. Oklahoma Territory was at its best in the fall. The sky blue, the sun warm, the wind cool. A white-tailed hawk soared above them, then swooped so low they could see the brown flecks on his feathers. A blacksnake glistened in the sun as it raced across the road. Squirrels chattered and ran through the waving branches of the pecan trees. Tomorrow it would be five years since the Run. They drove past Jackrabbit Schoolhouse.

"When's school going to open?" Lainey asked.

"Just as soon as the last cotton's in. Miss Swenson . . . Mrs. Pritchard, that is . . . is bound we're goin' to have a new schoolhouse. This one's not near big enough."

"I know. Last year the primer had to sit three on a bench."

"Mary Hampton's working up some kind of to-do to raise more money so's we can start building." He shook his head. "Looks like everything takes money now'days. When we built that schoolhouse nobody had a dollar in his jeans. We each gave a day's work and four logs. We traded loads of fence posts for those window frames."

Lainey glanced back at the schoolhouse. It was little and dumpy, but it would seem strange . . . and sort of lonesome . . . not to be there when the fall term opened this year. She had gone every term since it was started, but there had been no real class for her for two years past. Mrs. Pritchard had just taught her and what older

264

ones wanted to come from whatever books could be assembled. Now, she insisted, Lainey was beyond her. Besides, Lainey knew with the enrollment so large it wasn't fair for her to take up the room.

"I wish we could have sent you to normal school," Bush said. "Next year, maybe."

"I don't care," she lied, wincing at his casual use of Arch's words. She did care, but what was the use of going on about it. Part of the money had gone for the train tickets back to Missouri, for in the end Bush had been unable to let Allegra accept Ellen's generosity. "I have my certificate and I'll start looking for a school as soon as Mama gets back."

She stopped, realizing what she had said. Then in spite of herself she blurted, "Bush, when *is* Mama coming back?"

"I don't know," Bush said slowly. The wheels turned many times in the red dirt of the road before he added, "Sometime, I reckon."

When they reached town Bush did his best to make it a gay occasion. He took Lainey to the dry-goods section of the general store where he did his trading and had the saleslady cut off a wide satin ribbon for her hair. He took her to the hotel for oyster stew instead of buying cheese and crackers and eating them in the buckboard. He walked with her to Eastmans' for a visit after dinner. But somehow everything went wrong. The clerk was snippy about Lainey's choice of color. The oysters in the stew were lonesome, and cove oysters at that. And at Eastmans' they discovered that Merry had gone to Edmond to the college. Mrs. Eastman spent most of the time inquiring about Allegra and telling about Merry's triumphs and her wardrobe. When she urged them to stay for supper Bush said they had to get home on account of the stock. For once Lainey was glad of the countrified excuse.

The street was crowded with wagons and buggies as they walked back to the hitching rack.

"Makes me think of that first day," Bush said. "The way Allegra looked, driving that team through all the crowd. All dressed up in her pretty dress and hat. Who're you looking for, Lainey?"

"Who? Me? Nobody," Lainey stammered.

"I thought the way you looked you must know that tall fellow over acrost the street. The one with the tan hat. Kind of a cowboy-lookin' man."

"I don't have the least idea who he is."

"Plenty of cowboys around. Guess breaking up the Strip put a lot of 'em out of business. Not but what it was a good thing. Nobody's got a right to hold that much land from people that want to farm it. Dave Payne was a great man and time will tell, no matter what they say. Why if it hadn't been for him and his Boomers . . ."

It was a favorite theme. She let her father talk, asking the proper questions at the proper time so that she was free to watch (without seeming to) the lazy saunter of the tall man on the other side of the street. He swung his hat in his hand and the late sun gleamed on his black hair. Yes, he did wear cowboy boots, and even from across the street she could see that they were very fine and very, very fancy.

On October first Lainey was seventeen. Allegra sent her a length of moss-green silk, silver buttons to trim it with, a gay green ostrich tip and a yard of soft velvet ribbon just the shade of willow leaves in the spring. Mary Hampton came over to help her make up the silk, but in spite of the way it fit, and the way it picked up the green light in her eyes and made her cheeks look pink, Lainey's birthday was not a success. She quarrelled sharply with Arch who had ridden over to bring her a present. A photograph of himself, done by the new photographer in Randall. With his head in a clamp, his neck choking in a high starched collar, his cowlicks watered down to skull level, it was the picture of a stranger.

The quarrel came up out of nowhere. Not even to herself would Lainey admit that she had expected something more than this on her seventeenth birthday. But on the Fourth of July Arch had said "Next year." She had been sixteen then and now she was seventeen and surely this *was* next year. And he had just thrust that dreadful picture at her and started talking to Bush about the likelihood that the Free Homes Bill would be pushed through.

Finally, Bush yawned off to bed and pulled the calico curtain. They heard him drop his heavy boots on the floor and as if a signal had been given, they began to whisper together in harsh, hoarse, sentences.

They pretended the quarrel was over Lainey's promise to go to the magic-lantern show at Jackrabbit School with Doris Shipp. Arch had not asked her, Lainey whispered, and she wasn't going to sit around and wait till he got ready. If she had sense enough to pound sand down a rathole, Arch retorted, she'd know he was goin' to ask her. He had to get the last of the cotton in and he didn't have time to come around every time the wind changed. If he didn't have time he could have sent word. She supposed he'd sold his cotton high to get money to spend on votes for Dotty Sullavan at the popularity contest. He just might do that, Arch said coolly and as Lainey sputtered her opinion of Dotty he grinned and ran his curved fingers over the oilcloth table cover in imitation of a cat's claws. Jealous? The very truth of it was a red rag to her fury. You . . . you . . . you . . .

Then he reached across and took the photograph.

"Seein's you don't like this anyway." He tore it, across and up and down, and threw the four pieces in the woodbox. Lainey cried out angrily, suddenly seeing the photograph as a dear possession.

"What's the matter?" Bush called, the bed creaking as he hoisted himself on his elbow and looked at his watch. "Bedtime. Arch's got work to do."

She could have slapped him. Or Arch. Men were hateful! Hateful!

Later in the darkness Lainey groped her way back downstairs, her long flannelette nightgown tangling around her feet. Feeling around in the woodbox she came upon the scraps of the picture. A splinter slid under her thumbnail and set up a fiendish throbbing. Sucking at her thumb and shivering in the night chill she shuffled the four scraps of paper. At last she put them inside her nightgown and pressed them against her bare flesh as if by her own warmth she could piece them together again. But in the morning

267

when she looked at the tattered bits she saw the damage had been done and nothing could make the picture whole. She put the pieces in her keepsake box, under the silver spoon, and the ring Addie Bucklin had given her that was too small to wear now, and a small rounded quartz stone she had picked up somewhere.

There was such a crowd around Jackrabbit School you could hardly see the building.

"Hope more'n half can't get in," Bush said. "Then maybe we'll get a new schoolhouse."

Lainey, sitting with Doris in the buckboard, saw Beauty hitched to a tree and felt a twist of regret. Arch should have known she didn't mean all that. He ought to have asked her earlier, anyway. The green Studebaker wagon, no longer new and trim, rattled up. Children boiled over the edges.

"There's Sullavans," Doris sniffed. "Dotty thinks nobody's got a chance for the cake but her."

Dotty Sullavan, a blue fascinator over her red curls, lifted her blue merino dress daringly high as she stood up to climb over the wheel. Her plump legs in embroidered stockings could be plainly seen in the lantern light.

"Would you look at that!" Doris said righteously. Two young men ran up to the wagon, but Dotty jumped into the arms of a third.

The schoolhouse was already crowded. Lainey located Arch, pretended not to see him, then began to edge in his direction, looking back and calling greetings to the neighbors. Doris got her arm in a firm grip. "C'mon. There's a place not taken."

Helpless, she let herself be dragged to the other side of the room. The bench was only a few from the one where Dotty Sullavan sat holding court, twirling the silver heart on its long chain. It tinkled as it wound around her finger.

"Bell a cat!" Doris said.

Dotty gave her a superior look. "Takes a cat to know a cat," she countered.

"Ladies an' gentlemen. Boys an' girls o' Jackrabbit School, I'm sure we welcome each an' every one here tonight." Mary Hampton

268

began in a formal manner then looked at the crowd clogging the doorway. "My land, you boys, there, move over an' let those folks in. Well, as I was saying, you folks know why we're here tonight. We got to get a new schoolhouse. We've had pie suppers, box suppers, fruit suppers, an' oyster suppers till we've just about suppered out. We hate to just cold-out ask for money so with Miss Swenson . . . Miz Pritchard, that is . . . helpin', we got up this entertainment. A program put on by the pupils. A magic-lantern show . . . Fletch Brubaker borrowed the lantern an' slides from the drug store and we thank you, Fletch . . . An' then we're gonna have a contest to find out the most pop'lar young lady in the district. Votes to be sold for one cent each and a cake to go to the winner, and we hope you'll take it in good part. Careful of that lamp, Tommy! You're boundin' about like a dog in high rye!"

Mary waited till the lamp stopped swinging and then went on. "Most of us came to the Territory for a better chance. Now it's our part to pass that chance along to the boys an' girls we got comin' up in school. If we can't do that, we'd just about as well give up an' go back home. And now," she returned to her prim manner, "I'll turn the program over to Miss Swenson . . . Miz Pritchard, that is."

"Spartacus to the Gladiators," was given by Junior Roche. Mary Meegey obliged with "Lips that Touch Liquor Shall Never Touch Mine." Deany Pritchard recited, "Curfew Shall Not Ring Tonight!" A male quartet thundered, "Many brave hearts are a-sleep in the deep, so be-ware, beeeeee-ware." Bill Doggett's bass led them far beyond their depth. Jethro Bates tried Mark Antony's oration over Caesar but stuck on the second "Brutus was an honorable man," and sat down. The first reader sang "Toodlededoo was a Dandy Cock Robin."

The program went on and on. Mary Hampton was not one to give scant measure. It was nine o'clock before Fletch Brubaker set up the magic lantern. Arch was helping him and Lainey wished with all her heart that he would look her way. When he did she turned to Doris with a sharp, "I wish he'd let me alone!"

Now the lamps were turned out amid much giggling. The images from the magic lantern wavered across the sheet hung on the blackboard. A smell of hot oil from the lantern penetrated the room and John Empy fanned Dotty Sullavan with a spelling book. The slides were simple line drawings, brightly colored. An apple, a bunch of grapes, a Chinese pagoda, a comic series with Punch and Judy. The audience was growing restless. The popularity contest was what most of them had come for.

It was a sure way to make money for a cause, but until now Jackrabbit School had not used it for it was known to leave bad feelings. Over at Taney the "wrong" girl had won, and the "right" girl's supporters came back and tore up the schoolhouse. At Jackrabbit School it was easy to guess that Dotty would be the candidate of the crowd that ran around to square dances and wore showy clothes. But who would represent the others? The heart of every girl in the room beat faster. Eyes shone, voices took on a high-pitched quality. Even Doris looked almost pretty when the lamps were lighted again and the cake which was to be the prize was put on the teacher's desk.

It was a magnificent cake. A three-layer burnt sugar with car'mel icing. The winner would cut it with her principal supporters after the contest.

A buzzing knot surrounded Dotty. Bluebell Shimer, as her best friend, would be in charge of canvassing for votes. Already Bluebell had a chalk box ready for contributions.

Doris almost tipped the bench back, leaning toward a bunch of girls behind them. "I don't see why not . . . I'll tell her she's got to." She straightened up and caught Lainey's arm. "They want you to run against Dotty. You've got to!"

Lainey gasped, pulling away. "I . . . I don't want to. Let somebody else." But Doris had made up her mind. "Well," Lainey temporized, "at least I ought to ask Bush."

"Lainey Sheridan, you're seventeen and you've got a teacher's certificate. You don't have to ask *anybody*." Doris signalled the others. "She'll do it. Now, Anna May, you go after Tom Eckart. Edith, grab Lem Novak. We'll show that Dotty!"

Some of the young men were shouting for the girls to be put up where they could be seen. Dotty paraded up to the front of the room and perched on the edge of the teacher's desk. Lainey fol-

270

lowed after Mrs. Pritchard's nod of permission. The two girls sat back to back, the cake between them.

"Penny a vote," Bluebell was calling. "Dig down deep, heap good pup, as th' feller says."

But Doris outdid her. "Free Homes Bill is gonna pass! You won't need all that money you've got hid out. Free Homes an' Lainey Sheridan! Penny a vote."

Lainey was miserable. She had nothing to do with Free Homes. Somebody must stop Doris. She looked at Christina imploringly.

Doris reached Arch and Lainey saw him dig in his pocket and drop in two silver dollars. She melted inside. Dear Arch! Then Lyle Smith pitched three dollars to Bluebell Shimer. The ring of them in the chalk box was like a death knell.

Dotty's going to beat, Lainey thought, and though she had been sure of it from the first it hurt just the same. But I mustn't let on. I've got to act like I don't care. And I don't, only . . . Aunt Ellen said, Hold up your shoulders and remember who you are, and it'll carry you through.

Lainey straightened her shoulders and her young breasts lifted under the moss-green silk. The silver buttons gleamed in the lamplight. Mama was A Beauty, she remembered, and a Saunders. Then she was able to smile and she saw Bush nod in approval.

Doris came up, her face set in fierce despair. "We haven't got a chance! Look at those fellows ogle, and her dress half up to her knees."

"Well, I don't care," Lainey lied. "It's all for the schoolhouse."

"I care!" Doris flared. "And you would too if you had good sense. She's been tryin' to get Arch away from you since the fifth reader." She looked at Arch speculatively. "He oughta give more money. He oughta be tickled you're so pop'lar." Then she scanned the room. "Who's that, over by the door?"

Even before she followed Doris' pointing finger Lainey knew whom she would see, lounging against the door frame, as quiet and relaxed among the restless patrons of Jackrabbit School as he had been in the crowd on the Fourth of July. And she knew, too, as she met his eyes, that he had been watching her for a long time.

"I'm going to ask him," Doris said.

271

"No, you can't. He's one of Dotty's fellows."

"I can, too. I'm sick of lettin' her have everything her own way."

A quiver of excitement began at Lainey's breastbone and spread outward. Hold up your shoulders and remember who you are! To cover her fear she smiled at the tall dark man by the door. He was idly flipping a silver coin. Flip, catch, flip, catch. It spun, a silver globe in the lamplight.

Lainey heard Dotty whisper hoarsely to Bluebell, "That's Quirt Kearney, you ninny. Make him shell out. He made a stack on the horserace last week. Tell 'im I said to kick in!"

Quirt? Quirt? The short harsh name had a fascination about it. Doris was already talking to him when Bluebell approached. The people in the over-heated stuffy room sensed a conflict and craned their necks to see. Talk quieted.

"C'mon, Quirt," Bluebell shook the chalk box over Doris' shoulder. "Vote for your best girl. C'mon, kick in."

"You get outa here," Doris shrilled. "I was here first."

"You had no business askin' Quirt," Bluebell gave her a shove. "He belongs to Dotty."

"Hey," Quirt Kearney said in a mild, lazy voice. "I'm not roped an' branded a'ready."

Laughter filled the room. Behind Lainey Dotty groaned, but Bluebell, goaded by the laughter went on.

"She said you were. Dotty said for me to tell you to kick in."

The spinning coin went high. Quirt Kearney reached for it and came to his full height. Putting Doris and Bluebell aside he sauntered up to the front of the room where Lainey sat. She tried to speak, but no words came. Instead she smiled, feeling her lips tremble as she did.

"Hello," he said, as if they were alone. "Hello, Greeneyes."

Everyone in the room was staring at them. Malice and good will, curiosity and cruelty, jealousy and neighborliness beat about them like waves but it didn't matter.

"Hello, Quirt," Lainey said, lowering her lashes, then lifting them again.

Doris came pushing up, chattering, demanding. Ignoring her outstretched hand Quirt reached into his pocket. A shower of

272

silver dollars fell into Lainey's lap, the moss-green silk sagging under their weight.

"For the schoolhouse, ma'am." He bowed, a slight, formal bow, and walked past the teacher's desk. As he went by Dotty he pinched her plump cheek and she jerked away but said nothing. Then Quirt went on back to the door and out into the night. There was a puzzled silence, then a sudden blast of applause.

Chapter 24

"Twenty dollars!" Doris marvelled on the way home. "And you never saw him before?"

"I didn't say that," Lainey said conscientiously. "I saw him on the Fourth of July in the crowd, then at the platform dance, but he was with Dotty and I didn't even know his name till tonight."

"I don't like it," Bush slapped the reins on Stretcher. "Feller nobody knows, walks in, makes a grandstand play, walks out."

"But Mister Sheridan . . . twenty dollars . . ."

"That's not so much. How about what the rest of us've put in at the school? Day labor, sweat, lumber. Why Mary Hampton's put in a hundred times that, but you don't see anybody hoorawin' her about it."

"Did you see Arch's face?" Doris babbled. "I bet they get in a fight!"

"It's no compliment to any girl to have a couple of young fools get in a fight," Bush said sharply. "I hope my girl wouldn't behave so to bring that on."

Bush wants me to promise something, Lainey thought. But I won't. Greeneyes, he called me. Greeneyes.

"I don't want to hear any more about it," Bush said, giving Stretcher a cut with the whip that sent him lunging forward. The buckboard careened, straightened.

"Yessir," both girls chorused, Doris' fingernails digging into Lainey's arm.

As they got out of the buckboard and Bush started to unhitch they heard him mutter, "I never yet cottoned to a cowhand, and I doubt if I ever will."

"I reckon I was a little rough on you last night," Bush said. Doris had gone home early, subdued by Bush's disapproval and Lainey was scalding the dinner dishes. She turned her face away. Part of her wanted to run to Bush and say it didn't matter. But another part, a strange, cold part, that seemed to have grown within her since last night said, Hold back, bargain, let him hurt a little.

"That feller, now, likely didn't mean a thing out o' the way. It's just that . . . Well, you're growin' up. I used to think when you were a little tyke an' Ellen kept coming between us, that everything'd be all right if I could just get you to myself. You and Allegra. So I did. And now . . ." He spread his hands on the table in a curiously forlorn gesture. "Last night I was so proud o' you I liked to popped. 'That's my girl,' I kept thinkin', 'My girl.' Then it was like that feller'd taken you away from me. I guess I just got mad."

Still Lainey did not speak. Don't make it easy for him, a voice inside her whispered.

Finally she said, "I thought you'd be proud I helped raise the money for the school."

"I am, honey. We need a new schoolhouse; no two ways about it."

"If it'd been Arch put that money in you wouldn't've cared," she jabbed in the dark.

"No. I reckon I wouldn't. But Lainey . . ."

"I guess you don't trust me," she said and put a quaver in her voice. "I guess you don't really love me any more."

The dishes jumped as he struck the table. "Great day, Lainey! It's because I do love you I'm talkin' to you. Stay 'way from that cowhand. I don't want him on my place."

Then his anger vanished as abruptly as it had come, and Bush got up and patted Lainey's shoulder.

"I didn't aim to scare you, honey. I guess . . . I'm scared myself. I only wish your mama'd come back."

But Allegra did not come back. Instead, she wrote: "Missouri is beautiful this fall. I've never seen so much red and gold in the trees. The maples on the driveway have all turned. I climbed up the tower yesterday and thought of Lainey and how she loved to be there, and how much I miss both of you. When the crops are laid by, why don't you come up for a visit?" Bush dropped the letter on the table. One of the pages fell into a puddle of cold coffee and the ink began to run in the stain. "You finish. I got to get back to work," he said.

Lainey picked up the letter, dried off the coffee and put it back in the envelope. She would read it sometime. Right now she was lost in a dream of Quirt's coming to see her and what he would say to her and what she would say to him. She invented endless conversations that went on all through the day and at night they held her sleepless in her bed. Every morning she dressed with finicky care, disregarding the washing and ironing that was piling up. This might be the day! Every evening she brushed her heavy hair till it shone and sat before the mirror looking at the bright-eyed stranger reflected there. To think she had hated the color of her eyes! Greeneyes, she whispered. Greeneyes.

The middle of October, and autumn, travelling down from Missouri, slathered the Territory with color. Day after bright day the weather held.

"The man that doesn't believe in Heaven on a day like this is blind, deaf, and dumb," Brother Gordon said from the pulpit. The congregation nodded in agreement. Plenty to be thankful for. Prices were improving; crops had been good. This might be the session when Dennis Flynn, the indomitable Dennis, would bull the Free Homes Bill through Congress and relieve them all of the payment of a dollar twenty-five an acre for their homesteaded lands. In November William Jennings Bryan was sure to be elected, and even though most of them in that section were staunch Republicans, they cherished a secret hope that the Free Silver Millennium might come true. With all these blessings before them they bowed their heads and spoke a hearty, "A-men."

"A-men, brother Ben, shot a rooster and killed a hen," came from one of the wart-dotted Sullavan twins. His mother cuffed him but his wail was drowned in the shuffle of benches as the congregation got ready to leave.

This was the moment Lainey dreaded. Somebody was sure to ask, "When's your mama comin' home?" She parried the question as well as she could and heard Bush doing the same. When they got into the buckboard he handed her the lines. He looked more tired than when he had worked in the field all day.

Once home Bush took off his boots and lay down across the bed. It was the first time Lainey had ever seen him do such a thing. She took off her church dress and hung it up, put on a brown calico, ripped it off, and settled on a green calico with a white collar. Humming a nameless tune she set the table for supper, then went out into the late sunshine.

She walked slowly at first, then a west wind came up and teased her skirts, urging her to hurry. It was a cool clean wind that carried the tang of smoke, of falling leaves and drying grasses. At the long slope of the hill she paused to look at the glory before her. Down in the draw the tree with the catface brand flaunted its golden leaves. It was much the same as it had been the first time she saw it. The land around it had never been cut by a plow, and if it hadn't been for a back road that wound over from beyond Morehouse's quarter through the edge of the Sheridan place, a person standing there would not have known that the Run had ever been.

The wind whispered at Lainey's ear and she remembered how it had been a friend when she first came to the Territory. She began to run with the wind. Down the hill, down the hill, gathering speed, the tumble weed catching at her skirt. Down and down, jumping the patch of prickly pear, stumbling on the boards of the sled Bush had made for last year's brief snow. "Hello!" she called to the wind and the echo died in her mouth and answered in her drumming ears. Hello! Hello! She ran and the wind ran and through wind-flattened eyelashes she saw the golden leaves of the tree with the catface brand.

That was how she came on Quirt Kearney, running almost straight into his arms. She came to a stop before him, her face lifted and laughing, as he stepped out from a clump of persimmon trees.

"Hello, Greeneyes," he said.

Lainey gasped for breath, but not from surprise, for it seemed right that he should be there, the proper ending of the dreams she had lived in since the night of the magic-lantern shown.

"Where . . . where'd *you* come from?"

"Blew in on the tail o' that west wind," he smiled. It was idle talk, but it fitted the way Lainey felt. The wind had led her, hurried her to him. The wind, her friend. "Where *you* goin'?"

"For a walk," she said primly, tucking back her hair.

"Mighty fast walk. I couldn't keep up with a clip like that, but if you'll slow down . . ." He put her hand in the crook of his arm and whistled to the bay quarterhorse standing with dropped reins. "I'm shot with luck today. Ride out lookin' for one o' Morehouse's flea-bitten dogies an' end up with the prettiest girl in Oklahoma Territory."

For one moment her fast-beating heart believed him. And together they walked toward the tree with the catface brand, tossing talk back and forth. Never had she been able to talk to anybody as she talked to this stranger. His dark eyes looked down on her attentively; his mouth curved in a smile at whatever she said. He walked badly, but even that was in his favor. Cowboys never walked, they rode; still, for Lainey Sheridan he would *walk*. She shivered with sheer delight.

"You cold?"

"A little." She had learned since Arch asked her. This time there was no dusty buggy robe but Quirt's arm, warm and protective around her.

"That better?"

"Ummmmm," she said, a soft purring sound that committed her to nothing but did not protest, either.

They reached the tree with the catface brand. Quirt ran his finger over the puckered scar the surveyor's axe had left, while Lainey talked to him about the Run.

"You think a lot o' this place, don't you?"

"It's the best quarter in the whole Territory," she said. Then for the first time she wondered if it really were. "Bush . . . that's Bushrod Sheridan, my father . . . thinks so."

"I reckon he'd know." There was nothing you could object to in

278

his words, yet Lainey knew Quirt was laughing at her, and Bush, and the whole Territory.

"I thought maybe you came down to the Kickapoo opening last year."

"Me? I'm no nester." His contempt was unmistakable now. His lazy smile had turned cold. "I was ridin' for the Circle Z up in the Strip when the durn' fools opened up the country. I hope every single Boomer starves! An' they will. That's cow country, not garden patch."

His anger frightened her; she must get him away from it. "What . . . what did you do then? After that?"

"Wrangled hosses for an outfit in West Texas. Then I took a notion to drift." She considered gratefully the miracle that had led him to the Sac and Fox country.

"I headed for the Osage Nation, but I got sidetracked. Came down here to see what was left. This used to be ranch country, you know. The old K spread. Griffensteins. Th' Turkey Track." He jerked a piece of bark from the tree, threw it on the ground and set his fine high-heeled boot on it. "What'd I find? Patch o' cotton. Patch o' corn. Patch o' turnips. An' a fence every time you turn around."

Lainey was at once ashamed, apologetic for the Territory.

"This feller Morehouse's got a few cows. I'm ridin' for him, if you c'n call it that." Quirt scowled. "Son of a gun wanted me to take a hand plowin'. I sure settled his hash on that." From his shirt pocket came a sack of tobacco. He untied the string with his teeth, rolled a cigarette with one hand and placed it between his lips. Lainey watched, fascinated, while he flipped a match on his thumbnail. The smoke that trickled from his nostrils seemed to put him back in good humor. He pointed to a fallen limb, silvery gray in the dry grass. "I'm talkin' too much. You set down over there an' let me take a good look at you."

She sat down, spreading her skirts around her, conscious of how she looked with the reddening sun at her back. Quirt made her feel as if she were in a picture frame. Crouched on his heels his jeans tight on his long slim legs he looked at her, drew on his

279

cigarette, and let the smoke wander out his mouth and up his nose again. She began to blush and leaned over to pick a piece of dry foxtail grass.

"Yep," he said, "that's the way you looked first time I laid eyes on you. Sittin' up there in that old float in the hot sun. You made the rest of 'em look sick. I said to myself, 'There's a lady. A sure 'nough thoroughbred.' "

"Did you? Really?"

"You're mighty right I did. Then at that dance. You dancin' with that ol' big-footed boy . . . now don't pucker up, I'm not sayin' a thing *against* him, but he dances like he was hoein' cotton."

Lainey laughed, unashamed. The years of thinking of Arch almost as part of herself, relying on him, delighting in him, disappeared in that one deft flick of ridicule. He did dance exactly that way; like he was hoein' cotton.

"Then there at the schoolhouse. You up there like a little queen, your eyes shinin'."

"How'd you happen to come that night?" She longed to hear him say that it was because he thought she might be there, but Quirt drew back a little and let his look wander over her shoulder.

"Just happened along. Just shot with luck like I was today."

"It was nice of you to give so much money to the schoolhouse."

"Now you know better'n that." The intimacy between them was restored. "I just wanted to see you smile real big. Just wanted to see you show your pretty teeth."

"Oh, Quirt!"

"Easy come, easy go," he shrugged. "I had it then, now I'm flat busted." The shocked look on her face made him laugh. The bay quarterhorse nickered and they turned together to see the palomino mare trotting up the road, Arch on her back.

Lainey felt as if the trees and the brush had dropped away and left her sitting with Quirt on a high pinnacle. Arch lifted the mare to a full gallop as he went by, and she knew that he had seen them. With an impulse she did not stop to understand she called and waved. Arch did not answer, his face set on the road ahead. In an instant he was gone around the turn.

"Friend o' yours?" Quirt asked pointedly.

"Just one of the neighbors."

The savor was gone from the afternoon. Try as she would, Lainey could not bring it back. The light talk turned clumsy and halting. She was halfway glad when she heard Bush's long drawn-out, "Cooooooo Boss, Cooooooo Boss," as he called the cow in for milking.

"I've got to go now," she said.

"Want me to walk you home?"

"No. No, I'll just . . ." Lainey fumbled for words, unable to tell Quirt that Bush had forbidden her to let him on the place.

He mounted the quarterhorse and sat easily, looking down at her, but she dared not look him full in the eyes lest he see the naked longing there for him to return.

"G'bye, Greeneyes." His voice laughed at her, and suddenly it didn't matter if he knew, or if Bush had forbidden her, or anything at all. She *had* to see him again. But before she could tell him so he wheeled the horse and cantered off, pressing through the blazing red of the brushy sumac.

As long as she could see him she watched, tiptoe, but he was soon gone and it seemed right that the sun chose that moment to drop behind the hill. Slowly Lainey turned to walk back up the slope. Milking had to be done. Milk strained. Chickens fed. Supper put on the table. Dishes washed. Quirt Kearney had come and gone.

Quirt came back on Tuesday and again on Friday. Lainey met him at the tree with the catface brand where golden heart-shaped leaves twirled down on them in the cool autumn wind. If she remembered that Bush had forbidden Quirt to come onto the place she ignored the memory. She lived in two worlds, now. The house on the hill where she slept, cooked, ate, washed, and scrubbed, and the world of the cottonwood tree that she shared with Quirt. The time she spent with him became far more real, more important than the dragging hours passed in the house.

One night as she brushed at her hair . . . Quirt said it was like satin in the sunshine . . . she thought of the round red rocks she had found long ago. They had held jewels that waited for Lainey

281

Sheridan to set them free. Now, she, in her turn, had been found and set free by this tall soft-spoken man with the lazy smile. Free to laugh and make fun, to let the tiresome work of the claim be forgotten, to feel a warm arm around her when the wind blew cool and they sat close together on a fallen limb. Free, one day, to take and give a kiss.

But if the talk and laughter, the hand-holding, the long secret looks were light and easy, the kiss was not. Lainey was shaken and half-scared. A girl at Jackrabbit School had vowed that her mother told her if you kissed a man you got a baby. Lainey could understand now why the mother had told such a tale. Kissing was . . . dangerous. But danger could be fun, too. The next time he came she ran straight into his arms and when Quirt didn't kiss her she was painfully disappointed and ashamed of her own disappointment. Mama and Aunt Ellen said nice girls didn't want to be kissed. That day they found a persimmon tree laden, waiting the first frost, and they pelted each other with the hard orange fruit, laughing and shouting like children.

Quirt never stayed long, and he never said when he was coming back. Or if he were coming back at all. So each meeting had to be enjoyed to the utmost because it might be the last. Each time Lainey ran out to the chickenyard . . . the only place on the hill from which she could glimpse the tree . . . wild excitement or sick despair awaited her. The hens never got used to her running among them and scattered, squawking, as if they had spied a hawk. There were fewer and fewer eggs in the nests, but that was small price to pay for the heady knowledge that Quirt might be waiting.

He never asked to walk her to the house again, seeming to understand from her first awkward refusal that he would be unwelcome. That was one of the things about him that she loved . . . the way he sensed what she was thinking and did not force her to say everything out. But every time they were together was not happy for Quirt had a dark, moody side to him that Lainey dreaded. He would sit, smoking, his eyes sullen and withdrawn, and not say a dozen words. Or he would lash at the brush with the short-handled whip he carried. He'd got his name from it, she guessed,

282

but how or why she did not dare ask. These dark, guessed-at things were part of his strangeness and that, too, Lainey loved.

Quirt fitted into no life she had known before. Neither the tradition-filled life of Riverview, nor the hard-pressed life of the homesteaders. He never mentioned where he had come from any more than where he was going and she was content to take him as he was. A man who could drift, leaving a place when he "took a notion." A man without ties that were forever pulling him "back home." A man who carried all he owned on a fancy saddle. A man who could throw twenty silver dollars into a girl's lap just to see her smile.

So they met and talked and laughed and kissed and met again. A nice girl didn't meet a man in the woods. Lainey knew that. And Lainey knew that nice girls and bad girls were the only two kinds. But she preferred to forget it for a moment, as she forgot Bush's command that Quirt not come onto the place. This was different.

If Bushrod Sheridan had not had his eyes turned inward he might have seen the change in Lainey. The way she sang at her work, her sudden concern over her clothes . . . the Jenny June sewing machine hummed late in the night . . . or even the way a frightened melancholy would overcome her and she would stand, hand at her throat, thinking how Quirt might "take a notion" to drift out of the Sac and Fox country as he had drifted in. But Bush saw nothing because he was blinded by his own inner torments. Fear that Allegra might never come back had put lines in his face and shaken salt on his hair. He paid little attention to Lainey, and having once forbidden her to see Quirt it never occurred to him that she might disobey. Besides, he was busy.

After church one Sunday when he had been plagued by the neighbors' questions, he said to Lainey, "I've been thinking. It's time I built Allegra a house. A real one. I never meant her to go on cooped up in this place." He looked with dissatisfaction around the crowded room with the curtained-off bed. "It's not right, raised the way she was."

And because with him to think was to act he rode off to Randall on Monday morning to talk plans, money, lumber, and to try to find a carpenter. Word got around quickly and it was a cause for head-shaking among the neighbors.

"Buildin' it for her, I reckon," Mrs. Shipp said to Sis Pritchard. "But she'll never live in it. Too high'n mighty for the likes of us."

"I wish she'd come back," Sis Pritchard shook her head and her third chin quivered. "You never really knew her the way she was right after Sunny came. Why on Sundays we all went over an' had the tore-downdest singin' you ever heard."

"I like folks that's the same all the time," Mrs. Shipp sniffed. "Off ag'in, on ag'in don't set good with me."

"I feel sorry for Bush. An' Lainey too."

"They say," Mrs. Shipp held up her hand and spoke behind it, "that young feller that gave in all the money at the schoolhouse's hangin' around Lainey. I don't know m'self, but it's what they say."

"Looky here," Sis Pritchard said sharply, "It was your Doris that asked him first off for the money. I guess I was there an' I know."

With the house to plan and start Bush had little time for other things. As long as meals were cooked and he had clean clothes Lainey could do as she pleased. She scrambled through the housework and made a dozen trips to the chickenyard every morning, standing on tiptoe among the scattered feeding and drinking pans to catch a glimpse of Quirt or of the bay quarterhorse tethered to a tree.

One day she took a slice of cake with her and Quirt praised her cooking so from then on she always brought something for them to eat. The tree with the catface brand became more than a trysting place. Rather, it was a roofless home that they shared, the fallen limb becoming the table where they ate from a fringed napkin. Lainey often raided the chicken flock, excusing herself that the hens were not laying. Fortunately, Bush didn't care for white meat and he never noticed that the "pulley bone," Quirt's favorite, did not get on the platter. Lainey experimented with dried fruit turnovers, molasses candy, gingerbread, anything that could be eaten out of hand. Nothing was too much trouble. And since she never knew when Quirt was coming she cooked something special every day. Bush declared she was better than Mattie. It was nice to hear him say so, but his praise meant little compared to the look on Quirt's face when she offered him sliced ham, pink and succulent, between cold biscuits, tea cakes, crisp and sugar crusted, or quarters of spicy pumpkin pie. To a man condemned to eating old man Morehouse's meals it was pure heaven, he said.

"An' to think you think this much of ol' Quirt," he marvelled.

Her heart swelled so big with wanting to do things for him she could hardly breathe. "Whatever you like . . . whatever you want . . . just say . . ."

He looked at her for a long minute.

"Better be careful how you say that, Greeneyes."

"I don't care. I mean it. Every word."

That was a warm sunny afternoon and after they had finished eating Quirt slid from the fallen limb to the grass and put his head against her knees. The pressure of his head, the male smell of tobacco and hair oil, the sun shining on his smooth, tanned cheek, filled her with shimmering ecstasy. At just the right moment Quirt reached up, pulled her face down to his and kissed her.

"Nobody like my Greeneyes," he murmured. "I'd like to take you up behind the saddle and ride outa here some night. Take you to a real country. Idaho. Texas. Montana. Ranches a hundred miles wide. Just you'n me."

"Oh, Quirt, Quirt," she breathed against his face. "Tell me about it."

His arms dragged her down and the dry grass crackled as she came close to him. For an instant the breath of each was warm on the other's face. Then Quirt stood up.

"I gotta be gettin' outa here," he said.

Without another word he mounted the quarterhorse and dug his spurred heels savagely into the bay flanks. Wide eyed, frightened, Lainey stared after him until the last sound of his going was swallowed up in the sound of the wind in the trees.

Bush came home from Randall with a wagon-load of studding for the new house, his face like a thunder cloud.

Lainey met him, her chin at an angle very much like his. Nothing he could say would make much difference. Quirt had not been near the place for three whole days.

"What do you know about a fight between Arch an' that Kearney?"

Her heart lurched. Maybe Quirt was hurt. Maybe he needed her. "I don't know anything," she said truthfully.

"Don't you lie to me! I get to Randall and find the whole town talking that Arch jumped Kearney outside the Red Dog. They fought till somebody called the law and he pistol-whipped 'em apart. Some said it was over who had the best horse, but some," he choked in anger and humiliation, "some said it was over a girl . . . you. Now I want the truth!"

"I don't know why you're asking me," she fended. "You just called me a liar. As for Arch, I haven't see him for a month. And Quirt Kearney might have a dozen girls . . . for all I know."

Bush's angry disbelief subsided slowly into puzzled confusion.

"I reckon that's right," he said, nodding as if to convince himself. He washed, sat down at the table, arranged his knife, fork, and spoon into a triangle, then swept them into a pile. "But it's funny about Arch. He's not the kind to pick a fight."

Lainey's poise deserted her. "You said yourself he jumped Quirt. A person'd think Arch Hampton had wings! I'm sick and tired of hearin', 'Arch . . . Arch . . . Arch . . .' !"

Bush said slowly, "I always thought you an' Arch'd make a match of it. Sometime."

"Well, you can just unthink it!"

He started to speak, clamped his lips together, served the plates and ate in silence. Lainey became aware that he was watching her with a hurt, suspicious look. It meant nothing to her now but that she must be careful. Careful.

After supper Lainey walked out to the chickenyard. The wind was chilly and the ghostly skeleton of a castor-bean plant rattled dry leaves by the fence. It had come up as a volunteer from the crop she had raised to buy Arch's Christmas present. She hoped Arch would forgive her and find someone else, only, as she ran over all the girls in Jackrabbit School, or even in the Jolly Mandolin Club in Randall, none of them seemed quite suitable. The sky was bright with stars and though Lainey could not see the tree with the catface brand just to look in that direction made her feel better. Tomorrow Quirt would surely come.

Chapter 25

The next morning Bush hung around the house until Lainey thought she would go crazy. Then he went just outside and paced off space for the new house, setting corner stobs cut slaunchwise to sight by. He stacked the studding by the side of the house, then called in at the door that he was riding over to Doggetts.

Right away Lainey ran out to the chickenyard but Quirt was not in sight. Yesterday's applesauce cake had fallen in the middle and she decided to make some pumpkin pie. Quirt liked that better, anyway. Having something to do helped to keep down the uneasiness that rose inside her like bubbles in bread dough set too close to the stove. She rolled piecrust, beat eggs, measured spices. Soon the house was full of a sweet rich smell of baking. Lainey had just begun an elaborate dream of being with Quirt in the wild ranch country, when the Pritchard buggy, sagging with Sis's weight, stopped outside. Frowning, she went out to greet her visitor and invite her inside.

Sis Pritchard sat, uncomfortable, in Bush's chair, her short legs not quite reaching the floor.

"Bakin', are you? Smell fair makes my mouth water."

"Just some pies. I made cake yesterday but it wasn't much good."

"Sounds like ol' Bush's livin' high on the hawg." Sis fell to reminiscing. "'Twasn't like that when we first came, no siree! Pie an' cake were scarcer'n hen's teeth. First pie I made in the Territory was out of sheep sorrel, stewed down an' sugared and thickened with flour. I baked it in a Dutch oven Ab made for me to set up in front o' the campfire. Next day the wind took that oven outa camp and I never saw it ag'in."

She chuckled into her chins and settled back, "All the store meat we had that winter was bacon with a double row o' buttons. Ab

287

got it in pay for a load o' fence posts. It wasn't bad cooked with greens. That's where I met your mama, gatherin' greens that first spring. Neither one of us knew what to take but we saw Miz Halfmoon out there and we watched her and took same as she did. Dock, pig-weed, lamb's quarter, pepper grass. She dug some wild onion so I did too, but it was mighty strong. Went through me like a dose o' salts."

"Yes, ma'am," Lainey said, hearing only half of it. If Quirt came and left while she listened to this gabby talk! Sis sighed, frowned, and began to pleat her serge skirt with her fingers, her face turning serious.

"Lainey, I'm not one to beat around the bush," Lainey's spine stiffened. "There's talk about you an' Quirt Kearney."

She had known it all along but had refused to admit it. Now Sis Pritchard's fat troubled face forced her to and she hated Sis for what she had done. In icy imitation of Aunt Ellen Lainey said, "I don't know what you're talking about."

Splotchy red mottled the neck and face before her, but Sis held her temper.

"It's this, honey. With your mama gone and just Bush . . . well, men don't know a thing about young girls . . . some of us thought . . . that is . . . when we heard . . ." Lainey's outrage heightened. They had talked her over! The tree with the catface brand was no longer a haven but an invaded domain with the neighbors leering and peering from the bushes. Sis squirmed, half put out her hand. "Now don't go off half-cocked. He may be just all right, but the way he's been sneakin' around . . ."

"He is not sneaking!"

"Well, however you put it. Meetin' you down there in the draw an' all looks kind of funny. Miz Doggett heard that he got the money he gave so big at the schoolhouse bettin' on a hoss race with some gawk over in the Kickapoo that didn't have it to lose. An' Jurd Morehouse gave out that he wasn't wuth his salt to work. Just a fancy roper 'n' rider."

"Jurd Morehouse! Do you know what he puts out to eat three times a day? Beans!"

"Oh, lotsa folks gets by on beans. But what I'm gettin' at . . ."

"Mrs. Doggett didn't make any fuss when Quirt took Dotty Sullavan out."

"That's different. Dotty's older'n you and she's got her ma to look out after her, whether she does it or not."

"It's just because he's a stranger . . ."

"Mary Hampton asked me to come over. She'd o' come herself but she was scared Arch might get wind of it an' cut up. An' that's another thing—the way Arch's takin' it. Mary says he won't half eat and he's about to kill himself workin' all that land."

"So he jumps onto Quirt and tries to beat him up in Randall!"

"Did, huh?" Admiration sparkled in Sis's eyes, half hidden behind her cheeks. "Who licked?"

"I think you're dreadful! I think you're awful, every last one of you." Lainey cried out with her fists clenched. "It's none of your business who comes to see me and where, and I'll thank you to tell the rest of 'em the same. Peekin' . . . prying . . . nosey . . ."

"All right, all right," Sis got up heavily. "I told Mary this wouldn't do no good, but she would have it. Young folks got to burn their own fingers." She plodded to the door. "I just hope yours ain't burned too bad a'ready. G'bye."

Lainey did not answer. Sick with anger and the quick growth of fear that followed it she stood in the doorway. The south wind had warmed the day but a chill crept through her. The house behind her was quiet, too quiet, except for the crackling of the wood in the stove. Quirt. I've got to get to Quirt. A senseless pounding began in her head. Quirt. Quirt.

As if she had called aloud he came cantering up the road. Lainey blinked, unbelieving. Was it really Quirt and not just the dream of him that lived with her night and day? Around her lay all the familiar household things, the things that meant safety and the known world of her seventeen years, but in the instant of Quirt's dismounting at the gate she knew that none of them was worth anything without this man. Better the tree with the catface brand and Quirt than the claim without him. She did not run out to meet him but stood, framed in the doorway, conscious in every part of her being of his smallest movements, the sound of his high-heeled boots on the hard ground and the faint metallic click of his spurs.

Then he was in the room beside her and she shut the door after him.

"You shouldn't have come," she said, "my father . . . the neighbors . . ."

"Yeah, I know," Quirt shrugged. "But it don't matter. I came to say goodbye, Greeneyes. Time for me to drift."

"You mean you're going away?" Lainey asked stupidly.

"Yeah. I've been here too long a'ready." He ran his fingers along his jaw and she saw a dark bruise under the smooth, tanned skin, split flesh on his knuckles. "I didn't want you to think I was bein' run off. Or anything."

"Oh," Lainey cried, "you're hurt."

"It's nothin'. I'da cut him down to size if that fool at the Red Dog hadn't called the law."

"But he should have put Arch in jail," she said angrily. "He started it."

"That's no way to settle a fight," he told her, "callin' for the law. But maybe this time it's best. Might make trouble for you when I'm gone."

"I'm not afraid of trouble. I wish you'd hit every one of them." She was half-crying and he gathered her into his arms, not asking who "they" were but understanding that the two of them stood together and all the world outside were their enemies. Close to his hard, lean body she heard a fluttering in her ears like the upward flight of the pigeons around Riverview tower on a summer morning. I love you, she whispered, too low for him to hear. I love you. I love you.

"You're a real thoroughbred," he was saying, "my Greeneyes gal. I'll not forget you in a hurry. Wish I could take you with me. Right up behind the saddle. Ride off and never come back." It was the beginning of her favorite dream but this time it was going bitterly wrong.

"Where're you going?" she mumbled into his jacket.

"Maybe the Creek Nation. Maybe Texas." He stepped away from her and picking up a chip from the woodbox spat on it. "Wet or dry. Wet's east, dry's west." The chip flipped and hit the woodbox dry side up. "West it'll be. Texas." He smiled down at her, his lazy smile, hands on his slim hips, and it was as if he had already started. As if he were gone. She knew then that no one could hold him. There was only one way.

"Don't! Don't go," Lainey begged, despising herself for being unable to keep from saying it. "Don't go now, anyway, wait till tonight." She must not let him see what she was thinking so she put her face against his arm.

"Please, Quirt, I want . . . I want to fix you a snack for the road." It was a weak excuse but better than none. Then deliberately she turned to him. "We've never been together at night. I want to have that to remember."

"Greeneyes," he said and his voice was husky. She saw a fire begin in the depths of his dark eyes and she was proud because she had kindled it. "Greeneyes!" After he kissed her he said, "Tonight? The tree?"

"Not there. Too many people know. At the schoolhouse." She felt that she had planned it days ago and now all that she had to do was to open her mouth and the right words would come. "Eight o'clock. You'd better hurry, now. Goodbye."

She almost pushed him out the door, afraid that Bush might come home and spoil everything.

As Quirt rode away, his hat lifted in a sweeping arc, his spurs jingling, the sun flashing on his fancy saddle, the breath caught in Lainey's throat. A little way down the road he began to sing and the words drifted back to her on the south wind. "Oh that girl that pretty little girl, the girl I left behind me . . ."

But she was not going to be left behind. She was going with Quirt, to be with him forever and ever.

The smell of burning sugar filled the kitchen and Lainey ran to the oven. The pumpkin pies were scorched a leathery brown. As Lainey was throwing salt in the oven to cut down the smell Bush came in.

"I've got a chance to get a carpenter," he reported. "Feller over by Taney. Bill Doggett says he's A-one at building, but he can't farm for sour apples. He's lookin' for work right now and if you don't mind staying by yourself this evening I'll ride over and see him."

Lainey could hardly believe her luck. It must mean that what

291

she was planning to do was right. Of course the chance to get a carpenter should not be missed, she agreed, and she wouldn't be lonesome with all the sewing she had on hand. Almost timidly Bush suggested that she could ride over to Hamptons' for a visit but he did not press her when she did not reply. Putting his arm around her shoulders he said, "You're a fine girl, Lainey. If it seems like I'm hard on you . . . well, I don't mean to be."

All Lainey could do was nod. One word, one show of tenderness and she would have poured out the whole story.

The afternoon alternately sprinted and dragged.

For a while she would work frantically cleaning the house and cooking things in an effort to "make up" to Bush. Then she would stop, putting her cold hands against her burning face and whisper, "Quirt. I'm going away with Quirt."

Reaching for something on the top shelf of the kitchen safe her hand brushed the Haviland plates and she remembered Allegra's word on the Fourth of July . . . the very day she had seen Quirt for the first time . . . "Some day I want you to have those plates for a home of your own."

Now she was turning her back on all of that. There would be no place for Haviland china in the life she was choosing. Time enough for plates and walnut tables and braided rugs when she and Quirt would ride back home to be forgiven. Maybe they'd even take up land nearby. Quirt was set against being a nester but she was certain that she could somehow make him change.

No, a horse and saddle was all she needed. And the new riding habit with the divided skirt that Aunt Ellen had sent, and the moss-green silk if she could roll it small enough. Heavens! It was getting dark already. The towering flat-bottomed clouds that the warm wind had brought out of the south were already touched with gold and rose. While Lainey was milking and feeding the stock the sun disappeared and it was almost cold before she went into the house.

Too excited to eat she packed a snack . . . two of everything. They could eat it somewhere along the road to Randall. If only Brother Gordon could marry them, but he might refuse without Bush's consent. Better ask at the Methodist parsonage where they were forever changing preachers at the whim of some far-off authority. Married, I'm going to be married! Her heart jumped and beat faster. In the chest of drawers at Riverview was a lace veil like a spun cobweb. Aunt Ellen had said . . . But a veil's not a marriage. A marriage is going with the man you love. Mama and Bush. Jeb Saunders and Laice. Lainey and Quirt.

Taking a small carpet bag from under the bed she went upstairs to pack. She rolled the moss-green silk into the tightest ball she could but still it was bulky. Never mind, she would not go without it. She jammed it on top of the white nainsook nightgown that made her blush when she folded it. A hair brush. A green-velvet ribbon. A hand mirror with daisies painted on the back. Looking for handkerchiefs she saw the keepsake box. She remembered now, the round quartzy stone was the one the little Indian boy had given her for a piece of candy. And there was the silver spoon; it had begun to tarnish again. She rubbed it a little, then dropped it in the box. Too late for that now. Then she saw the four pieces of cardboard that had been Arch's photograph. She pushed them into place so that the torn face looked up at her. Please, she whispered, please understand. Then with one quick motion she scattered them apart.

In the low ground, in the dry gulch and the draws a fog was settling. It was not visible from the house on the hill, but it seemed chilly upstairs and the sound of the wind was gone. Fog was rare in Oklahoma Territory, but it could come like the ghost of the buffalo herds that had once covered the plains. It crept up the hill with a steady, silent motion, thick and white.

Downstairs the clock struck seven. Lainey dropped the keepsake box, scrambled the contents together, and stuck it back in the drawer. The garnet cross fell to the floor and as she picked it up and put it around her throat she could feel her heart beating there. She put the note she had written to Bush by the mirror. It had taken a long time to write and she had torn up a dozen attempts. "I have gone with Quirt Kearney," it read. "Please don't try to find us. Love to you and Mama, Elaine Saunders Sheridan." It seemed fitting to sign your whole name when you were going away to be married.

The minutes were slipping by. She could reach the schoolhouse in ten minutes but Quirt might be early. Nothing must go wrong now. Lainey picked up the carpet bag and opened the front door. She stepped back, gasping, as the fog confronted her, a tall, sheeted ghost. An eerie silence covered the claim. But after her first fright Lainey realized that this, too, was on her side. The fog would hide her and Quirt as they rode to Randall. Ducking her head she went out into the dripping night. Nellie was reluctant to leave the barn. As Lainey rode out she pulled the mare close to the house and with a rush of tenderness touched for one last time the rough cottonwood siding. Then Nellie trotted out to the road and the fog closed around them.

The cornfield, the dry gulch, Pappy Vickers' turnout, Sunny's grave, she checked off the places hidden in that swirling white blanket. The road was so familiar she was not afraid of being lost, but still she peered anxiously ahead over Nellie's pricked ears.

If only she had told Quirt to meet her nearer home. Maybe he was already waiting at the schoolhouse. Maybe he would ride up the road a ways. She strained her ears in the cold silence. The carpet bag flopped at her knee and she forced the handle down over the pommel. Her hands were cold and stiff. Gloves! Of all things, she had forgotten to bring gloves. With longing she recalled the glow of the fire through the open stove lids. The thought shamed her. If she couldn't stand a little fog! The schoolhouse must be close. The turnout should be along here.

Then she was sure she heard a horse coming up the road. Coming slowly, the way a man will ride when he is scanning the road ahead. Coming right toward her! "Quirt," she called, "Quirt, I'm right here!"

"Helloooooo, where are you?" The fog took the voice and twisted it out of all semblance to Quirt's voice, but Lainey forgot caution, forgot everything but that he might pass by unseeing in the mists. She caught at the saddle horn and half-rose in the stirrup calling again.

"Quirt! It's Lainey!"

They were almost upon each other, the two horses that moved in the fog. Nellie stopped, stock-still. The other horse nickered inquiringly, then came alongside.

"Lainey?" Arch Hampton said, and for a split second she wondered why she had not known his voice before. "I got Bush up behind, here. He's hurt."

Together they got Bush into the house on the hill, his right leg almost useless. He wavered in and out of consciousness, using Lainey and Arch for crutches and his bulk, made awkward by pain, brought them closer together than they had been for weeks. Once their hands touched around his neck and each drew back, then caught again as he stumbled.

"Chair, not bed," Bush grunted and they eased him into his chair. Arch propped his hurt leg up on the woodbox. In broken snatches Lainey got the story as she stirred up the fire, put the tea kettle on, found the whisky, and looked for the liniment made from Jimdandy's secret recipe.

The man at Taney had not been at home so Bush turned around and started back. But it was low country around Taney and the fog had come up early making travelling slow. Thinking Lainey might be worried he had forced Blackjack to hurry. Somewhere the horse had wandered off the road and stumbled into a gopher hole. He had fallen with Bush under him at the edge of a draw, the ground gave way and they went down.

"He screamed," Bush said, his face gray under the tan, "then he never made another sound. Broke his neck, near's I could tell in the dark. Best hoss I ever . . ."

"We got to get that boot off," Arch said. "Can you stand it?"

Bush nodded, took a swallow of straight whisky and shuddered as it went down. "Then I crawled a ways up the draw and made it to the top. Don't hardly know what I did do. First thing I knew, there was Arch."

"Beauty found him," Arch straddled the woodbox and took hold of the boot. "We were late over't the other place and got caught by the fog. She nickered and snorted and wouldn't go on. Then I heard Bush an' I durn near fell in the draw gettin' to him." He gave a tug to the boot. Lainey saw the sweat pop out on Bush's forehead. He held out his glass and she splashed whisky into it. Arch tried again.

"Whoa, there!" Bush gritted.

Arch looked at Lainey. It was the first time, she realized, that

295

he had looked at her since they had come into the house. It was an impersonal gaze but under it something seethed. Anger? Hurt? Contempt? She didn't know. Had he heard her call for Quirt? She looked away.

"Guess we better cut the boot off," Arch said. "Hate to, but that ankle's swelling."

It was a tricky thing to do. The knife blade worked through the heavy leather barely stopping outside the home-knit sock. Once Arch's knife slipped and the white flesh puffed through the gray fabric, a tiny trickle of red at the knife point. Bush winced but said nothing. Only once was there any sound except the sawing of the knife blade. It was the clock striking eight.

Lainey, kneeling by the woodbox, holding the foot steady, did not look up. Eight o'clock. Quirt would be at the schoolhouse. He would ride away thinking she had not cared enough to come. My love, my love, she thought, wait for me, my love. But even as she thought it she knew Quirt was not a man to wait. The luck she had had all day, the monstrous luck that led her to think everything was on her side, was a cruel trick.

"You're holdin' too tight," Bush said through his teeth. She tried to let go.

"That'll do it." Arch put down the knife. The boot came off. He peeled off the sock. The foot was a sickly white, the ankle swollen and discolored. Bush wiggled his toes experimentally.

"Not broke, I guess, but it hurts like it." He lowered his foot into the hot water Lainey had placed before him, then leaned back, panting.

Half-past eight. If Quirt had been late . . . and he might have been with the fog. If she went now and rode fast . . . or even walked. You can't go off and leave your father helpless, one foot in a bucket of hot water. You can't walk out with Arch Hampton watching you. Just walk out and not come back. Oh, but I can't let Quirt go without me. I can't. She went on cutting long strips of sheeting for a bandage. Then Bush betrayed her.

Eyes still closed he asked her, "What were you doin', out on a night like this, Lainey? Get scared, or something?"

She clutched at his words and built on them. "I got scared. The fog and all. I was on my way over to see Doris. I left you a note."

Then she knew she had made a mistake. Shipps lived in the other direction. "I guess I got turned around." Arch knew she was lying. Let him. Let him think what he wanted to. At this very minute the bay quarterhorse was taking Quirt away from her. She put down the scissors and tore the last strip. The scream of the muslin was like the scream she felt inside her.

"I'll go put up your horse," Arch said. Remembering the carpet bag on the pommel she tried to think of a reason to stop him, but it was too late.

Bush said, "This'll be hard on you. I'll be laid up for a while."

"I don't mind," she said dully. Then it came back to her how she had made him and Bud Menifee laugh, years ago, and with an effort she added, "Root hog or die."

There was no laughter now, but a thin smile washed over Bush's haggard face. Arch was at the back door. He handed Lainey the carpet bag without a word.

"Thanks," she said, and started to add that she was going to spend the night, or that she had been taking her sewing, or that she had borrowed the bag from Doris and was returning it, but one look at him told her it was no use. He knew, and knowing he despised her.

"Want me to go after Doc Harter?" he asked Bush.

"Not tonight. Tomorrow, maybe. If I could just get some sleep." Lainey rubbed liniment on the ankle, the puffy flesh holding the print of her fingers as she worked. Then they bandaged it tight at Bush's direction and helped him to bed. Lainey fixed a sack of hot salt to put on his knee which was beginning to stiffen. Arch filled the waterbuckets and brought in wood by the armload. Weariness and whisky eased Bush into sleep.

"I'll be over in the mornin' to do the chores," Arch said at the door.

"You needn't. I can get along," Lainey said.

"I'll be over." He ran his hand across his cowlicks but they had risen again in rebellion before he got his hat on. "If you need anything, fire three shots. I c'n hear."

"I'll be perfectly all right," she insisted but he was out the door. Only when she heard Beauty start down the road did she realize that she hadn't thanked him, or said a word about his bring-

297

ing Bush home. Must you thank somebody for ruining your life?

It was half-past nine. She and Quirt would have been in Randall now. They would have been standing in front of the Methodist preacher. Bush began to snore. They had put him on his back and she could never lift him alone so the snoring would go on and on. The snores which began with a gurgling rumble went up and up to a crescendo, broke on a snort and started all over again. Her thoughts began to follow their jolting rhythm. Up, up, up, snort, down, up, up, up. I'm going crazy, she thought, or maybe I've been crazy all the time. I must have been to come back. Why didn't I ride on to the schoolhouse? Why am I here now? Up, up, up, snort, down, up, up, up.

Presently Bush muttered aloud and she went over to the bed. "You want something?"

"Blackjack," he said. "I had to leave him out there. Those damn' coyotes . . ."

She wanted to shake his shoulder, to dig her fingers in his flesh and scream that more than Blackjack had died that night. That her life was ruined and she would never love again. Raving about a dead horse when his own flesh and blood stood in mortal pain!

"He got the claim for us," Bush said. "If it hadn't been for him . . ."

"Go to sleep," she pulled the wool quilt up over him. "Go to sleep. Arch'll ride over in the morning."

When he started snoring again Lainey went upstairs and un-packed the carpet bag. The moss-green silk she would never wear again. She unhooked the garnet cross and put it in the keepsake box with the scraps of the photograph of Arch. It was strange that it took the sight of his torn face to make her cry. She pressed her head into the pillow her body abandoned to racking sobs. After the tears were over she sat up on the edge of the bed and took the note from the mirror. Without unfolding it she held it over the lamp chimney. The paper browned, curled. A greedy blue flame licked at the edge. She held it as long as she could, then dropped it into the hand-painted china pin-tray and watched it burn to a black ash.

Chapter 26

So began the dreary month of November when the few leaves left on the trees were brown flags of surrender, and the wind mourned across the Sac and Fox country remembering the lost summer. In the house on the hill Lainey went doggedly about her work. Arch came to do the chores, morning and evening, but he spoke to her as little as possible and she answered him the same way. At night, as soon as Bush was settled, she went upstairs and sat in the darkness dreaming of Quirt. The picture of him waiting at Jackrabbit School returned again and again. Was he somewhere in the vast land of Texas? Would he write to her some day and ask her to come to him? My love, my love, she whispered, if you had known you would have ridden up the hill and carried me away from them. And when she said these words Arch and Bush became two captors who had taken her by force, holding her against her will.

The fog had been gone by morning. A brisk wind erased it utterly and it lived only in the minds of the neighbors who loved to brag about the kinds and varieties of weather in the Territory. " 'Member that fog? Wasn't that a booger? Couldn't see my hand before my face." They talked about it when they came to visit Bush, for with the news of his accident they forgot the coolness that had risen between them and Allegra after Sunny's death. After all, this was old Bush and it was up to them to rally 'round. So they talked about the fog and the election, and especially their hope that the Free Homes Bill would pass.

When the neighbors came Lainey excused herself and went upstairs or out in the barn lot, or even down to the cyclone cellar. She was sure they were eying her furtively and snickering behind her back. "Got her comeuppance, didn't she?" "Tried to tell her but she was too smart." "Feller with an itchy foot like that's no good." She rejected all their offers of help whenever possible and the food that the women brought she served only to Bush, preferring to eat her own hurried cooking.

The day she saw Sis Pritchard driving up she ran to the back door and rode over to Halfmoons'. Lydia Halfmoon served her coffee and sat in polite silence, looking at the floor. Try as she would Lainey could find no way to reach her as Allegra had. It must have been the music that had made the bridge. She asked about Annie who had gone, now, to school at Carlisle in far-off Pennsylvania.

"Come back this summer, maybeso," Mrs. Halfmoon lapsed into "reservation talk." "Your mama home?"

"No, ma'am. She . . . I . . . this fall." She said it as if she had a real promise. "One letter said she had been to Kansas City and bought some new music. I wish you'd come over and play the organ."

"Maybeso," Mrs. Halfmoon said again, but Lainey knew she would never come until Allegra returned. And when would that be?

Back at the house she found Bush hobbling around the room with the cedar cane old man Morehouse had whittled for him. "You missed Sis Pritchard. She wanted to see you."

"I didn't want to see her," Lainey said, tired of pretending. "I left on purpose."

"I guessed you did." He hobbled over to the window where the pile of lumber was still stacked. "She told me about . . . she said she had some words with you. She feels pretty bad about it."

"She can just go right on feeling bad!"

"I know Sis's pretty flat-footed, but she meant well."

"I guess you think all of 'em meant well. The whole nosey bunch. I hope they're satisfied." It was a relief to blurt out what she thought. "Just because he was a stranger . . . What are they? Nothing but strangers themselves. But just because they got here first . . ."

"Lainey, I hate to see you take it that way. I guess I shouldn't have told you not to let him come on the place. I never thought . . ."

"The place," she stormed. "The Sheridan place! You act like it was so fine. It's just a little old quarter section of land. Patch of cotton. Patch of corn. There's places that are a hundred miles wide. But you won't let somebody I . . . I . . . love come on the Sheridan place. Well, Quirt came to see me plenty of times and I'm glad he did and I'll love him till the day I die." She looked around wildly as if searching for a weapon. "I don't blame Mama for going back to Riverview and staying. I wish I could go, too!"

If she had struck him in the face Bush would not have winced so violently. Lainey ran up the stairs to hide herself from what she had done but his face haunted her, and not even with the pillow over her head could she escape from the bleak look in his eyes—the look of a man who has staked everything on one throw and lost.

Later in the day Dr. Harter stopped by to see Bush on his way home from a call at Wellmans'. The need to stand together and cover up for the family brought Lainey downstairs, her hair combed, face washed and clean apron over her dress. The two men were swapping views of the coming election.

"You're a good nurse," Dr. Harter said to Lainey, closing his bag. "Bush's ankle is in fine shape and that knee'll work out in time. But you don't look very perky yourself."

"I'm all right," Lainey began to set the table. If the doctor would stay for supper it would put off the time when she would have to be alone with Bush.

"Bush is mighty lucky to have a girl like you."

She waited, steeled against what Bush might say, but he answered quickly, "They don't make 'em any better'n Lainey. She's my girl."

The old phrase was comforting.

"I'm going to leave her a tonic." He handed Lainey a bottle of thick brown medicine. "One tablespoon before meals, Lainey. And get out and around a little. You don't need to stay in so close. Bush is all right."

Dr. Harter couldn't stay for supper so Lainey walked him to the buggy.

"When's your mother coming home?" he asked abruptly.

"I don't know," he startled the truth out of her.

"Does she know that Bush was hurt."

"No. He wouldn't let me write to her. He told me twice not to."

"I see."

"Do you think I ought to? Anyway?"

He tugged at his moustache. "No, I guess not. But . . . a doctor ought to stick to muscles and let hearts alone. Still, the heart's a muscle, too." He smiled at her. "Don't pay any attention to me. I'm just talking to myself. And remember to get out and get around. You and young Hampton, now, ought to take in that minstrel show at the Knights of Pythias lodge hall tonight."

He drove off with a flourish of his whip. Lainey stood at the gate until he was out of sight, anger flickering within her. Why couldn't people leave her alone? She looked down the road where she had last seen Quirt, riding off in the sunlight, his hat in a sweeping, graceful arc. From far off a ghost of singing whispered, "Oh, that girl, that pretty little girl, the girl I left behind me . . ." Hoof beats made her turn, a wild hope leaping within her. It was Arch, coming to do the chores.

There was no sense in running and hiding whenever anybody came around.

From now on she would stand her ground. Especially with Arch. Deliberately Lainey walked over to the stretch of ground the mare would cross going to the barn lot.

"Hello, Arch," she said.

"Good evening," he lifted his hat, solemnly, formally, pulled the reins and rode around her. With her cheeks burning she went into the house.

"I've been thinking about what Doc said," Bush started. "Sis Pritchard said there's a play party at Jennings' tomorrow. I'll ask Arch to take you and . . ."

"I wouldn't go with him if he was the last man on earth," Lainey choked. "Now or any other time."

William Jennings Bryan lost the election for president on the Democratic ticket. Dennis Flynn lost the election as territorial representative on the Republican ticket. It seemed fitting and

302

proper to Lainey that both these things should happen in a year when nothing went right.

She and Bush never mentioned Quirt again. And Bush stopped trying to urge her to go out with Arch. He stopped doing many other things too. As Dr. Harter predicted, the ankle and the knee healed, but Bush, seemed to have lost his driving force. He took over the chores from Arch now and did what farm work had to be done in November, but he made no effort to get ready for the spring. The lumber for the new house lay untouched, as Bush sat for hours staring at the fire that winked through the open holes of the stove, his big hands idle on his knees. One day Lainey caught him staring at himself in the mirror.

"Gettin' old," he touched the threads of silver in his beard.

"I think white hair is very becoming," Lainey said politely, and wondered at his wry grin.

"Honey, how old do you think I am?"

"I . . . I don't know."

"I'll be thirty-seven my next birthday." Then he added, "Allegra's thirty-six."

He rarely mentioned her name any more. The letters from Riverview, brought out by the neighbors were likely to wait a day, or even two, before being opened and read.

Christmas was coming and Lainey dreaded it. The program would be held in the new schoolhouse this year. It had been built in front of the old one which was left standing to be used as a storehouse. The new schoolhouse had a teeter-totter in the yard, a rope swing, a home-made flying jinny and a cyclone cellar.

Most of the homes had cellars these days. People from east of the Mississippi contemptuously called them " 'fraid holes" but those from the western states who had known the fury of tornadoes shrugged and went right on digging. Another group said a cave was a lot of foolishness, but, after all, Ma had to have some place to put her canned fruit. Mary Hampton insisted on one for the schoolhouse. "I lived in Kansas," she said. "I know what I'm talkin' about. And make it plenty big."

Christmas was only a week away when Doris rode over to ask Lainey to help with the trimming of the tree. They were all going to meet at Mrs. Wellmans' house that night and get the decorations ready. Lainey had already decided that nothing in the world could make her go to the program and see all those people. She could almost hear them whisper, "Yeah, that Lainey Sheridan that's always been so high 'n' mighty, she sure got left! Feller made a big grandstand play then high-tailed it outa here." But trimming the tree was different. This was the first year she had been considered grown-up enough to be asked and she had not been off the claim since the night of the fog except the time she rode to Halfmoons'. Going anywhere seemed in a way unfaithful to Quirt but she remembered what Dr. Harter had said. After all, it was "doctor's orders."

The Wellman house was full of women and girls. Lainey took a long time hitching Nellie, and then stood awhile with her hand on the horn of the sidesaddle. I don't want to go in at all, she thought, and pressed her face against Nellie's satiny neck. They hate me. Quirt liked me best and they all hate me. Quirt! Quirt! Come back and take me away. Nothing in the world can stop me from going with you this time.

The front door opened and the light fanned out, the far beams catching Lainey. Bluebell Shimer called out, "Well, look who's here!"

Her retreat cut off, Lainey answered in falsely bright tones, "Better late than never!"

Two pans of popcorn were rounded up like mounds of snow. Yards and yards of popcorn strings were in the making. In one corner of the room Mrs. Shimer carefully gilded walnuts with a bottle of precious gold paint. Mrs. Wellman and Mrs. Shipp covered stars and crosses with the tinfoil hoarded from between the layers of plug tobacco. Doris, Grace and Bluebell were putting bright-colored candy into red mosquito-netting sacks.

"We need you over here," Doris called. "You stand by me and put in three red pieces and two white ones. Bluebell's got it all messed up."

"I can't see that it makes any difference. It all tastes alike."

"Girls, stop eating that candy," Mrs. Wellman said. "There's hardly enough as 'tis. The committee had a hard time raising the money this year, with the election and all."

The bad minute was over. Lainey's hood and cloak were on the bed with the others, her hands already sticky, a piece of candy in her mouth tasting good at first and then faintly like glue.

Once she tensed at whispering behind her from around the pans of popcorn. Her sharpened ears heard, "I don't think she ought to go on any longer. All those big boys in school. I'm surprised at Curly's putting up with it."

A snicker. "Always heard schoolteachers wore the pants."

It was about Christina Pritchard, then. Once she would have turned, angry, quick to defend. Now she was only relieved because they weren't talking about Lainey Sheridan.

"Here," Bluebell whispered, "now, while nobody's looking." She slipped Lainey a piece of candy. It was white with a coating of yellow and a red four-petalled flower outlined in the center. All her life Lainey would remember how that candy looked and how it tasted. Even the smell of Christmas candy was something she avoided for years and years.

Bluebell said, "Dotty Sullavan got a letter from Quirt Kearney. She let me read it."

The wooden bucket seemed to tilt. Lainey groped for the edge.

"He took Dotty out the night of the big fog. She met him at a dance over at Miller's barn. I hear they really cut a wide swathe! Didn't get her home till 'most morning, then he took out for Texas." Then in mock concern she put her hand over her mouth. "But I guess I oughtn't to be talking this way with Lainey around. Guess she knows all about Quirt."

There was malice in the pale-blue eyes. A little silence fell on the room. The ticking of the clock was as loud as the beat of a horse's hoofs. For once in her life Lainey was grateful to Doris and her bossiness.

"Lainey Sheridan! Pay attention," Doris snapped. "That's the second time you've put in *three* white ones and *two* red ones. Go on like that and we'll never come out even."

The evening passed. How Lainey got through it she never knew.

305

Filling the candy sacks became a monumental task. She found herself in a panic, saying over and over, "Three red and two white . . . or is it two red and three white?" Oh, Quirt, Quirt, how could you? How could you?

At ten o'clock Mrs. Wellman said they had done enough. Tomorrow night they would meet at the schoolhouse and trim the tree. Everybody must be there at eight o'clock, sharp.

Eight o'clock at the schoolhouse. Eight o'clock at the schoolhouse. The words ran around and around in Lainey's brain. She washed the sticky candy off her hands. Then she said to Mrs. Wellman, "I can't come tomorrow night. Bush needs me."

"I thought he was about well."

"He is, but he gets lonesome by himself."

Lainey could sense Mrs. Wellman's disapproval. "When's your Mama coming back?" she asked sharply.

This time Lainey did not wince. Almost indifferently she answered, "Pretty soon."

It was a good thing Nellie knew the road back to the Sheridan place, for the reins lay slack on her neck. Lainey's hands were clenched and sometimes she beat her knee and sometimes she smeared the tears off her cheeks. Twice she cried out, wordlessly, like an animal in pain. Then short periods of icy calm came over her and she calculated, always coming out with the same result. Miller's place was on the other side of Randall. Quirt could not have been there at a dance and at the schoolhouse at eight o'clock on the same night. Bluebell might have been lying about the letter, but with so many people at Millers' she would not dare to lie about the dance. No, it was true. It was true. But he had promised . . . Or had he? Had she promised for him? Lainey twisted in the saddle and covered her face with her hands.

How could I have been such a fool? And Arch knows. He brought my bag in from the barn. She retched and the sickening taste of Christmas candy filled her mouth.

Quirt! Quirt! Come back and take me away. All this is a bad dream. The real days were the ones when we had our house by the tree with the catface brand and you kissed me and called me Greeneyes. They were real; this is a nightmare.

306

But if it was a nightmare there was no waking. Nellie brought her to the barn door and stood patiently while Lainey fumbled at the bridle, the cinch. A dull haze surrounded her . . . like the cold-white fog the night Quirt had gone. But it wasn't the fog that kept him away from her. He had found his way to Millers' to dance with Dotty Sullavan.

The lamp was low, a signal that Bush had gone to bed. She tiptoed into the house and stood, motionless, thinking that he called her, but he only mumbled in his sleep, "Allegra . . . Allegra . . ."

She felt a rush of pity. He wants Mama like I want Quirt. Poor Bush. But poor me! Oh, poor me! And she turned out the lamp and went up the steps in the lonely dark.

Chapter 27

"Looks like we'll get a white Christmas," Bush said idly. He was standing at the window looking out at the lead-gray sky, the cedar cane under his hand.

"Looks like it," Lainey was slicing salt pork for dinner. While part of her worked another part of her stood motionless, tormented. How can I keep doing this? Who cares if we eat? How long would it take to die if you didn't eat at all? A long, long time.

"That's a lot of meat," Bush said. "You must be hungry."

She looked down at the stack she had sliced. It was enough for four people. "I guess I wasn't thinking. Bush, when are you going to butcher? That shoat's ready and we don't have any fresh meat."

"I'll attend to it," he said. "Pretty soon, now."

She knew he hardly heard her. She would have to bring the matter up half a dozen times before it was done. His absentmindedness had annoyed her in the past weeks, but now she felt she understood.

"Did you have a good time last night?" he asked.

"We got a lot done," she evaded. "There's enough popcorn to string around the Territory. And the candy's all sacked up."

"When I was a boy back home," Bush said, "we never kept Christmas much. One time somebody told me about old Santy and I hung up my stocking. My ma filled it with little bits of rock. I cried the whole day."

"How terrible!" Lainey exclaimed. Bush rarely spoke of his childhood.

"One time, long after, I asked her why she did it." He smiled a little sadly. "She said it was to teach me that nobody gets something for nothing. We have to pay for everything we get, one way or another."

Lainey stood, knife in hand, taking in his words. We have to pay for everything. One way or another. She had had Quirt. For a little while he had belonged to her, no matter what anybody said. Now one way or another she must pay.

"Ma was a hard woman," Bush said, "but she had a hard life. Pa off to the war, the bushwhackers burning them out. Little old hill farm. I wish now I'd tried to make it easy for her, but I didn't know."

"Hello the house!" a voice called from outside.

"Sounds like Mr. Doggett," Lainey said, starting to open the door.

But the door blew inward and a woman rushed past her and there was a clatter of the cane on the floor.

"Bush! Bush! I've come home."

There was nowhere to look but at the embarrassed Bill Doggett, standing in the doorway with the familiar straw suitcase in his hand. He scuffed the floor and cleared his throat and Lainey took pity on him and asked him in. Then Allegra caught Lainey to her.

"I'm home," she repeated again and again. "I'm home, I'm home."

The cold of the outdoors lingered in her long cape and her face was pink, her eyes bright. Lainey felt, pressed against her cheek, the wetness of tears that might be Allegra's and might be Bush's, or might even be her own.

"Look here," Bill Doggett said, "I didn't aim to bring on a freshet!"

It was easy to laugh. Two who had thought laughter had gone forever found it on their lips. "Glory be!" Bush said on a rising note that shook the house. "Glory be!"

Then Allegra saw the cane. "It's nothin'," Bush tossed it in the corner. "Just an excuse for old man Morehouse to whittle a chunk. Sit down, Bill, sit down."

"Well now," Bill Doggett said, "I think I better get on my way. My wife sent me to town for some Christmas doin's. She'll be looking for me back."

His going was hardly noticed in the flood of questions and

309

answers. No, Allegra had not written on purpose, to surprise them. Yes, Ellen and Hod were fine. No, the trip was easy. Yes, she came by way of Guthrie, and then on the stage. No, nobody in Randall knew she was coming. She was going to ask Eastmans to drive her out but then she saw Bill's team hitched to the rack at the drug store.

And through it all Bush kept a fold of her cape between his fingers as if he could not believe she was really there.

Lainey got up and reached for the skillet. "I guess I better start dinner. You'll be starved."

"Here," Allegra pushed her down by the shoulders and tied on an apron over her travelling dress. "You sit down and let me cook. It seems like a year since I've cooked for my family."

"Four months and twenty-one days," Bush glanced at the clock shelf. There was a folded sheet of tablet paper with little pencil marks checked on it. He took it down and dropped it in the stove. It flared up brightly, lighting his face.

"Oh, Bush, Bush," Allegra hid her face against his arm. "What have I done?"

"Hush," he smoothed her hair as he used to Lainey's. "You're home now. That's all that matters."

They were all going to the Christmas program at the new school-house, Lainey could think of no excuse to stay at home. Bush had put aside his cane. Allegra was bubbling with happiness and full of plans. She had brought Lainey a brown wool dress with just the suggestion of a bustle. It was bought, ready-made, in Kansas City.

"To think," Mary Hampton fingered the seams, "someday maybe we'll all buy ready-made clothes like that. What wouldn't I give to get shut of shirt-making!"

"Now you know you wouldn't let anybody else make shirts for Hamp," Allegra said. "Or for Arch, till he gets married." She smiled at Lainey. "How is Arch? I hope he's not still trying to work all the land in the neighborhood."

There was a moment's strained silence. Then Mary Hampton said, "Arch's fine. He won't be to the program because . . . be-

310

cause . . . well, I don't know for sure but I think he's sparkin' one of the Thompson girls over by Taney."

She was glad, Lainey told herself, glad that Arch was no longer on her conscience. If he wanted to take up with that fancy Sue Thompson just let him go ahead. She put on the new dress and the coral beads Aunt Ellen had sent and rubbed a little color on her cheeks from the moistened petal of an artificial rose. Let them think what they want to! Hold up your shoulders and remember who you are.

She remembered. She was Lainey Sheridan who had thought Quirt Kearny loved her.

On the day after Christmas Bush went to work on the new house. As he shovelled out a foundation, the red dirt flying over his shoulder in the cold, clear air, he sang:

> " 'Way down South on Beaver Creek,
> Sing-song-kitty-cantchee-ki-me-O . . .' "

Allegra ran in and out of the house, never stopping for a coat, jumping up and down with her arms hugged around her, as she remembered this and that bit of news to tell him. The work would never get done at this rate, Lainey thought sourly, for every time Mama came out Bush stopped and looked at her as if he had never seen anything as wonderful. The way they laughed and talked together made her think of Quirt and the tree with the catface brand. She felt painfully in the way. Wrapped up in their delight at being together again, Bush and Allegra seemed to have forgotten her. Quirt was gone. Arch was gone. School was gone. Allegra took over cooking and running the house. The girls Lainey knew were getting married. Grace Wellman's wedding had been announced at the Christmas program with a package addressed to *Mrs.* Pug Barton. Merry Eastman was back at Edmond after a gay vacation which was extensively written up in the Randall *Recorder*. Getting a teaching job this time of year was difficult. Lainey tried to keep up interest in her studies, but working on square root, or parsing, all by yourself is dull work.

311

Then one day in January Jane Baker stopped the team of mouse-colored mules at the Sheridan place and asked her to come over and visit at the mission. To Lainey it was as if the plain dark hood Jane wore over her severely combed hair was a shining halo.

Life at the mission was simple and orderly. The pattern of days centered around working with the Indians was a balm to Lainey's sore heart. Will and Sara Gwynne made her welcome and let her come and go about the place as she pleased. But most of the time Lainey stayed in the schoolroom, watching the cedar pointer with which Jane led her pupils through the adventures of Cat, Mat, and Rat. There were seven little Indian girls in the school now, two more than when she and Arch had come to see the dead panther. Once in a while one of the mothers would slip in during the lessons and sit cross-legged on the floor at the back of the room. These signs of progress seemed very slight to Lainey but when Jane talked about them her plain face shone.

After a week Lainey felt rested. In two weeks she was full of plans for the school she was going to teach. It had been fine to be at the mission where nobody knew about Quirt, where she was safe from the gossiping, prying neighbors. Then, suddenly, it was time to go home and Bush was coming for her on Sunday afternoon.

"I wish you'd come with me," she said to Jane. "You could give the school a holiday and stay a little while."

"Thee knows Friends do not travel on Sunday," Jane said.

"Well, but . . . I hate to go home. I just hate to."

"I am glad thee likes it here, but home will seem good when thee gets there."

"Maybe. But I'm . . . safe . . . here. I feel safe."

"Thee does?" There was mild amusement on the plain face. "Remember what thee thought at first? On the train? That the Indians were fearful creatures?"

"I guess I didn't know much," Lainey rolled the looking glass into her nightgown. She knew that Jane regarded it as a frippery but Mama had put it out for her to take. "There are worse things than Indians. I found that out. I was sure glad you came by when you did." A sudden question popped into her mind. If she didn't

312

ask it she would always wonder. She put the packed carpetbag on the bed. "Jane, did you know about Quirt?"

Jane looked away. "Yes. I heard."

So even they knew it! Jane and Sara and Will Gwynne had talked her over behind her back, pitying her. Even the Indians who came and went at the mission must know.

"Of all the nosey, hateful, prying people!" she was half crying.

"Lainey," Jane said quietly, "I did not know thee had so much conceit."

"Conceit?" She gasped. Conceit in Jane's code was near kin to the sin of pride.

"Two months and more have gone since this young man left, and still thee thinks that two heads together, two whisperers together must talk of thee? Whenever thee sees women gathered, thee is certain that they talk of thee. Nothing but thee. That is conceit."

"But they do. They did. They sent Sis Pritchard . . ."

Will Gwynne called from the front, "Bush is here. Ready, Lainey?"

"I'm ready," she said resentfully. "I'm more than ready."

Jane brushed her hand across her eyes. "Tell him to wait a minute."

But Lainey was already out the door.

She said polite goodbyes to the Gwynnes and got in the buckboard with Bush. With a flick of the whip they were off.

"Sure missed you." Bush began talking of the new house.

She thought of the days behind her when the peace of the mission had been a balm. Now it was shattered. She would never go there again. Never see Jane.

"Got the foundation dug. Going to start on the framework."

Conceit. A nasty, hateful thing to say. I'm not conceited. I'm not.

"That man over by Taney's promised me a week's work later."

But I did think they were talking about me. How did she know?

"Wish I could get some brick."

"Bush, I want to go back."

"Back to the mission? Forget something?"

313

"Yes, I forgot something."

"Jane'll send it over. We're a mile past."

"Please, Bush. Please!"

He looked at her curiously, backed the horse and cut the wheels sharply. "There. Turned on a dime and had a nickel change. What'd you forget that's so all-fired important?"

"Just . . . something."

She ran up to the mission and burst inside without knocking. Jane was sitting almost as Lainey had left her, a queer, strained expression around her eyes.

"I'm sorry, Jane. I guess you're right. I mean, I *know* you are."

The smile she saw was like sunlight in a darkened room.

"I was very hard on thee."

"But how did you know? The way I felt when I saw them whispering? I didn't tell you that."

"Because it happened to me. Long ago."

"To you?"

"Did thee think I was born an old-maid schoolteacher?"

"Oh no. But . . . please tell me."

"Sometime. Not now. Bush is waiting."

She walked with Lainey to the door. There she put an arm around the girl's shoulder in a rare, shyly given caress.

"I thought I had lost thee," she said. Then she hurried Lainey out to the waiting Bush and stood in the door calling after them, "Come back . . . Take care . . . Come back . . ."

Lainey did come back. She rode over on Nellie often as the weather opened up. And she went other places, too. Jane was right. No one was talking about her . . . Not now, anyway. To realize it was a relief and yet, somehow, she felt a little cheated, too.

It was the middle of February when Christina Pritchard came over to have a talk with Allegra, after school. Lainey was shooed out and she went resentfully to feed the chickens. She stood with her back to the sight of the tree with the catface brand but it was still as clear in her mind as if she stared at it. The corn hurt her thumb as she shelled it. The chickens flocked around her feet and she dropped grains on her shoes to watch them come up, necks outstretched, and peck off a grain then run as if she pursued them with an axe. Quirt said she could fry chicken better than anyone in the world, but she must not think about him any more. He had left her. He had broken a promise. Or did he really promise? Anyway, how do you forget part of your heart?

At last they called her in. Their faces were pink with excitement. By the way they looked at her she knew it had something to do with her but thinking of Quirt had taken the edge off whatever they had in store for her.

Allegra said, "You tell her, Christina."

"Lainey, we want you to be the teacher at Jackrabbit School."

"Jackrabbit?" her jaw dropped. She had wanted 'a school' but she never in the world had thought of Jackrabbit. "But you're the teacher."

"Yes, but I vant . . . want . . . to stop now. I mean we, Curly and I . . . Oh, you tell her." She put her scarlet face into her hands.

"You mustn't get upset, Christina, after all, it's the most natural thing in the world. Lainey, Christina and Curly. . . that is, Christina is . . . she's . . ."

"I'm going to have a baby!" Christina blurted out. "There, now you know."

"Well," Lainey said weakly. "Well."

The whispering she had overheard at Wellmans' dropped into place like a piece from an abandoned puzzle.

"And Christina wants you to be the teacher. Isn't that fine?" Allegra prompted Lainey with her eyes. It was the same as when she was little and was given a present; she could never say "thank you" quickly enough to suit Mama or Aunt Ellen.

"Thank you very much," she said, automatically. "But I don't . . . I don't . . . I don't think I know enough."

"You're the best pupil I ever had," Christina took her hand. "You have your certificate. I've talked to Mrs. Hampton and to Sis and now to Mrs. Sheridan. They all think it's a good idea."

"But they're not on the schoolboard," Lainey said, bewildered.

"Lainey!" Allegra was scandalized. "She couldn't speak to those men about a thing like this. Mary and Sis talked to Hamp and Ab, and I'm sure I can answer for Bush."

"You can start in Monday. I'll come for the first week to help you get started out. Oh, Lainey, I'm so glad!"

"But, wait a minute. I . . . I . . ."

Neither woman was listening to her. Allegra led Christina over to a padded packing box used as an extra seat. It had not been opened for a long time.

"I want you to have all these things," she said. "Sunny's. You were here when he . . . when he . . . I thought I'd never give them up, but we can't hang onto the past forever. It isn't fair."

So, once again, Lainey Sheridan took her place at the Jackrabbit School. For one evening she had been the most popular girl in the district. Now, she had her chance to be its most respected person, the teacher. Out of the misery of nervousness that she suffered there was a small grain of comfort that Mary Hampton and Sis Pritchard wanted her to have the job. She remembered the talk when Old Slackpants had disappeared, "A teacher ought to be better than other folks." She vowed she would never disappoint them.

But at the end of the first day she was ready to forget any such foolish vow and cut and run! Her mouth went dry, her tongue would not work, the problems in arithmetic might have been written in Sanskrit, geography might have been a tale of an unexplored planet. It was awful. Awful!

"You did just fine," Christina said as they prepared to bank the fire for the night.

"I was terrible!" Lainey wailed. "I said Montpelier was the capital of Maine and I've known the capitals since I was ten!"

"You'll be all right. Why the first day I taught I went out in the middle of the morning and threw up, I was so scared."

"You? Scared?"

"Yes, and somebody saw me and started a story that I was going to have a baby and I thought I'd die. And now I'm really

316

going to have a baby and I'm tickled to death. Time makes a lot of difference."

"Oh, Christina, do you remember the night I won the cake? And Quirt?"

"Yes, Lainey. You looked so pretty, nobody could have looked prettier."

"Will I get over Quirt? Will I? Ever?"

"Yes, you will. And teaching will help. Now let me show you about tomorrow . . ."

At the end of the second week Lainey decided that teaching was like picking cotton. You can get used to it. You can even get to like it.

Forty pupils faced her every day. Some were as old as she was. Some knew more, especially about arithmetic. Some had come from other districts where the lessons were more advanced or far behind. The schoolboard tried to insist on books alike, but hard times made a joke of their rules. The pupils brought whatever books they had, or what their older brothers and sisters, or even their mothers and fathers had used. Still, they managed to make progress.

It was hard to get used to being called "Miss Sheridan." Only Uncle Guy had ever called her that. Some of the older pupils called her "Lainey," but Bush said she must put a stop to that. It took her a week to get up the nerve to do it. Then she wrote out her full name on the board and added the "Miss" as an example of proper grammar. She was congratulating herself on her cleverness, when she came in after recess and found written under "Miss Elaine Saunders Sheridan," "Mrs. Quirt Kearney. Ha. Ha." She never knew who wrote it, but she suspected Bluebell's youngest sister. It took her a minute to get control of herself, but then she picked up an eraser and cleared the board without a word to the snickering schoolroom.

The problems of teaching and living at home, where Allegra expected as much help with the housework as before, took so much time that she rarely thought of Quirt, now. She was glad they were in the new schoolhouse; the old one, still standing in

317

the back and used to store wood, would always be haunted for her by his tall slim figure, lounging by the door frame.

Occasionally she saw Arch for he was breaking sod in a field that joined the school grounds, but he never stopped by and she tried not to look in his direction when he rode past.

Doris told her that Arch and Sue Thompson had broken up and that a girl in Randall had asked him to a church social. Life levelled out in front of Lainey. She would be a teacher all her life. Like Jane Baker. She would never be anything else. It was decided and she was glad.

Chapter 28

One morning in March Bush hitched up early. He had offered to drop Lainey off at school on his way to Randall for more lumber. There was a twinkle in his eyes and he whistled all the way down the road.

"You're up to something," Lainey accused him, but he only shook his head and whistled louder.

When they were nearly at the schoolhouse they saw Arch, down the field, the heavy clay of the Hampton land peeling back from the plowshare he held in the furrow. Blackbirds followed him, perching on the clods, calling in the clear morning, swooping and swinging around man and horse. Bush stopped his whistling and sighed. Lainey gathered up her books.

"That boy's a real worker. It's a shame he has to go it alone."

She was about to answer him hotly, speaking of Sue Thompson and the girl in Randall and maybe others.

"Hamp don't put in one good day's work a week at home. If I had a boy like that . . ." She knew he was thinking of Sunny and touched his hand. "Well, here we are, Jackrabbit Junction, everybody change!" He handed down her stack of books. "Don't get scared when you get home tonight at who you see."

She asked him a dozen questions but he only shook his head and drove away.

When Lainey went outside to fill the water bucket Arch was at the end of the field nearest her. She could almost smell the strong, damp odor of the turned earth. All at once he jumped back; the plow, untended, lurched; the horse stopped. Arch grabbed a heavy clod and threw it into the furrow. Another and another, slamming them into the ground so that they exploded and little bits flew up in the air. A snake must be down there. A copperhead,

319

likely. Arch leaped across the heaped furrows to the fence row and picked up a long stick. He forked the squirming snake onto it and pitched it toward the edge of the plowed land. It was done calmly, the way a man does a necessary thing, but there was something in the very arc of the pitch that suggested revulsion.

Shivering in the morning wind, Lainey went into the school-house.

She hurried home that afternoon, walking with the children who went by the Sheridan place. At the door of the house a tall stranger grabbed her and she jerked away from him before she realized it was Bush with his beard shaved off!

"Got sick of hiding behind all that brush," he said.

He looked years younger. Just the way he had when he first came to Riverview, Allegra insisted. She told the story over again though Lainey knew it so well she could have told it herself. "There I was drying my hair. I'd washed it in rain water the way I always did and I was sitting out on the back steps in the sun. My hair was longer then. Down to my waist. Here came Bush. I didn't know his name, then; I just knew he was the one that waited on the customers at Blanton's. He said, 'Do you need another hand around the place?' And I said, 'Goodness, no,' and I felt like going through the floor because my hair was down and all. And then Bush said, 'You go tell Hod Crump I've hired myself on. If he don't like my work he don't need to pay me!'

"And in a month I married her," Bush said, rubbing his pale shorn face with his brown hand.

"I was engaged to Tom Bridges, too."

"How is old Tom?"

"I forgot to tell you! He has a horseless carriage! You'd never believe . . ."

They had forgotten her again. Lainey went upstairs, took off her dress and hung it carefully behind the calico curtain. A scrap of the moss-green silk showed from behind the other garments. She started to push it back, then let her hand linger on its softness. Bush had come to Riverview, a stranger, just as Quirt had come to the Sheridan place. What had happened? What had gone wrong? If only she were pretty like Mama. If she had had blue eyes and long golden hair, if she had had pink-and-white cheeks and slender white hands, would it have turned out like this?

"Any more news in town?" Allegra asked at supper as she spooned out bowls of wild greens cooked with hog jowl and passed the vinegar in the cut-glass cruet.

"Yes, there is." Bush looked grave. "The talk's all that the Indian Territory's going to bolt and get statehood all to itself. I hate to think of it."

"I never did see why you cared so much," Allegra said. "If more want it as two states, then what difference does it make?"

"I'm not so sure 'more' do want it that way. It's just the boys at the head of things. They talk so big and you never can tell in either territory, just what's what. If a person could just sit down and talk to some of those fullbloods, the way me'n Henry Half-moon talk," he reached for a corn pone. "What're you mumbling, Lainey?"

"Henry Halfmoon and I," Lainey said automatically.

Bush's face turned red. "Dog take it!" He mumbled "But any-way, a bunch of us are going to get together in Randall in a week or two and try to get lined up to go over to Guthrie and build a fire."

"With all the farm work and the new house hardly begun?" Allegra's eyebrows rose, alarmingly. It was the first hint of dis-agreement since she had come home.

"I know. But a man has to do some things for the place he lives. The way I look at it this single statehood's the most important thing there is right now. I've got to do what I can."

"But what can you do? Clear down here? It's going to be de-cided up in Washington."

"I know. But I've got to do what I can. It's the right thing."

Allegra pressed her lips together in a firm line. The meal was finished with only "Please . . . Thanks for the butter . . . Peaches? . . . No, thanks." And the whistling of the teakettle on the stove.

Lainey began to gather up the dishes. If only one time Mama

would say, 'You must be tired from teaching. Go sit down.' But the truth was that Mama did not think schoolteaching was real work.

Allegra went to the organ and opened the new music she had brought from Missouri. Then she pushed it away and turned the pages of the old green songbook. The left pedal squeaked and the bellows gave a soft preliminary wheeze. Then the music began and the words were not needed for they hung in the air, sweet, cloying, dragging Lainey back to another day, another world.

> *"Soft o'er th' fountain, lingering falls th' southern moon.*
> *Far o'er the mountain, breaks the day, too soon . . .*
> *'Nita . . . Juanita . . ."*

She had sung it, longing for an unknown love, a dark stranger. She had whispered it, not knowing that love means pain; that never, never in this world do you get something for nothing.

> *"Ask thy soul if we should part?"*

A saucer cracked as it struck the floor.

"Lainey!" Allegra whirled the organ stool around. "For goodness sake, be careful."

"I hate that song," Lainey said. "I wish you wouldn't play it any more."

"Well, of all the . . ."

Lainey wiped the soap suds from her hands. "I'm not going to wash dishes after supper any more. I'm tired and I have to get ready for tomorrow."

She ignored the gasp, the look that passed between Bush and Allegra as she untied her apron, hung it neatly on the nail by the stove and went upstairs.

Bush doubled up on his spring work to get a clear space to go to town for the statehood meeting. But no matter how much he did there was still more. The framework of the new house gaped, untouched. He shook his head one night at supper.

"End of March and cotton to chop and corn to cultivate and the house waitin', but I'm going tomorrow anyway." He looked belligerently at Allegra and Lainey. "For some things a man just has to quit his own work and help out."

"Hamp was by here yesterday," Allegra said sweetly, "on the road over to Turners'. He said they needed help worse than he did."

"If you mean that I'm like Hamp . . ."

"Why the very idea. I just mentioned he was going by."

Thank goodness I'm going to be an old maid, Lainey thought as she went up to her room and made out questions for the history class. The warm wind brought the sweetness of spring in through the window and it was hard to keep her mind on the Continental Congress. Tonight the trials of Thomas Jefferson, John Hancock, and Benjamin Franklin were as old and musty as abandoned hay. She folded her pencil into her book and going over to the window stood staring into the soft, mysterious night.

In the morning Lainey was as tired as if she had not slept a wink. The day was warm and humid. The pupils at Jackrabbit School were as hard to manage as forty whirling dervishes. At recess, instead of playing Black Man or Duck on a Rock, the boys ganged up on the girls in a water fight. The smallest Pritchard boy climbed the roof and dumped an unfortunate cat down the chimney. It came out unhurt but squalling and covered the room with ashes. Lainey was at her wit's end. Where was the calm serenity of Jane Baker? The capable competence of Christina Swenson? Given a chance to spell for the last thirty minutes . . . a concession on any day but Friday . . . the pupils insisted on cyphering and the biggest Shimer boy got Lainey tangled up on a trick problem. She dismissed the school ten minutes early, giving a twitch to the hands of the clock she kept in her desk. The pupils scattered. They were out of sight before the sound of their raucous catcalls died away. There would probably be a dozen fights on the way home, but that was not her problem. She sighed with relief and set about straightening up the schoolroom. How hot it was for March! In two more days it would be April. April Fool's

323

day! Her heart sank. What devilment would she have to cope with then?

Now what's the matter with me, she wondered. I wanted to teach school. I like it, too. Only not all the time. Days like this . . .

Lainey fished a wad of gum out of the water bucket. That Ed Novak! She had told him to get rid of his gum and this was what he did! She went back to her desk, the same desk on which she had perched in the old schoolhouse the night of the popularity contest. "Hello, Greeneyes," Quirt had said. "Hello." Picking up a spelling book Lainey wrote a list of words on the blackboard to be learned. The light was getting dim. It must be later than she thought. Better write out some problems, too. The big boys were getting out of hand about arithmetic; thought they knew more than she did. Maybe they did, but in her own arithmetic book were problems in long division that Arch had worked out, answers and everything. She began to copy figures on the blackboard, then stopped, chalk upraised. It was too quiet. Outside the light had turned from gray to green.

Lainey put the chalk down on the tray as quietly as if she were afraid of waking someone. The air in the room was stifling. The thud of her heart sounded against her ears. There was a swish in the treetops, then quiet again. She walked to the front door, her footsteps sounding unnaturally loud. In the livid green light the schoolyard looked like an underwater scene. The rope swing swayed lightly but there was no other motion.

Then suddenly Arch came running across the field, the red clods spinning backwards from his heavy boots. He vaulted the fence and came straight for the schoolhouse. She stood, transfixed, hearing but not understanding his call.

"Lainey! Lainey!"

He caught hold of her arm and jerked her down the step. She stumbled and fell toward him.

"Run!" he shouted. "Cyclone."

Then she saw it, briefly, terribly, as he spun her across the yard to the cyclone cellar. A tall twisting black funnel bearing down with nightmare speed. It came from the south. It came with fury. A roar like an oncoming freight train filled the air. They reached the cellar. Arch fought the heavy door with one hand and pushed Lainey down the steps with the other. She was falling, falling into the dark cave. The door slammed down and there was no light. No light at all. Lainey huddled on the earth floor. Fears of darkness, of being buried alive, of creeping, crawling serpents swept over her, and the cellar shook with the mighty roar of the wind.

Then Arch was leaning over her, pulling her to her feet. She could smell the sweat on him and feel the heat of his body in that cold airless place. He was panting and he had not spoken a word since his warning. His chest brushed against her; then he caught her to him seeking and finding her face, her mouth.

He kissed her, not once but many times. Not gently but with bruising force as though he hated and loved her at the same time. She clutched at him. A fierce eagerness burned in her that she had never known before. Not Quirt, not a dark stranger, not a golden knight, but Arch. Arch. Arch.

Then it was over. The roar of the cyclone diminished and died. The roar in Lainey's ears subsided. As suddenly as he had caught her to him Arch shoved her away. Standing, trembling, in the blackness of the cellar she heard him stumble up the steps. As he threw back the heavy door with a crash, gray light spilled down the steps. She glimpsed a set, tormented face. Then Arch was gone.

Carefully, carefully, as though she were made of glass, Lainey walked up the steps and out into the air again. The schoolyard was strangely untouched, except for the rope swing that jerked crazily back and forth. A tall elm tree had crashed into the old schoolhouse. The branches of the tree were still settling and one of them cracked like a pistol shot.

Arch? Where was Arch? He had disappeared as completely as the cyclone. Then as she stood there alone, watching the empty swing, the gray air seemed to thicken and a cold driving rain, stabbed through with hailstones, poured down. Lainey was completely drenched before she could close the cellar door and run to the schoolhouse.

I won't think about it, she said to herself. I'm too mixed up. I won't think about it till later. The ashes in the stove were cold

325

and gray. With a few scraps of paper and some kindling from the bottom of the woodbox she kindled a little fire that drove the chill from her flesh, but it could not stop the trembling that went on within her. I've got to stop it, she fought herself, I've got to. Think about Mama, she may be hurt. Or Bush? No, he's in Randall; he'll be all right. Is Nellie all right in the shed? The rain was slacking; the hail was thick on the ground outside. If Arch would just come back I'd . . . What would I do?

Hoofbeats on the road outside. She ran to the door. Arch! But it was Mama riding on Stretcher, her long wool cape soaking across her shoulders.

"Are you all right, Lainey?"

"Yes, I . . . I got to the cellar. Are you?"

"Yes. Up high that way I saw it in plenty of time. The house stood, but the barn's ruined and the new house . . . it's all gone." She spoke without concern as if she reported a catastrophe in another country. "If you're all right . . ." she picked up the reins. Stretcher looked around.

"Where are you going?"

"I've got to get to Bush."

"But Mama, he's in Randall. You know he said he'd be late getting home and with the storm and all he'll probably spend the night with Eastmans and . . ."

"I've got to get to Bush." She clucked to Stretcher. "All right, boy." Lainey caught at the stirrup.

"But the storm . . . there may be lots of trees down . . . and it'll be dark."

"Will you take your hand off my horse?" It was a cardinal sin to touch a horse a Saunders was controlling. Looking up in the gathering twilight Lainey saw Allegra's white face and the set of her jaw. It was all Saunders. Stubborn as mules and touchy as blooded horses, Pappy Vickers had said.

"I'll go with you. Wait till I get Nellie."

"Hurry."

Hurry. The night closed in and the horses slipped and floundered in the mud. Hurry. The main path of the cyclone, a quarter of a mile wide, snaked aimlessly this way and that across the country leaving trees across the road, heaped-up brush that had to be circled, and strange sinister heaps of timber that might have been houses or barns. Hurry. There was no friendly light in any house to guide them. There was no passing team or any horseman or even a man on foot to give a hail. Only the two women and the horses and the need to hurry. Hurry.

Once as they rode down the steep sides of what had been a dry gulch but was now a rushing watercourse, Lainey said, "I think we'd better go back. Bush won't like it; you know he hates to be worried over."

"I've got to get to Bush," Allegra said monotonously. "You heard the way I talked to him about going. You were there. All right, Stretcher, take it eeee-asy." Then a long time later as they splashed through the mud of a plowed field, "I thought I'd learned. All those months at Riverview and not a minute I didn't want to be with Bush. And then . . ." Lainey saw her shadowy figure lean over the saddle horn and pat the horse's neck. "Hurry, Stretcher, we've got to, we've got to."

They came to Randall, mudcovered, sodden, chilled to the bone and found the town a nightmare. The cyclone had struck at the main street and tossed the houses like a malicious giant playing with a child's blocks. It had come at five o'clock and in many of the houses fires were lighted to cook supper and the coals scattered by the wind blazed up. The rain and hail had put out some of the fires but others still blazed and in them men caught and held by timbers begged to be shot. And now, in the night, the tale of bloody death mounted and mounted. The dead and the dying were carried into a church, one of the few places in town left with a roof. White-faced women tore up bandages and Dr. Harter with his shirt ripped and his glasses gone went from one broken body to another.

The fires that lighted Allegra and Lainey into town turned the familiar place into a shifting weaving horror of destruction. They saw a man sitting on the timbers of his house beating at his bared head with his hands.

327

"My God! My God! My God!" he said, over and over and over.

A speckled ox, one of a team that had won the stone-pulling contest, wandered blindly down the street.

A man on a black horse loomed up suddenly before them. Lainey looked into the chill eyes of Al Colwater, the sheriff. His hand rested on one of his guns.

"Get back. Get back." Then he leaned toward them. "Mrs. Sheridan?"

"Yes. I'm looking for Bush. Have you . . ."

The second's hesitation was enough. "Over at Eastmans', ma'am."

"Is he . . ."

"I don't know." He glanced back at the fire. "I'll take you. We've had to deputize half the town. You'd never get through. Hey, Jim . . ."

They followed him through the maze of destruction. A section of board sidewalk was upended across the street. Al Colwater swung out of his saddle and smashed at it with booted feet. A familiar bell tower rakishly crowned a little restaurant. "Why . . . it's the Methodist Church!" Lainey gasped.

"Yep. No prayer meetin' tomorrow night," Al Colwater said with bitter humor. "Drug store's gone. Gin's down. Bank's blown in."

"Sheriff . . . Sheriff . . . Hey, Al!" A man yelled out of the darkness. "Found a woman under this house. Give us a hand."

He looked at Allegra. "Can you get to Eastmans' from here?"

"Of course. Go on. But . . . was he . . . when you saw him . . . ?"

"He was alive then; I hope he is now. Bush's too good a man for us to lose. We wanted him to go up to Guthrie to speak for us." Then the sheriff was gone and somehow Lainey and Allegra found the street. There was Eastmans' with every lamp in the house burning. Through the lace-curtained windows they could see Mr. Eastman standing in the door and Mrs. Eastman bending over the bed in Merry's room. The same bed, Lainey remembered, she had slept in on the Fourth of July.

Allegra ran into the house. It was the first time Lainey had

328

ever seen her leave a spent horse saddled, with the reins dragging. Lainey tied both horses to the iron ring of the hitching post and followed.

"Thank God you're both here," Joe Eastman was saying. "I was going to try to make it out to your place but Eleanor didn't want me to leave."

Allegra brushed past him, past the weary, frightened Eleanor and knelt at the bed.

"Bush! Bush, darling!"

He opened his eyes and smiled, then he frowned, "Allegra . . . you shouldn't have come . . . dark . . . dangerous . . ."

"Whole chest crushed," Mrs. Eastman whispered to Lainey. "One leg and one arm broken. They said it was no use to try to get Dr. Harter, but he came anyway."

"Don't," Lainey said sharply, "don't tell me."

Joe Eastman patted her shoulder. "Easy . . . easy . . ."

He thinks I'm a horse, she thought, or a mare, or a filly. How can I take it easy when Bush is . . . is . . .

Merry's canary, forgotten, cage uncovered, sang a shrill cheerful song, over and over.

"Bush, it was right for you to go to the meeting," Allegra said clearly. "I want you to know I think so. I thought so all the time, really." He smiled again and moved his good hand nearer her.

"Territory's good place . . . got to do . . . what . . . I can . . ."

"I know." Allegra bowed her head against the white counterpane. The sodden dark hood slipped from her golden hair that curled in tendrils as it dried.

"Lainey," he wiggled the fingers of his big brown hand. She came to the bed and leaned down to hear him. Behind her the sobbing of Eleanor Eastman swelled, diminished and swelled again, and the canary sang on. "My girl . . ."

I can't stand it. I can't stand it. I can't stand it.

Yes, you can. You can stand what you have to.

"It's . . . a . . . good claim," Bush whispered.

"The best one in the Territory," Lainey answered automatically. Allegra lifted her head and listened.

329

Running feet outside and a man shouting at the door. "Joe, we got to have help. Fire broke out at the livery stable." The feet pounded on. Joe Eastman shifted his weight uneasily.

In a normal tone Bush said, "Go on, Joe. I can handle this myself."

"Well, so long, Bush."

It sounded so natural that Lainey let hope gush up in her heart. Then she saw Allegra's eyes fixed on Bush's face as one memorizes a beloved object and she knew her hope was false.

Bushrod Sheridan spoke once more. "Allegra!" he cried out, and struggled up on his good elbow. His wife caught him in her arms and held him, her cheek against his beardless face. "Allegra!"

In that cry Lainey heard the love and passion of a lifetime. Her own grief was overcome by wonder for she knew, suddenly and surely, that the differences between these two, the quarrels, the clashes, the separations were as nothing. Their love was deep-rooted, strong. All the rest was on the surface. But Lainey turned away now for it was not fitting to watch this lovers' farewell.

Time enough for weeping tomorrow and all the days when Bush was gone.

Chapter 29

Lainey pressed her hand against the coolness of the glass window and watched the spring landscape running by as the Santa Fe carried them north. Already it was plain to see that the season was not as far along as it had been in the Sac and Fox country. The leaves were smaller, the flowers paler, the grass still showing patches of last winter's brown. It was as if they were going backwards in time. There must be things out there in the countryside to look for. Changes that had come since the Run. She should be watching for them, but she could not force her thoughts to focus.

Things had happened too fast. She could not put them in proper order any more than the town of Randall could ever be the same place again. No matter how long Randall existed or how big it grew it would always carry the scar of the roaring fury that had come out of the sky that March day. Time would be measured there as people said, Before the cyclone, After the cyclone.

The day had set its mark on Lainey, too. A mark of violence. Arch's kisses, angry, bitter, and sweet were a part of it. The long ride through the night to reach Bush. And the end of the ride beside Merry Eastman's bed. Never again could she say, "Bushrod Sheridan, my father," and feel coming toward her the strength and warmth that had been his.

They had planned to have the funeral on the claim. There was a mass service for the dead in Randall but Mama would not have things that way. "Bush belonged to the claim," she said with a trace of bitterness in her voice. "He'd want to be buried here. And . . . there's Sunny."

So Bush's friends had done their best to give her what comfort this would bring. It had taken all day long for the lumber wagon to carry his body home across the torn-up countryside. Bush's blue roan had been tied on behind the wagon with the saddle empty. No one cared to ride it. Watching the wagon start out Lainey knew why the Indians buried a man's things with him. A horse and a saddle were part of a man.

The next morning when people began to arrive at the house on the hill Mary Hampton came to Allegra with tear-streaked face.

"This house will never hold 'em all. You ought to have it at the schoolhouse. You really ought."

And after opposing so many things Allegra suddenly agreed.

No work was done all that spring day because Bushrod Sheridan had died. People came to the schoolhouse leaving ruined barns and unroofed houses, they came over roads blocked by fallen trees. They waded creeks, forded streams where bridges had washed out, bucked the mud. And still they came. Lainey would never forget their faces. Hamptons. Wellmans. Doggetts. Pritchards. Sis had put her arms around Lainey and her tears had washed out any trace of anger. Novaks. Henri Gervais. Halfmoons. Curly Pritchards. Jurd Morehouse and his uncle. Thompsons over by Taney. Eastmans from Randall. Bud Menifee and Kate Tillery who had driven all night to get supplies in to Randall. The Negro family who had picked the Sheridan cotton. Gartons from the agency. Jane Baker and Will and Sara Gwynne. They came and they came.

And there were unknown men and women who strode up to Allegra and Lainey and took their hands. "He stopped to help when my team got stuck in the Run." "He was always so friendly, goin' past our place. Never too busy to say 'howdy' and pass the time o' day." "He lent me a hamestrap one time; I have to say I never gave it back." And most often, "He was a real good neighbor."

Brother Gordon preached the service. He could only stay a little while because there was so much to be done everywhere. It was some comfort that he took as his text the same one he had used the first time they had ever heard him preach, "But now they desire a better country, that is, an heavenly . . ." Bush—in a new country.

332

Allegra sat with her eyes closed, her head resting on the green plush seat. The shaking of the train made the black ostrich tips on her black hat quiver. It was all exactly the way it had been when they went down to the Territory, except for the terrible, the terrifying, absence of Bush. He had stayed in his seat very little on that journey, but Lainey had always known he was visiting with folks in the day coach, or the train crew, or hopping off and on at each stop. Now Bush was gone.

The claim was gone, too. It was a thing Lainey could not think about without bitterness. On the very night after the funeral when the last tiptoeing neighbor had gone, when Lainey filled the woodbox, which was always Bush's bedtime chore, Mama had said, "Now we can go home."

Vainly, Lainey pled that Bush would want them to stick by the claim. Vainly, she pointed out her responsibility as a schoolteacher. She even tried to argue that they could get more for the place, later, after the Free Homes Bill passed and that it was sure to go through the next session of Congress. Allegra only repeated to each argument, "As soon as we can sell out we're going home."

Too tired and heart-sick to do more, Lainey had finally agreed when Allegra lashed out in one of her rare angers, "I've given enough to this red earth! I won't stay here and see another one of mine put into it."

Still Lainey had gone on teaching, hoping some miracle would happen. But none did. The spring work was getting heavy and the school was down to the small children. It would close, soon, anyway. The April moon was hardly half full when Arch came riding over on Beauty. Lainey saw him from the upstairs window and she was ashamed of the throb of gladness she felt. With Bush gone she ought not to feel that way about anything. Still . . . She reached for a fresh dress.

Downstairs Allegra was asking Arch in. He did not mention Lainey's name. She stood, half dressed, listening.

"You might get a better offer," Arch ended, "but if you don't, mine'll stand."

"I don't want to wait," Allegra said. "Besides, I want you to have the place. I think Bush would have liked it."

"I thought a lot of Bush," Arch said. "I'll try to farm it the way he would. He had . . . he had a real fancy for the land." Arch stumbled and it was a lot for him to say. Lainey wondered if Allegra really knew what he meant. "But, if you want to wait . . ."

"I don't want to wait. I'll take your offer and we can go to Randall tomorrow and get it fixed up. Now have some coffee, and I'll call Lainey."

"Thank you, ma'am, but I've got to be getting along. I'll come past for you tomorrow morning, around ten."

He was gone! She heard him riding off, Beauty's hoofs squishing in the soft April dirt. The fresh dress was a stifling tent over her head. She jerked it off, hearing a seam rip, and threw it on the bed. He despises me! He wants the claim just because he knows it will hurt me to give it up.

She put on her nightgown and pretended to be asleep when Allegra called.

At the depot in Guthrie Uncle Guy had appeared. Allegra's face worked.

"You shouldn't have done this Guy, come so far. But I do appreciate it!"

"Now, now," he patted her shoulder. "There's little enough we can do when . . . Bertha sent her love. She wanted to come but some club meeting at the house . . . She wants you to come back for a visit. Real soon."

"I'll never come back, Guy. Never."

"Well," his freckled hands played nervously with his watch-chain, "we'll miss you. But I can see . . . Now if there's anything you need, I'd take it as a favor if you'd let me help. Bush was my friend, you know."

"No, thanks, we'll get along. Bush was everybody's friend. He liked . . . everybody." Was there a tinge of resentment in Mama's voice?

Then Uncle Guy turned to Lainey and handed her a big box of candy. "Something for the trip. And if you ever need any help, let me know."

334

"I will," Lainey promised, ignoring Allegra's little frown.

"And if you ever come back . . ."

"There's no use talking, Guy, we never will." Something in Lainey rebelled at the finality in Allegra's voice. She wanted to protest but the Santa Fe was whistling, Uncle Guy was picking up their bags, the journey back home was about to begin.

They opened the candy box between Guthrie and Perry. On top was an envelope filled with greenbacked bills. Allegra read the note aloud.

"I knew you'd be stubborn but take it as a loan. That's a banker's business."

"Do we need money?" Lainey asked, conscious of the three months' pay from the schoolboard packed in her keepsake box. Ninety dollars less the ten she had proudly paid for three months' room and board. How Bush had bragged on that!

"We have a little with what Kate Tillery paid for the stock and what we got from the claim and the sale. But it was nice of Guy. I'll send it back tomorrow."

Lainey did not like to think about the sale. To have people . . . just anybody . . . come and look at your things, finger them, make remarks about the quality had been almost past endurance. When Mrs. Sullavan complained about the color of the cushion on the rocker, Lainey had been hard put not to slap her face. But Allegra seemed to mind less. To her the sale was just an obstacle to get past on the way to Riverview.

They had kept a few things. The Haviland plates. Bush's chair. The footstool he had made for Sunny. The rest of their household goods was scattered over the countryside. They must realize every cent they could, Allegra insisted. Then with the impulsive generosity that marked the Saunders family, she gave the organ to Lydia Halfmoon.

"It's yours. I don't want to see it any more. I'll never play again."

Lydia shook her head with a half smile. "Yes, you will. I said that, too, one time. If you ever want it back . . ."

"Never!"

"KANNNNNNNsas City!"

Two women looked at each other. They had come back to a starting point. Each felt the bleakness of the moment. To get up and collect the baggage, to descend into the crowded depot, to be pushed and buffeted by the crowd, all of those things meant that Bush was gone. That they were women, alone.

"You take the lunch box, the straw suitcase, and the carpet bag," Allegra said briefly. "I'll bring the other things."

"Yes, ma'am." You can stand what you have to stand. You can do what you have to do. Together they stepped off the train.

Then out of the crowd they saw Ellen Crump. Her hat was perched on her pompadour exactly as it had been when Lainey saw her last. Her back was as straight, her eyes as blue, and people stepped out of her way in the depot at Kansas City just the way they did in Marney. It was a heavenly relief to lean for an instant on her spare, steel-corseted frame. To hear her say, "Lainey! Allegra! Thank goodness you're home!"

And then to smile for the first time in a long, long time at the sight of Aunt Ellen mopping her eyes and scolding Mama, "Allegra, a lady never cries in public."

They had almost reached the depot at Marney when Lainey felt a warning prick. Allegra was telling about the sale and what she had done with the organ.

"You don't mean to tell me you gave that organ to an Indian squaw!"

"You don't understand, Ellen. She was my friend. A neighbor."

"Your friend? The idea! The very idea!"

It was not going to be easy to come back to Riverview.

Chapter 30

Six months at Riverview and I'm still looking in my shoes for centipedes! Lainey jerked on her shoes and sat on the edge of the bed kicking her feet.

Why can't I change? Why can't I be the kind of person Aunt Ellen wants me to be?

The first few weeks had been wonderful. Worn out as she had been by the loss of Bush, teaching, and the upset of selling the claim and the furniture, it had been heavenly just to let everything slide, secure in the knowledge that Aunt Ellen was so competent. But the warning prick that had come as they rolled into the Marney depot returned again and again. When, at last, it had brought Lainey wide awake, it was too late. From a grown-up who had taught school and kept house she had been demoted to an inexperienced young girl . . . an *unmarried* young lady in the home of her elders.

It bothered her, too, that nothing was as big, as high, as steep as she remembered.

It took Pappy Vickers to straighten her out on this.

"It's natcheral. I rec'clect when I got back from my first trip up the Santa Fe Trail . . . up to then I'd never seen anything bigger'n St. Joe and I thought it was pretty fine. Man! How things had swivelled down!"

"You mean Santa Fe was so much bigger?"

"Naw, it wasn't much in those days. 'Dobe houses and some churches. But it's just that a feller gets a different way of lookin' at things when he goes around a leetle. An' another thing," he squinted at her, "you're a heap taller'n you were when you left here. Makes a difference where you're sightin' from."

But Allegra had no such trouble. She slipped back into the routine of the big house as easily as the Haviland plates had gone back to their old place in the china cabinet. In the morning she worked at whatever Ellen selected, and in the afternoon she and Ellen went visiting, sewed, or entertained company. Mattie still ruled the kitchen and there was a new helper now, Roselda, whom Mattie alternately shielded and persecuted. So there was no place, really, where Lainey was needed. She was painfully conscious that the tasks given to her were the same kind of "busy work" she had managed to find for troublesome pupils at Jackrabbit School.

And just as in the days when Bush had first gone to the Territory, the evenings were worst. The endless backgammon games, the rustle of Uncle Hod's pages, the flutter of moths at the high narrow windows. Sitting with her crocheting in her lap . . . a mess of knots and tangles . . . Lainey wondered if she had ever gone to the Territory, or if it was all a dream. At least once an evening Aunt Ellen would catch her crossing her knees.

"A lady crosses her ankles, never her knees."

Then Uncle Hod would look up from his book. "Let the child alone, Ellen."

Child! Child! That was what she had become. An overgrown, awkward child. She looked at her hands, so inept with the crochet needle, and thought of the cotton they had picked, the rabbits they had skinned, even the times they had swished a long limber willow switch over the pupils of Jackrabbit School.

Still Lainey did have to give Aunt Ellen credit for trying to make her happy. She had done her best to arrange company among the young folks who lived in Marney or up and down the river. But it just hadn't worked.

All the girls had gone to seminary together, and were either married or engaged. Lainey got along better with the young men, but too often she found herself saying, "When I lived in the Territory . . ." Then a look of glazed boredom would pass over the face of Henry, or Lee, or Sterling, and presently he would leave.

Even Addie Bucklin, who, much to the amazement of the county had married the youngest Bridges' boy, had changed so much that it was hard for Lainey to find enough to talk to her

338

about to fill an afternoon. That is, unless they talked about Bucky, Addie's fat, white-faced baby boy, whom Lainey privately thought was a horror.

"I know more about that baby than if I'd had him myself," she grumbled.

"What a thing to say!" Aunt Ellen frowned. "An unmarried young lady . . ."

Oh Lord! Lainey moaned inside and went up to her room.

It was odd, she thought, that the one person who seemed honestly interested in life in the Territory was Mr. Bucklin. He dropped in often on his way to and from town with a basket of fine peaches, a setting of fancy eggs, or a bundle of St. Louis papers for Uncle Hod, and he was never in a hurry to leave. Best of all he let Lainey talk about Bush.

"Bush was a fine man," Mot Bucklin said one day as he leaned his gangling length against the back-porch railing. "He was my right bower when most folks in Snyder County wouldn't give me the time o' day. I don't forget it."

The county was taking to Mot better, now. He turned up as owner of property in the most unexpected places, buying land at tax sales and by a knack of picking the right men to work it turning it back into producing farms. A good trader, he had run a horse, a wagon, and a washed-out farm up to a substantial holding. There were even rumors that he had come out ahead in trading on the cash grain market in Kansas City. But money, Mot said, didn't mean much when a man's wife was gone, his children married and he sat, lonesome, in a house built for a family. Then a man needed friends.

"Friends in Snyder County aren't for sale," Aunt Ellen said sharply.

It never failed to amaze Lainey the way Mr. Bucklin took her rebukes, with a nod and a grin.

"For one thing you ought to get that river riff-raff out of your house." Since Mrs. Bucklin's death and Addie's marriage a man and his wife and a horde of bare-shanked, runny-nosed children had been living at the Bucklins'. The man farming, the woman "keeping house."

"Alvy's a pretty good farmer," Mr. Bucklin gnawed his moustache.

"Then let him farm and build him a house to live in. Nobody that's anybody is going to come near you with them around. That woman looks as if she'd never scalded a milk crock in her life. How does the butter taste?"

"Now that you ask me, it *is* a mite high."

"Send 'em packing and I'll get Mattie to find you a good cook. They're hard to get these days but they can still be found."

"Thanky, Miss Ellen. That would be a real help."

Early in the fall Mot came over with a basket of hickory nuts.

"Bart Saunders asked me to lodge meetin', Miss Ellen. I reckon I've got you to thank for that."

"Nonsense, Bart's got sense enough to know a hawk from a handsaw. Be sure you go and have a good time." She hesitated, then went on, "But Mot . . . don't wear those clothes. They just plain look . . . trashy."

His face turned red as a turkey gobbler's as he looked down at the bright-yellow shoes, the pin-checked suit, the vest edged in white, the heavy gold watchchain looped back and forth through the buttonholes.

"Why, Miss Ellen, I never thought . . ."

"I know you didn't, so that's why I'm telling you. And, Mot, if there should be a card game after the meeting . . ."

"Now Miss Ellen," he smiled slowly, "you don't need to worry about me all the time. From there on, I'm on my own."

He said it politely enough, but Lainey, listening, knew that Mr. Bucklin was a man you could push only as far as he wanted to be pushed, and in the direction he wanted to go.

Christmas was a quiet holiday. The number of the Saunders' kin who came to dinner was smaller than usual. The children's table was not really needed, but Aunt Ellen insisted on it. The food was superb and abundant as usual but instead of staying on for a cold supper, most of the family were gone by sundown. Only a half-dozen remained to fill their plates again with Smithwick ham, cold turkey, cranberry jelly, and Mattie's raised light rolls.

"Where *is* everybody?" Aunt Ellen looked bewildered and indignant.

Cousin Martha May started methodically. "Well, Emmitts' went to *her* folks. And Azalea told Gem she was going to have Christmas at home for once in her life. And John T. is . . . uh . . . sick." It was unnecessary to mention that John T. was on a spree. "Molly and Breen went to St. Joe because her father died in November. And . . . "

"Oh, I know all that," Aunt Ellen interrupted, "but I just can't get used to it. There was a time when not one of them thought of going any place else."

"*O tempora, O mores,*" Uncle Hod said. "How about some music, Allegra?"

"Why Hod, I haven't played in . . . I don't know how long."

"Then play for us now. We need it."

He led Allegra to the square grand piano that had come up-river by flatboat the year the house was finished. The lamplight fell on her face and spilled over her hands on the yellowed ivory keys.

"I guess Lydia was right," Allegra said quietly to Lainey.

When the last of the kinfolks had left Allegra and Lainey started up the curving stairway together. Riverview was very quiet. Snow had begun again and every sound was faint and muffled.

"When I was a child," Allegra said, trailing her hand on the bannister, "they always stayed all night at Christmas. We had pallets all over the place. The Saunders were a big family then."

"What happened?"

"Oh, that's the way with big families. All at once they seem to scatter." She looked back into the dark stairwell. "I'm glad the day's over. Holidays are worse than other days when you've lost somebody you love. And with Sunny's birthday so close . . ."

Lainey squeezed her mother's hand. When you've lost somebody you love. She had lost Arch, and, now, she knew that she loved him. On a Christmas so long ago that it seemed to be in another life he had given her an autograph book with a red cover. He had written on the middle page, so that she did not find it for days, "As sure as the vine grows 'round the stump, you are my darling sugar lump, Arch W. Hampton." Down in one corner he

341

had put XXX. It seemed childish and foolish to remember it now, but she couldn't help it. If I keep on like this I'm going to cry, she told herself, and once I start crying I'll never stop.

There had been very little that was happy about the new year of 1898 so far. In February the explosion of the battleship *Maine* in Havana harbor rocked the country and with flags flying and bands playing the United States went to war. Dewey sailed past Corregidor in darkness to capture Manila and destroy the Spanish fleet. The Rough Riders charged up San Juan Hill. Lainey read every account in every paper she could find and dreamed that Arch had been wounded on the battlefield. She burned to be needed, to do something to help, and spent long afternoons at Cousin Marian's making bandages. But this was salt in an open wound for every other girl there wore a red, white, and blue badge and looked starry-eyed at the song, "When Johnny Comes Marching Home." Lainey considered making up a sweetheart in the Territory who had gone to war . . . the Randall *Recorder* was full of the organization and progress of the Territorial Volunteers . . . but to do so seemed not so much dishonest as unpatriotic.

Then Cervera's fleet was destroyed off Santiago, and, suddenly, the Spanish-American War was over. From now on in cemeteries all over the country there would be flags honoring the young men who marched away as the bands played and won a war. But Lainey Sheridan had done nothing at all and her sense of defeat was as keen as that of any Spanish grandee who sat at the peace table.

She climbed to the tower often that summer. She could think about Arch there. The further she was away from him, the more days that slid by, the realer he became, the more she ached to touch his hand, or see the rebellious cowlicks rise up on his head.

When Lainey had first known Quirt she had spent long hours in making up conversations with him. With Arch there was no need to talk. She could just sit remembering how it had been to be with him. A series of pictures flashed before her as clear as the stereopticon views Cousin Marian kept on the parlor table.

Arch fighting her battle at Jackrabbit School. Arch bringing her home safe when the panther stalked the night. Arch pulling her into the game of hide-and-seek. Arch going forward to take the blame when Sunny was lost. Arch in the dim pre-dawn light doing the chores when Bush was hurt. Arch, running toward her, forgetful of his own safety, as the black fury of the cyclone hurtled down.

He had done all these things and many more and asked no return but loyalty and she had sat under the tree with the catface brand and laughed at Arch and his dancing. It was intolerable to remember!

Lainey looked out at the soft gray twilight of the Missouri summer evening. A few stars had come out. The pigeons that circled the tower in the daytime had gone to their nests around the barn eaves but their chuckling murmur sounded, faintly. The sweet scent of honeysuckle rose from the trellis by the porch. The peace around her only made her inner turmoil worse. It was as if everything in the world was in harmony but Lainey Sheridan.

Would it be any different if I had it to do over again? No, she answered herself in bitter honesty. No, it wouldn't. The whole thing had been like starting to run down the long hill on the claim. Once you started you had to go on, stumbling, falling, leaping, running, until you reached the bottom. From the first time she had seen Quirt on the street in Randall she had yearned toward him. It was not Quirt's fault. He had not meant to do her any harm. It was as natural to him to make a girl smile and tell her she was pretty and kiss her as it was to breathe, or to roll a cigarette.

Would he have come to the schoolhouse that night if I had told him, straight out, that I was going away with him? For the first time she asked herself that question and the cold silence of the fog blotted out the familiar sights and sounds of Riverview as Lainey sought her answer.

No. Quirt didn't want to be tied down. He had told her so in a hundred ways, but she wouldn't listen. He wanted to be free. He might have taken her along, just the way he promised to meet her, because he hated saying 'No.' But he didn't want her. She'd have been a nuisance, a burden. Something to get rid of along

343

the road. Maybe he did know what she was planning. Maybe that was why he hadn't come. Not the fog, or the dance, or Dotty. Just Quirt.

I ought to hate him, but I don't. I think I'll always love him a little. Because he was what he was. Just Quirt.

Someone was coming up the ladder.

"I thought you might be up here." Allegra crossed the tower and put her arm around Lainey's waist. "Smell that honeysuckle!"

"Ummmmm." Lainey tried to keep the irritation out of her voice at this intrusion. The tower belonged to her, alone.

"Lainey," Allegra said gently. "Mot Bucklin wants to marry me."

Chapter 31

If the tower had crashed to the ground she could not have been more surprised, Lainey thought, hours later, as she sat up in bed, her arms around her knees. And with the surprise came a rush of unreasoning anger, and a flood of harsh, hurting words.

Allegra stood still until she had finished, her head bowed.

"I was afraid you would feel this way," she said at last.

"Anyway, Aunt Ellen won't let you," Lainey added triumphantly.

"Ellen has changed," Allegra said. Then she admitted, "A little, I mean."

"But marry . . . Why Mr. Bucklin's father . . ."

"Mot's father has been dead for twenty-five years. Maybe he did do some things that were wrong, but I think a lot of things were done back there that wouldn't pass muster . . . on both sides. I know Bush would say it didn't matter."

"I don't know how you can even speak his name," Lainey flared.

"I loved Bush with every bit of me. My heart and soul . . . yes, and my body, too. I loved him so much that when he died, I died. But you can't stay dead, Lainey. There are different kinds of love. Mot's lonesome; so am I." The wind stirred in the leaf-heavy maple limbs. "Do you know how old I am?"

Oh Bush, Oh Bushrod Sheridan, my father . . .

"I don't see what difference it makes, how old you are," Lainey said sullenly.

"I'll be forty soon. The women in the Saunders family live to be old. Old." As she repeated it, it became a knell. "Seventy. Eighty. Ninety. That's nothing for the Saunders women. I don't want to live all those years alone."

The Saunders' women. I'm half Saunders, no matter how much Aunt Ellen says I'm 'all Sheridan.' And I'll be old. I'll live on here at Riverview. Alone. Sewing for other people's children. Gathering receipts. I'll be the one that the Kentucky kin writes to. I'll be the one who has the dinners and they'll get smaller and smaller until at last there'll be nobody left. And I'll be here. Alone. No, no! Lainey cried in her heart, not knowing that the cry came also from her throat.

"Well, if that's the way you feel," Allegra said quietly. "I just wanted to know."

She turned away, her hand at her throat. It was almost dark and Allegra stood silhouetted against the starlit sky. A memory came back to Lainey of a day, long ago. A day in the first camp on the claim when her mother had stood just this way, her gold wedding ring winking in the sun.

Allegra had not wanted to go to the Territory, but because she loved Bush she had pulled up her deep roots and gone. She had borne Sunny while the norther screamed outside the makeshift house. She had made a home and welcomed the neighbors and made friends with Lydia Halfmoon. She had seen Sunny die and she had wavered but her love for Bush had brought her back to the claim. Now Bush was gone. In that moment between the twilight and the night Lainey saw her mother as she had never seen her before. A beauty? Yes, but far more. A woman.

And now I'm asking her to give up something else, just because it's not what I want. Bush would want her to be happy. I can't . . . I won't . . . be glad, but I can . . . I can . . .

Suddenly her arms were around Allegra.

"Mama, you're the best . . . the bravest . . ."

"Hush, I'm not any of those things. You mustn't say . . ."

"Whatever you do, it's all right with me."

"Bush liked Mot."

"Yes, ma'am."

How Bush had suffered when he thought Allegra had gone back to Riverview for good. But it hadn't mattered to him in the end. No, not at the last when he called out to her from Merry Eastman's fancy bed with the shrill singing of the canary piercing his cry. Maybe pain is a part of love. Maybe it's a part of living.

"Mot wants to buy back all the old Riverview land. He wants

346

to have the place the way it used to be. And he wants to send you to school. To Lindenwood in St. Louis. But I haven't given him an answer yet. I told him I wanted to ask you first. It's been more than a year since . . ."

"Sixteen months," Lainey said.

So it had ended that way. Through the long hours of the night as Lainey turned and twisted and wadded the pillows under her head, she tried to make herself face the years ahead. Bush. Mama. Mr. Bucklin. Aunt Ellen. Riverview. They spun around and around. She slept in uneasy snatches and once she dreamed of Quirt standing by the tree with the catface brand, a remote amused smile on his face. She wakened with tears on her face.

The letter with the postmark, Randall, Oklahoma Territory, came in a batch that Mr. Bucklin brought out from Marney. He came almost every day, now. Lainey tried to avoid him, but he cornered her as she slipped out the back door on her way to the pear tree.

"I'm not much of a hand at talk," he said, "but I'd like you to know I don't blame you a bit for feelin' funny about your mama and me. I thought the world of Bush, and I know it'll be hard for you to see me in his place." In spite of herself she winced. "But remember this, you don't have to do a thing you don't want to, and if I can give you a hand at what you *do* want . . ."

She ran away, sure she would cry if she stayed.

The limb of the pear tree where she used to sit and dream of the Princess Elaine was uncomfortably cramped. She moved to a larger limb. If Aunt Ellen sees me she'll have a fit. She flipped a piece of curling bark down to the chickens and watched the hens crowd around. The great, great grandson of the old Dominicker rooster strutted past.

The forgotten letter crackled in Lainey's pocket. She looked, frowning, at the handwriting. In a way it was familiar, but the letters staggered across the envelope. Who . . . ? She laughed, remembering Mary Hampton, and opened the letter.

It came from Jane Baker. With the same calm with which she

would have spoken she wrote that she had been having trouble with her eyes and that Will and Sara made her go to see a doctor in Guthrie. He said she was going blind.

". . . and since a blind teacher would be a burden in the mission, I am going back home to Ohio. I go by way of Kansas City and I would like to see thee, if thee is not too busy."

It wasn't fair! It wasn't fair! Jane who had given her life to helping others . . . blind. With unsteady hands Lainey swung down from the pear tree. The hens clucked around the pans and the rooster flapped his wings. In a fury she ran at them, scattering them. The fool things! With Jane going blind.

Mr. Bucklin drove Lainey and Aunt Ellen to the depot in Marney. It was unthinkable that Lainey be allowed to go to Kansas City alone, as she had wanted to do, but Aunt Ellen had some shopping, and besides she wanted to see Trenny who was ailing. Make the best of it, Lainey gritted her teeth, that's how it's going to be from now on. Make the best of it. At the depot Mr. Bucklin lifted a sheaf of late roses out of the back of the surrey. They were wrapped in wet newspaper.

"I thought your friend might like 'em," he said to Lainey, almost shyly. "I knew a blind man one time that raised roses. Said they were his family."

She liked Mot better at that moment than she ever had before.

To Lainey's relief Aunt Ellen and Jane Baker took to each other at once. But she was equally relieved, when, after a good deal of talk, Aunt Ellen said that she was going to visit Trenny and that she would be back in an hour and a half. Lainey was on no account to leave Miss Baker, or the depot.

"That's the way she treats me," Lainey said, watching the departing back. "Like I didn't have sense enough to come in out of the rain."

Jane lifted her face from the sheaf of roses.

"Thee is very like her. I think I would have known thee came from the same family, even without my eyes."

Lainey gaped. Like Aunt Ellen? Impossible. Jane must be los-

348

ing her mind along with her eyesight. Then the force of Jane's tragedy came back to her.

"Oh, Jane, it isn't fair! It isn't fair!"

"Thee must not say that. Thee must not question the goodness of God."

"But I do. I . . ."

"Hush!" the big squarecut hand pressed firmly against Lainey's mouth. "Do not . . . do not make me doubt."

"Well," Lainey said, "anyway you're going home."

Jane shook her head. "The mission was my home, because that was where I was needed." She took up the roses and pressed her plain face for a moment against the soft pinks, reds, and yellows.

"And now," she said in her usual cheerful tone, "I will tell thee all the news."

Lainey drank in the talk. Because since Pappy Vickers' death . . . George reported that the old man died in his sleep and a blessing, *he* thought, for he was no good to himself or anybody else . . . there had been no one she could talk to about the Territory. For Mama seemed to want to forget about the years away from Riverview.

Now, in the bustle of the depot, Lainey heard again the familiar names, the places. She heard of the fight that still went on for statehood, in spite of setbacks, changing administrations, and shifting alliances. She heard it all, but she did not hear the name she wanted most to hear. It might have been an oversight, but that was not like Jane.

"How about Arch?" Lainey finally said. "Arch Hampton that came with Bush and me to see the panther? How about him?"

How about Arch with his blue eyes and his rebellious hair? How about his hands, big before their time, that held mine? Why did he kiss me, down there in the cave, if he despised me? Did he believe the things they whispered? Why didn't he make me leave Quirt and come back to him? Does he love somebody else? Is he married? Does he ever think about me?

All the unspoken questions crowded into the spoken one, How about Arch?

"Have you seen him? Lately?"

"I saw him the day before I left." Only someone who had known her well would have noticed the shifting of Jane's body. *There is something! She doesn't want to say it, but I've got to know.*

"How does he look? What was he doing?"

"He looked very well. I could not see much for he was in the bright sun coming toward me." *There must be more than this.* Jane began plucking at a rose petal. "I saw the Eastman girl when I went to Randall. It is much easier to get around, now that the train comes to the town."

"What was Arch doing?"

Jane put down the roses and folded her hands.

"He was hauling a cookstove in his wagon. There was a tarpaulin over it and it came loose and scared my mules, flapping in the wind. He stopped to help me quiet them."

"A cookstove? But Hamptons' have a good stove. They bought one the year before we left. A Wilson Patent."

A man doesn't buy a cookstove just for fun. He has to have a reason. A man buys a cookstove for his home. For his wife.

"He did not say who it belonged to. He might have been hauling it for a neighbor. He asked me about thee."

"He did? Oh Jane!" Then her delight subsided. *Arch would do that, of course. Mary brought him up to be polite. Or was it all so far behind him that it didn't hurt any more?* She saw a spare figure getting out of a hack at the front door of the depot. "There's Aunt Ellen."

"Lainey, once I promised I would tell thee something."

"Yes, I remember."

"I . . . I had a follower, once. We quarrelled and he went away and joined a wagon train. I never saw him again."

"Oh, Jane! I'm sorry!" *She hardly knew what she was saying, or what Jane said. Arch? Where are you, Arch?*

"I would not have thee think I spent my life regretting. I have had many good things. It was after he left that I found my concern, and I have had the mission and the children. But now I know that I should have sought him out. I should have humbled myself."

Arch, making a home in the Sheridan place. Arch, holding

350

someone in his arms, laughing and whispering in the darkness.
I can't stand it!

You can stand what you have to stand.

"Well," Aunt Ellen said, "I thought we'd never get back. Three
horseless carriages stuck on hills. Nasty-smelling contrivances!
Give me a horse, anytime." She put a shoebox on Jane's lap. "I
just had Trenny's Arminda put up a lunch for you while I was
there. No sense in paying those prices on the diner. Seventy-five
cents for one meal! Arminda has a heavy hand with bread but
she can fry chicken."

They put Jane Baker on the train and Lainey tried to realize
that she might never see her again. There had always been plenty
of time, before, but lately time had taken to rushing by like the
wind in the Territory, never still, never letting you stop and hold
one moment close before it was gone.

"If you're ever in these parts again . . ." Aunt Ellen was saying.

"Or if thee is ever in Ohio. Lainey has the address . . ."

"Wait" Lainey said brokenly, "wait a minute."

Aunt Ellen marched her out of the train. "Don't make her break
down. She's been so brave."

"I can't help it. I . . . can't . . . help . . . it . . ."

"Of course you can. Hold up your shoulders and remember . . ."

But the rest was lost in the snorting of the engine. The familiar
bonnet, the dear, plain weathered face peered out of the window.
Jane blinked in the bright sun. The train began to move.

"Goodbye," she called. "Goodbye, Lainey. Take care . . .
Goodbye . . ."

The night was hot and humid over Riverview. Lainey rolled
from one side of the bed to the other, seeking coolness. Her nightgown was soaked with sweat, her eyes aching. She had cried till
there were no tears left. She was thankful only for one thing; Aunt
Ellen's hard code of behavior had upheld her till she got to her
own room after supper. At least there had been no unendurable
tenderness, no sympathy. She was free, up here alone, to cry and
bury her head in the pillow. She had lost Arch. Jane's attempt to
keep the truth from her had only sharpened it.

In books girls who had broken hearts pined away and died.

She would not do that. Her hands explored the warm length of her body. It did not care if her heart was broken. It would go on, healthy and strong, and keep her living. Seventy. Eighty. Ninety. One of the Saunders' women in Kentucky lived to be 103. Did she have a broken heart? When did she get so she didn't care? Seventy? Eighty? Ninety?

Sleep came in the night. Sleep and a merciful little wind that wandered in at the open window and fingered the long dark hair, touched the tear-streaked cheeks. Then the wind grew bolder and lifted the damp white nightgown so that the girl on the bed grew chilly and one hand strayed out to find the sheet.

Lainey sat up, listening. The wind was moving about her as a lover's hands move about the beloved.

"I want to go home," she whispered. "I want to go home."

When Lainey came downstairs the next morning it was clear in her mind just what she wanted to do and how to go about it. But by noon she realized it wasn't as simple as she had thought.

To begin with she had been late for breakfast. As she went into the dining room Aunt Ellen looked up from her coffee. "Good after*noon.*"

It was a way she had and Lainey had heard it a hundred times. It might once have been meant as a joke, but this time it grated on her nerves and she snapped back. Aunt Ellen's indignation was heightened when Roselda entered a moment later with Lainey's plate and stood fidgeting at the sideboard.

"That will do, Roselda. If I want anything more I will ring."

"Yassum. Mis' Ellen, I won't be here tomorry."

"What in the world are you talking about?"

"My boy's goin' nawth. I want to see him to the train."

"This is a fine time to tell me. I suppose Mattie knows all about it."

"Yassum, but she told me to tell you ma'self."

"If there's no reason not to, why don't you let her go?" Uncle Hod stirred his tea, scraping the spoon against the cup.

Aunt Ellen's face was a study. The rule that a lady never raised her voice to a servant warred with the rule that discipline must

352

be maintained. And Uncle Hod had added trouble with another rule that a lady never differs with her husband in public. And Roselda was public.

"I'll discuss this later," she said icily. "Bring some hot biscuits. And tomorrow don't use so much soda. There's a saleratus spot in this one."

"Yassum. I'll tell Mattie. I won't be here tomorry."

She left through the swinging door with the least twist of her hips.

"Did you ever hear such impudence? She ought to be . . ."

"Now, honey, you can't have her whipped, or sold down the river." Uncle Hod twinkled over his teacup.

"Horace! You know no darky was *ever* whipped or sold off this place!"

"I apologize. I should have known it was too early in the morning for teasing. But I'd better take my share of blame. This boy of Roselda's is smart. I've let him borrow some of my books and I've talked to him. I think he'll have a better chance in the north."

Aunt Ellen's eyebrows rose ceilingward. "Whatever made you start a thing like this?"

"Same reason you got Mot Bucklin to give up yellow shoes and join the lodge. Because I couldn't keep from meddlin'." He dropped a light kiss on the top of her iron-gray pompadour. "Don't take things so hard, Ellen. Times are changing, but it could be they're changing for the better. There's a fifty-fifty chance, you know."

He left and Lainey went up to help Allegra change the beds. With Aunt Ellen's mouth as grim as a mole trap, this was no time to bring up her plan to go back to the Territory. And it was no time to tell Allegra, either, for she was full of Mot's idea of sending Lainey to Lindenwood.

"I know it would make Bush happy," she said as she slipped fresh cases on the pillows. "He wanted to send you to college at Edmond but it just didn't work out."

Does she think I don't know why it didn't work out? Shaking dried lavender blossoms between the sheets Lainey stole a look at her mother. I don't believe she knows it herself. Bush wouldn't tell her he had used that money for tickets back to Missouri, and she would never ask. A lady takes what her husband gives her and makes out with it and never, never asks questions. Lainey thought of the store of silver dollars from her teaching. Once you've earned money you feel different. If I ever get married . . . but there; that's all settled. I'm going to be a schoolteacher like Jane. And I'm going back home.

In the middle of the morning Lainey went into the library. The room was barred with sunlight and Uncle Hod sat reading in his chair.

He raised his head as Lainey entered, and marked his place with his thumb.

Lainey drew a deep breath and forced the words to come. "Uncle Hod, I want to go home."

"I know," he nodded quietly. "I've seen it coming a long time."

"But I didn't know it myself until last night."

"Everybody wants to go home, Lainey. Men spend their lives looking for a home. Sometimes they find it and sometimes they don't. The lucky ones, like Ellen, are at home where they're born."

He stood beside her, the book in his hand.

"When I got out of the army, after Appomattox, I had in mind to do a lot of things. One of the boys in our company was going to Texas to raise cattle. He wanted me to go along and I had a hankering to go. Texas was new country then, in some parts. But Ellen couldn't see it that way and I loved Ellen. So I opened up a store down at the crossroads, this side of Marney, and it looked at first as if I'd do all right." He smiled, his gentle deprecating smile. "Then I began to collect my accounts. I found I couldn't press this one and that one because they were my wife's kinfolks. Well, the wholesalers closed me out after a while. Ellen wasn't sorry. It never seemed fitting to her for a Saunders . . . even one by marriage . . . to keep store. I tried one or two other things, but they didn't go well. It was my fault; I'm no pusher. My chest got to bothering me and with one arm off it was hard to find the right thing. After a bit I just stayed here in the library. Ellen could run Riverview better than I could and she got used to being the boss back there when her father was gone. She let me have my say where folks could see, but where it really counted . . ."

Lainey nodded, understanding.

"Some men might have taken to liquor, but I didn't have the stomach for it. Books were more in my line. Jeb Saunders . . . for all that he was a tough customer . . . had a good start on a library. I've added to it." He looked up at the high shelves crowded with books. "I guess you might say I was searching for a home, too. Maybe I found it, after all."

"Jane Baker said home is where you're needed."

"That could be right," Uncle Hod nodded. "But then, again, home is where the things you need are." He gave her a gentle push. "Now shoo, or Ellen'll have me up for interfering with the housework again."

It was understood that she would go with Aunt Ellen and Mama to the meeting of the missionary society that afternoon, but she was in no mood to listen to the troubles of the heathen or help pack a barrel with outmoded clothes. By staying out of sight she managed to be left behind.

Up in her room Lainey fell to thinking of Arch and the cookstove he was hauling. Was it to the Sheridan place? Who would cook on it? She kicked viciously at a rag bag in the closet. All this thinking about Arch had to stop! She was going to be Miss Elaine Saunders Sheridan all her days, a schoolteacher in the Territory, and she was going to be calm and cool and never get upset about anything. In the morning she would tell Mama and Aunt Ellen what she was going to do. Tomorrow morning . . .

She took the keepsake box from her drawer and counted the money she kept there. The scraps of Arch's picture were in there, too, and the silver spoon that had come out of Buffalo Springs clinked against the coins.

Lainey arranged the scraps into a picture again. "I ought to throw these away," she said. "I really ought to." But she knew she never would.

Lainey placed the silver dollars in piles of ten each on the dresser. They made a nice clink as she stacked them. The eighth stack was two short. She shouldn't have bought that hat in Kansas City, but it had been so pretty in the window with its gay bunch of green velvet grapes on the side. She reached it down from the shelf and took off the swathings of tissue paper, and perched it on her head. The mirror showed her a smiling Lainey. A slender girl who had finally caught up with her growth. Her bosom had now achieved the proper swell demanded of the stylish shirt-waists, her hands and feet had dwindled to the proper proportions. Not as small as Mama's, of course; nobody had hands and feet like Mama. Still, Arch teased her about her small hands. He had said they looked sick around a hoe handle. But she had beat him to the end of the row chopping cotton! There she was, back at Arch again. She tilted the hat a little to the left.

Aunt Ellen had debated about letting her buy that hat, even though Lainey would be paying for it with her own money.

"It's too grown-up," she told the millinery lady. "Those grapes . . . flowers, now . . ."

"Grapes are all the go," the lady insisted. "But I could re-trim it."

Lainey held out for grapes. Now as she looked at herself with the hat on she thought about what Aunt Ellen had said. 'Too grown-up.' But I am grown-up. I *am*.

"And I'm going back home," she said to her reflection in the mirror. "And neither you nor anybody else is going to stop me."

She pulled her writing case out from under the bed and began to write.

Chapter 32

In September a smoky blue mist covers Snyder County in the early morning. Lainey blinked as she looked out the window and saw how early it was. The sound of wheels had wakened her. Who in the world? She slipped out of bed and went to the window in time to see the democrat wagon going down the drive with Jimdandy on the driver's seat and Roselda wearing a hat trimmed with red, yellow, and purple roses sitting beside him.

She's going! She really is! If she can, I can. If-she-can-I-can. She made a little song out of it that put her back to sleep, curled in the big high bed.

Mailing her letter took the tension out of Lainey. She finished up her crocheted mat and gave it to Aunt Ellen. Mama had sneaked it out of her work bag and done over the last inch, but who cared? If you're grown-up such things don't bother you. She went to a five-hundred party and won the prize. Fielding, who had returned from Kansas City to Cousin Marian's for a visit, looked with favor on her and took her for a drive. He had grown up into such a solemn young man she found it fun to make him laugh. The first time since Quirt left that she had really laughed.

Fielding lengthened his visit. Aunt Ellen looked at him speculatively, which Lainey thought was wildly funny. Allegra gave Lainey a petticoat of changeable green and pink taffeta. Mot Bucklin took them all to a band concert. The first cider was running at the cider mill. She never drank it without thinking of Pappy Vickers.

When Fielding took her driving again she asked him to stop at the cemetery so that she could leave some flowers at Pappy's grave. Two small boys were pulling weeds around it.

"He told us yarns," the bigger one said. "Ma said they were yarns, anyway."

"He said he'd been to Injun country," the other said, and held up a small tobacco pouch. Lainey had seen it many times. One of Henry Halfmoon's many uncles had given it to Pappy. "He said a real Injun gave him this 'ere."

"It's true," she told the boy. "I knew the Indian that gave it to him. His name was Kish-ke-hon-ah. He was a direct descendant of Black Hawk." She hoped it might be possible, but Pappy would not mind and the uncle was dead, too.

"Gee!" the boys said. "Gee!"

Life became almost pleasant. As Jimdandy said, "Long as I'm here I might as well enjoy ma'self." Lainey enjoyed herself for another week. Then one morning Mr. Bucklin arrived with the mail.

"And one for Miss Elaine Saunders Sheridan," he read out. "Picture of a bank on it, too!"

She knew he meant no harm, but Aunt Ellen stopped in the middle of opening a fat letter with a Kentucky postmark, Uncle Hod looked up from an advertisement of *Lives of the Poets* and Mama put down a new pattern of crochet she had ordered.

"Are you sure that's for you, Lainey? It looks like it was from Guy Mebane."

"I wrote to him," Lainey said, disgusted that her voice shook.

"Is he the one that married Bertha Tomset?" Aunt Ellen asked.

"Yes, he's the one I told you about. He's done so well."

They waited. Lainey fingered the letter, pretending to look at the picture of the bank on the envelope. Uncle Hod went into the house.

"Well?" Aunt Ellen demanded, "what does he want?"

Mr. Bucklin looked up at the sky, muttered something about rain, and sauntered out of earshot.

"If you aren't going to open his letter, why did you write him?" Allegra said.

"In my day unmarried young ladies didn't keep letters away from their families!"

358

"I'm not keeping anything from anybody," Lainey said desperately. She edged toward the door.

"But why did you write to Guy?" Allegra insisted.

When your mother asks you a straight-out question you have to answer her. Lainey took a deep breath.

"I asked him to help me get a school to teach in the Territory."

The sick white look that came over Allegra's face made Lainey's heart sink.

"Don't you . . . aren't you happy here?"

"It's not that. It's . . . I . . ." Please, please, don't let me hurt you, she wanted to beg. Please be hateful so that I can hit back.

"Well, you can just put the whole thing out of your head," Aunt Ellen said. "The idea! Traipsing around the country. A young unmar . . ."

"If you say that again, I'll scream," Lainey said between her teeth. "I'll scream and scream and nothing you can do will stop me." She saw Aunt Ellen open her mouth, glance a moment at Mr. Bucklin, hesitate, then clamp her mouth into a thin straight line.

Allegra came closer to Lainey. "Is it Arch? Do you want to see Arch?"

"Arch Hampton is getting married," Lainey threw the words like rocks. "Jane told me. I don't know who he's marrying and I don't care!"

"I don't know what you-all are talking about," Aunt Ellen said briskly, "but the whole thing is impossible. You can't go off down there without your mother and your mother is marrying Mr. Bucklin the fifteenth of October."

Lainey looked at Allegra and saw it was true. The finality of it brought back the surge of protest she had felt on the tower.

"I meant to tell you," Allegra said, "but lately you've been . . . been hard to talk to, honey. I want you to stand up with me. I sent to Kansas City for some more of that moss-green silk, just like the piece I sent when you were seventeen. Why . . . Lainey!"

Lainey was laughing. A high-pitched ugly laugh, close to hysteria.

"Stop that," Aunt Ellen snapped. "Stop that this very minute."

The laughter broke off.

"I hope you see what came of taking her off down there in the first place," Aunt Ellen said. "You should never have given in to Bush, Allegra. Never!"

None of them noticed that Mot Bucklin had come back.

"I wouldn't say that, Miss Ellen," Mot Bucklin said firmly, "Bush did what he thought was best."

"This is no concern of yours, Mot. I'd thank you . . ."

"That's where you're wrong. What concerns Lainey concerns me. You'd better tell me what's the trouble."

"Oh, Mot," Allegra wailed. "To think she wants to go to the Territory, all by herself. To teach school!"

Three women watched the man, hanging on what his words would be.

But Mot Bucklin had come out on top in too many horse trades to be hurried. He just stood there, chewing at his moustache and switching a willow branch at the porch rail.

"That all there is to it? Just *wantin'* to go?"

"She's written a letter to some man down there," Aunt Ellen said.

"*Mister* Guy Mebane and he's in the biggest bank in Oklahoma City and he was a friend of Bush's," Lainey said stiffly.

"What's he got to say?"

"I don't know. I haven't read the letter."

"Then all this to-do is about somethin' nobody knows?"

"She had no business to write without asking," Aunt Ellen said. "Downright sneaky."

"Oh, I don't know. I don't like to tip my hand, either."

"You're surely not going to uphold her in a thing like this!"

"Miss Ellen, I like folks with git-up-an'-git. I think it would be a real good thing for Lainey to go down there and teach school. Or just stay awhile. It'll settle her mind. She may want to stay, or she may want to come back and go to Lindenwood, but the way I look at it, that's something she's got to find out for herself."

"Do you *really* think so?" Doubt and relief mingled in Allegra's question.

"Sure. She's grown up. She's the one to decide."

Lainey wanted to hug him but some inner shyness held her back. He had risked something, coming over to her side like that, but he had done it without hesitation.

"Thank you, Mr. Bucklin . . . Mot," she blurted out. The twinkle in his eyes told her that he knew what she meant and that he expected no fancy speeches or promises.

The back door closed smartly behind Aunt Ellen as she went into the house.

"Go on and read your letter," Mot Bucklin grinned. "Your mama and I have some talkin' to do. Then when you know how you stand we'll see what can be worked out."

If I can live through Sunday I can live through anything, Lainey thought, but Sunday was gone and Monday was worse. Her trunk was packed, her keepsake box tucked snugly in one corner, and Jimdandy had put it in the back of the democrat wagon. The box of books Uncle Hod had selected had been sent express to Miss Elaine Saunders Sheridan, Living Water, Oklahoma Territory. Every time she thought of the address her heart jumped a little for Uncle Guy had not only put her in touch with a school that needed a teacher, but one that was not far from Randall. Home, I'm going home and nobody can stop me!

Aunt Ellen had done her best. She had brought up every ally she could find. Cousin Marian. The new preacher at Marney. Fielding, pressed into the cause by his mother. Mattie, wrinkled, sad, and white-wooled. Even Addie who was glad enough to take sides against her father as she plainly thought his second marriage would hurt Bucky's chances of inheritance.

No matter. Only one more day. Monday. I'm leaving on Tuesday. The Short Line to Kansas City. The Katy to the Territory, and then the Frisco which went right to Randall, now. Mot Bucklin had arranged it for her. The school-board man would meet her in Randall and drive her to Living Water. But no one, not even Mot knew that she had written the school-board man to meet her on Thursday instead of the day she would arrive, Wednesday. It was nobody's business but her own. Wednesday belonged

361

to her. One day to drive out to the Sheridan place . . . no, the Arch Hampton place . . . One day to look once more at what she had loved and lost and then to pick up and go on.

But first there was Monday. On the surface it was like any other Monday. White sheets billowing on the line, linen bleaching on the grass. Drawers, petticoats, and corset-covers hanging modestly on the line back of the smokehouse. Lainey, in an old dress of Allegra's that strained at the shoulder seams, stirred starch to a clear jelly. Aunt Ellen counted napkins and fluted ruffles. They worked back to back in the kitchen, but they might have been a hundred miles apart. Mattie and Roselda glowered at each other and refused to pass the beeswax across the width of the ironing board. Jimdandy retreated to the farthest field. Uncle Hod shut himself in the library. Allegra stayed upstairs, working furiously at the sewing machine, the thump of the treadle sounding through the house. All day Lainey hoped Mot Bucklin would drop in, but he stayed away. She supposed he did not want to intrude on her last day with her family.

After supper Lainey went to her room. It was too early to light the lamp and too dark to do anything without it so she sat at the window and watched daylight fade from Riverview.

A deep tenderness for all that she was leaving filled Lainey. I'm going, and I want to go, but . . . but this is part of me, too. I'll never forget it. Never. Never.

This house. This land . . . fought-over land. These people. They made me what I am. I thought I did it all myself, but I'm part of them and they're part of me and wherever I go I'll carry Riverview, Snyder County, Missouri.

Putting her arms out the window, Lainey pressed her hands against the solid brick wall of the house.

She was there when Allegra entered, hesitantly, carrying a lamp in one hand and a dress of dark green henrietta cloth over her arm.

"I just got it finished," she said. "I wanted you to have something new to wear."

"That was nice, but you didn't need to . . ." Then she looked

362

at her mother and altered what she had started to say. "That was nice and thank you very much. It's pretty."

"Ellen put in the hem."

The stitches were exquisite, barely visible in the cloth. Lainey thought of the long day in the kitchen, ironing, mending, sorting. "You shouldn't have let her. On Monday . . ."

"I couldn't stop her. I never could. Lainey . . . would you . . ."

"No, I can't! Please don't ask me." She was in a panic. If she weakened for one moment she might never, never go. And there was Arch. 'Thee will always have to go and find out.' Jane said that a hundred years ago and she was right. I do have to!

"All right. I just thought . . . I'll miss you, honey."

"I'll miss you."

"Well," Allegra turned to go and the light retreated with her, leaving the room in violet dusk. "Go over to our old place sometime and see about Sunny and . . . Bush. Mary promised she'd look after things, but somebody in the family . . ."

"I will."

"Goodnight."

"Goodnight."

The soft closing of the door meant the end of something. The day, perhaps, or the pain of parting. Or the long struggle to go home.

The sky was pearly when Lainey got out of bed. I'm late! I'll have to hurry! The new dress fitted perfectly. The hat with the green grapes was all the millinery lady promised. She picked up her carpet bag and heard the little jingle that meant the silver spoon Arch fished out of Buffalo Springs was settling against the garnet cross. She had taken them both out of the keepsake box to carry with her. The four-leaf clover pin rode jauntily at her throat. 'The color of your eyes,' Uncle Guy said! She started out the door, then went back and made her bed. A lady always, always, keeps her own room.

Too late for saying goodbye to each beloved object, as she had, years ago. Never mind. I'm taking with me what matters most

363

. . . the way they make me feel. She stopped outside Aunt Ellen's door, then opened it softly and looked in. Aunt Ellen was lying in bed, her face turned toward the wall, the sheet pulled tight across her shoulders. *If she just turns over, or even looks . . . but she didn't.*

Lainey went to the kitchen. She had thought Roselda might have a cup of coffee ready for her, but it was Mattie, stooped and cranky, her lip almost out to her chin. Coffee and bacon between biscuit helped the all-gone feeling. Lainey kissed the soft, wrinkled cheek. *The very first money I make teaching school, I'll send her some snuff.*

She had supposed Jimdandy would drive her to the depot, but there was Mama up in the democrat wagon with Jimdandy waiting at the horse's head.

"You didn't think I'd let anybody else take you?" Allegra laughed at Lainey's startled face. "Mot wanted to, and Jimdandy. Even Hod. But I wanted to the most."

"Goodbye, Jimdandy."

"Goodbye, Miss Lainey."

It was the first time he had ever called her 'Miss.'

Down the driveway, around the curve, and through the gate. At the pike Lainey turned back to see the tower. Three early-rising pigeons made a looping swing around the iron lace as the first rays of the sun touched their wings.

"Glory be!" she said in the morning silence. "Glory be!"

At the depot Mr. Buff's lamp looked sickly in the sunlight. He bent his head to the clicking telegraph machine, ignoring Allegra and Lainey as long as possible. When he spoke it was with the air of a man with weightier matters on his mind.

"Ten minutes, yet. *Railroad* time."

Ten minutes? Ten minutes to say goodbye? To make up for past mistakes and prepare for future changes? Ten minutes? The two stared at each other.

"Lainey, take care of yourself!"

"And you take care."

"Tell Lydia Halfmoon . . . tell Mary Hampton . . ."

"Tell Cousin Marian goodbye for me. And tell Mot . . ."

"Is it really all right with you for me to marry . . . I mean . . ."

"It's all right."

"Lainey, there's something else."

"What?"

"Oh, I don't know how to say it. But sometimes here in Missouri, at Riverview, sometimes I get to thinking about the Territory, and I find myself waiting for . . . the wind."

Wooooo . . . Wooooo . . . Waw-wooooo.

Bluestone crossing. In the fraction of time left Lainey tried to take in what Allegra had said, but it was too big an admission. She hugged her mother, picked up the carpetbag, straightened her hat. Allegra thrust a shoebox into her hands.

"Here, this is yours. It was on the seat of the democrat wagon when I went out this morning."

, The box was securely tied with string, knotted and cross-tied. Only one person tied a lunch like that! Lainey sniffed at the box. The smell of fried chicken was unmistakable.

Too late now. Too late to go back and say goodbye to the thin figure under the tightly pulled sheet. The conductor was frowning at Lainey, his watch in hand.

"It must have been Ellen. She wouldn't want you to be hungry. She . . . she loves you."

"I know." Lainey felt that she had always known. Aunt Ellen loved her and that was why . . .

"Booooard!"

Lainey stumbled up the steps. From the vestibule she caught one last glimpse of Allegra waving with one hand and fishing for her handkerchief with the other.

Chapter 33

They had built the depot at Randall at the foot of the hill and the hack uptown cost a quarter. But Lainey's carpetbag wasn't heavy and anyway it would be good to walk after all that time on the train. Vinita, Tulsa, the towns of Indian Territory had amazed her. No wonder Bush wanted them in the same state! She watched the Frisco puff away on its way westward, and started up the long hill on foot. She looked for scars of the cyclone, but like all young things Randall healed quickly. The main street was busy with horses, buggies, and wagons. The dust ruffle of the new green dress showed red dirt. A person almost wished styles would change and dresses go halfway to your knees. But no lady, certainly no schoolteacher, would think of wearing them.

She stopped at the drug store for a glass of soda water. Mr. Link eyed her.

"Aren't you . . ."

"I'm Miss Elaine Sheridan," she said, thinking of her status as a teacher. But when he still stared she went on, "Bush Sheridan's girl."

"Sure! Sure!" he shook hands with her. "Glad to see you folks come back."

"Just me," she said. "I'm going to teach school over at Living Water."

"Well, good luck to you. Never was a better man than Bush." He went back behind the counter, a new one with mahogany sides and a marble top.

Lainey finished her soda water and laid down a nickel. Mr. Link waved it away.

"No charge to homecomers. Come back 'n' see us."

At the door to the street she stood as if fumbling in her pocketbook, but really to rest her hand on the doorframe for a moment. Quirt had lounged there the first time she ever saw him, on that blistering Fourth of July.

A moment later Lainey went to the livery stable and hired a horse and buggy for the afternoon. The livery stable man looked at her just the way Mr. Link had.

"Say, aren't you . . ."

"Bush Sheridan's girl," she said, a little shortly. "Come back to teach at Living Water. I'll bring the rig back before sundown." She stepped into the buggy.

"Say, young fellow in here mentioned your dad's name lately. On the track of some furniture or somethin' you folks had sold when you went back to . . . where was it you went to?"

"Missouri," she snapped, and touched the horse with the whip. The livery stable man stood aside, gaping. I don't want to hear about it! What does he mean, hunting up our furniture? Oh, Arch, you didn't need to do that!

Lainey was half-crying but the horse was a hard-mouthed plug and she had to give him her attention to get any speed out of him at all. Then the unrolling of the familiar countryside blotted up the pain and the tears. This was the way they had first come to the claim, Mama in her surrah and her hat with the white birds. The grass had been so high it brushed the bellies of the team. The land had been untouched, unconquered. And she had slept, lulled by the wheels and the song Mama had brought from home.

The houses along the road fell into their proper places. To know which one would come next gave her a satisfaction out of all proportion to the deed. She had seen most of them grow from a campsite to what they were now. Small, comfortable farm homes. A new house, put up since she had left, annoyed her.

At Jackrabbit Schoolhouse she pulled up and sat, looking. After the cyclone they had torn down the old schoolhouse and added a second room to the new one. Did they have another popularity contest to raise the money? Did someone remember Quirt Kearny who tossed twenty silver dollars into Lainey Sheridan's lap?

No matter. What they said or didn't say was of no importance now. The only thing that mattered was driving up that road to

367

what had once been the Sheridan place. To see with her own eyes . . . But what would she see? And what would she do? The plan, made at Riverview, ended at the livery stable back in Randall.

The field where she had seen Arch kill the copperhead was empty in the September sunshine. She drove on up the road and stopped opposite the first campsite, hitching the horse to a persimmon tree. Bush was there, and Sunny. She did not weep, nor feel the sorrow she had expected to. They were safe in the red earth. They had loved it. Bush coming to it from afar as a man seeks his home, and Sunny because it was all he knew, and, at last, the earth had taken them into its inner, secret self. The red sandstone markers were warmed by the sun. Lainey put her hand on the one marked, BUSHROD SHERIDAN, and said, as if in answer to a question, "You were right, Bush. It was the best thing to come."

She wrinkled her forehead trying to recall just how he looked. A big dark man with a habit of pushing his hat back from his forehead. A man who looked out from green-brown eyes, unafraid. Fresh from her own struggle to leave Riverview with its safety and its deep roots she understood better what it had meant for him to come. Without guarantees, without promises, risking all that he had. And she knew, as she stood there with the western sun on her face, that he would have said it was worth the gamble.

Time was running out. She must go on up that long hill to the house that belonged to Arch. To see for herself the girl he had chosen to live among the furnishings that had once been Allegra's. To be polite and civil, and to walk down that hill, if she must, with unbent back. Time to do that or be forever ashamed that she had lacked the courage. 'I know, now, that I should have humbled myself,' Jane Baker said in her quiet voice. 'I know, now . . .'

The wind rustled the tumbleweeds that had been kept back from the graves only by the long stroke of a scythe. 'Go on,' the wind said, 'Go on.' But the wind had led her to Quirt, once, laughing and whispering in her ear. She stood, unable to move, caught in a panic of indecision. It would be simpler to go back to the livery-stable horse. To put the whip to him and hurry back to Randall. To go to the hotel she had spotted before she left town. Simpler, even, to go over to Eastmans' and walk into that room where Bush had died.

Something moved in the grass by Sunny's headstone. Lainey jumped, clutching her skirts around her. Snakes! But no sinuous length uncoiled, no menacing rattle sounded. A tiny spiked head and two bright beady eyes looked at her from the grass. A horned toad! Lainey pounced, caught him, held him on her open palm. The little creature's painted sides palpitated, his fragile claws scratched at her flesh.

"St. George, O.T.!" she said.

The first St. George had been a sign that Bush would come back with a claim. Now, this one . . . Her heart jumped, absurdly, and she forgot the speed with which a horned toad can move. He darted off her hand, hit the ground, scuttled out of sight. Was he a sign? She must get him back! Lainey knelt in the grass, scratching at the tough growth. A sandbur stuck in her finger. The new dress was dragging in the dirt.

She got to her feet and dusted off her skirt.

This is silly. It's just a horned toad. It's not a sign. The wind's not a sign. It's not telling me to do *anything*. It's just blowing the way it always does in the Territory. I'm grown-up and I'll have to decide for myself. If I'm going anywhere I'd better go or the sun will be down.

Lainey started walking, without a backward look, straight up the hill.

The place was in good shape. Arch knew the land, and, like Bush, he tried to take care of it. She noticed the filled washes, the plowing that went around the rises, and for some reason this gave her courage as she went along.

The house had an unlived-in look. Lainey could tell that even before she reached the yard. There were no chickens in the chickenyard, no horse or cow in the lot. Maybe the Arch Hamptons hadn't moved in yet. She opened the gate and closed it carefully. The yard had been scythed. Somebody had done that. Was a face looking out at her from the upstairs window where she had looked out so many times? In the reddening light she could not be sure.

"Hello the house!"

Her voice sounded wild and loud in the silence. There was no answer.

They could at least answer! They weren't so all-fired good that they couldn't pass the time of day! Lainey tried to get angry but her courage was oozing fast. She had come so far and now there was nothing to do but turn around and go back. But first she wanted to see in the house.

Stepping over the foundations Bush had laid for the new house, Lainey walked up on the porch and pressed her face against the glass window. Real, store-boughten windows. Her own face looked back. She shaded her eyes and peered in.

With growing sickness Lainey recognized each piece of furniture piled there. The big bed that had been Bush and Allegra's. The rocking chair where they had rocked Sunny. The kitchen safe with its pattern of pierced tin. The stove with the Oak Leaf on the door. It had been their stove Arch was hauling!

Everything was in disorder. The cushion on the rocker looked as if pups had chewed it. She rubbed at the glass and looked again. The dark spot on the table where she had set the iron one day showed up like a sore thumb. And somebody had let something sticky boil over on the stove and never cleaned it up.

At the step on the porch she whirled, arm half up as if to defend herself. A stranger, caught spying on what was never meant for her eyes.

Then she was in Arch's arms and he was kissing her, and she was a stranger no longer. She was Lainey Sheridan who had come home.

It was some time later when Arch had opened the house and dragged the rocker out on the porch for her to sit in that she asked him, "All our furniture, Arch? What made you round it up?"

His face turned red and he twirled his hat on his finger.

"Oh, I don't know. Made me feel like you were comin' back, I

370

reckon." Then he burst out, "Sullavans had that rocker and I couldn't stand it the way those kids tromped on it."

She would never tell him that the news of his hauling a stove to the claim had very nearly kept her away from him. But it wouldn't have in the end. Nothing would. She was very sure of that as she left the chair and sat beside him on the edge of the porch and put her cheek against his arm. She and Arch belonged together.

"I ought to get back to town," she said, not moving. "I told the livery stable man I'd be back by sundown."

"Let him worry about that," Arch said and slipped his arm around her. So they sat as the sunset flamed, red, gold, azure, and the colors gentled into copper, then grayed a little. Presently they walked around the house, stepping carefully over the foundations Bush had laid out.

"I had it in mind to start building when I got the furniture rounded up," Arch said.

"How'd you know I was coming back? How'd you know I hadn't gone off with somebody else?"

"I didn't," Arch said. "I just went ahead. Root hog or die."

The old phrase made her smile. That was the way it was with Arch and Bush and the others who had come in the Run. They had come on faith and by faith they stayed. It was the only way to do. It was the way she had come up the hill to Arch.

They stood at the back of the house and the tree with the catface brand waved, golden and beckoning, in the fading light.

"Arch . . . about Quirt . . ."

"Hush," he said, and bent toward her. "I don't care about anything so long as you've come home."

And in the fragile second before his mouth found hers she knew that no life was long enough for her to tell Arch how much she loved him, but she would try. Here, at home, she would try.

This was the 16th of November, 1907.

Lainey, going out to hang up the washing, stopped at the door of the house and let the wind ruffle up her hair and cool her face.

371

She washed in the old house, now. For five years they had been living in the new house. The morning was bright as a silver dollar. The wet clothes overflowing the basket sent up clouds of steam. I ought to have them up by now, she thought, drawing in a deep breath. And I will, in a minute. But the minute lengthened. The day with work that must be done snapped at her heels like an untrained pup. Still, she stood, watching the mare's tails feather out in the sky. In a minute. Just a minute.

She picked up the basket and went out to the clothesline. As she stretched up her arms the wind moulded the calico dress to her. She was no longer the slender girl who had returned to the Territory to teach a year at Living Water. Her figure was full and rich with the beauty of children borne and the expectation of another.

I ought not to put my hands over my head, she reminded herself, and let them fall on the clothesline. The tree with the catface brand had lost most of its leaves in the big wind last night. The sumac that had been scarlet since the first frost was taking on a purplish tinge.

I wish bittersweet grew in the Territory the way it did in Snyder County. Maybe Jimdandy could dig me a root and Mama could mail it down. No, better ask Aunt Ellen; she'll be sure to attend to it. Must get these clothes up. Have to bake today, too. And there's the piece to copy off for Maxie Pritchard to say at literary. You'd think Christina would do it herself, but with all those children . . . I wonder if she ever wishes she hadn't married Curly and had gone on teaching at Jackrabbit? Do I wish I'd stayed on to teach at Living Water another year when they wanted me to? They begged me to come back.

She laughed at her own foolishness. No, my goodness, no.

She pinned a blue shirt on the line with quick, capable hands, thinking how Sis Pritchard said the only thing she minded about her store teeth was that she couldn't hold clothespins in her mouth. Another shirt with a patch that showed dark in the sunshine. Then the little burst of energy died out and she leaned on the line, swinging idly back and forth. Why can't I get going?

The wind blew an answer against her ear. A haunting, teasing answer that coaxed her to run away from the basket of wet clothes, the two children, the baking . . . run down the hill to the very bottom. Some ghost of the wild exhilaration she had felt once came back to her. What had it been like to be that young? I wonder where Quirt is and what happened to him? But the wonder was like the wind, it came and was gone. She shook out little Ellen's pink calico print and hung it up. I'll never make her wear dark clothes, no, not if I have to scrub my hands off. But I didn't know how hard Mama worked. No wonder she thought school-teaching was easy!

Well, she has it easy now. Mot won't let her turn a hand and he's bought back all the Riverview land and a brand-new organ and a grand piano and a carriage and blooded horses! My! It took me a long time to get used to Mot . . . and Mama . . . but now I see it's all right. Mama told me there were lots of kinds of love but I didn't know then. What I had for Quirt was one kind. She smiled at the great golden tree. But what I have now is better.

Then she saw a tall blue-shirted young man coming up from the field. Her heart jumped and she scolded herself. After all these years! But something might be the matter. She ran toward him, lightly, in spite of the long dress, the apron, and the child she carried. She ran between the old house and the new almost stumbling in the trench little Bush was digging.

"Mama!" he fussed. "Look out!"

Dirt all over him. Red dirt. Now I'll have to wash again. Oh well, he's happy. She forgot him and little Ellen napping in the house.

"Arch? Are you all right, Arch?"

"Now why wouldn't I be all right?" He grinned down at her and there was in his blue eyes the laughter of the boy at the Run.

"But I thought you were going to work in the far field."

"Listen to her," he complained. "Won't let a man stop for a cup o' coffee."

"But . . . but you never did. You never just up and quit work in the middle of the morning."

"I believe she's forgotten," Arch addressed an unseen ally over her head. "And after all the to-do."

"Forgotten?" Then Lainey put her hand over her mouth. "Oh Arch, this is it. The day the Territories turn into a state!"

"Yep. The state of Oklahoma." He pulled out Bush's watch. How long, how long ago she had stood on the banks of Deep Fork and seen Bush look at the same watch and glance at the sun as Arch did now. "Nine o'clock. I guess old Teddy Roosevelt's got his pen out. I guess, in a minute or so . . ."

He did not finish. Instead she saw him swallow, hard. Then he reached out and pulled her to him with one arm and with the other he took off his hat. The November sun touched the blond hair and the wind lifted the cowlicks. I hope the new baby has hair just like Arch. She leaned against his strength and felt safety in the rock-hard muscles that the red earth had given him in exchange for the years of hard sod-busting, plowing, planting and harvesting. It was a fair exchange, she thought, putting her hand in his. A boy for a man. The Territories for a state. One state in which the differences and bickerings between the Territories would be forgotten.

"I wish Bush could have seen the day," he said.

Maybe he does. Maybe he's here, right now. Bush wouldn't leave this country, not even for a heavenly one, if he could help it. Why of course he's here. This is his claim. He built the old house and he laid the foundation for the new one. She could almost see the big black-bearded man coming up the road, the red dust blowing from his feet, the wind in his face. Lainey reached up and put her arms around Arch's neck.

"I'm glad I came," she said as the rattle of a train echoed in her ears and once more she looked on the long, unbroken horizon of new country. "Oh, Arch, I'm glad I came!"